The Medical Dete
Memoirs of A Most Unu

Although this is a work of fiction,
upon a real life event as experien
doctor in an English rural setting. T
described genuinely occurred, and the way of solving
them also occurred as described. However, names and certain details have been changed so as to make individuals unrecognisable and to improve the narrative. Occasionally two separate stories have been amalgamated to make a more interesting book for the reader.

These methods of solving medical problems are the results of individual anecdotes, this approach being practised by many doctors throughout the world. However, they have not been assessed by the FDA of America or other appropriate Authorities. Therefore no attempt should be made to use the information in this book to diagnose or treat individual conditions without consulting a medically qualified doctor.

Thank you Sylvia Alexander for the original painting that has formed the front cover.

ISBN: 978-1-84426-842-9

First published in Great Britain in 2010.
Published by Abaco Book Publishing Ltd
www.abacopublishing.com
Printed by Print On Demand-Worldwide

The Medical Detective

Chapter 1

"It's not like it used to be," said Maud Hughes to her grandson Patrick. "When the last doctor came, he really seemed to understand you. Don't get me wrong," she added, "This one is very caring and seems to know what it's all about. It's just that things are different. They are not the same."

At the age of ninety-three, Maud Hughes was entitled to her point of view. She had seen so many comings and goings in her long life. She had been born in the village of Stead Norton, gone to junior school there, had had to go to the senior school in the larger local town of Fulton, had been married in the local church when still a girl of only nineteen, had had all her four children at home, and had lived in the same village all her live. She had never gone on holiday because she had never wanted to. She had never gone further than Fulton, and even then not very often. She was quite simply content with her lot. Her lifelong love, her husband Ted, had died only a few years earlier, but at the tender age of ninety-one.

Although some people might think Maud's life was very narrow, she had been really happy, and particularly happily married. And despite what many people nowadays might think of her limited education, Maud was really quite an intelligent person but fortunately had never wanted for more than she had. She was born of very poor parents who had struggled to bring up their seven children, three of whom had died of pneumonia at a very young age. Maud had a wonderful saying that she told to everyone. "I was born with nowt, but I've still got some of it left."

Everyone in the village loved Maud. She was such a friendly person. No one came to live in the village without someone saying to them, "Have you visited Maud yet?" And when they eventually did visit her, she would say to them, "I wondered how long it would take for you to visit me! Come in and have a cup of tea and a slice of cake." Whatever time of day it was.

Maud was the oldest person in Stead Norton, and certainly the person who had lived the longest in the village. A number of elderly folk had died over the past few years, but none of them had lived there all their lives like she had. She knew everything about the place, yet she wasn't nosey. She knew the history of Stead Norton because she had been taught it by her parents and grandparents, all of whom had lived in the same village. Her four living children had grown up, had got married, had had their own families and had moved away. So Maud was the last of the line, the last of an era, as far as Stead Norton was concerned.

"But then life has accelerated", she would say, "Started to go faster. In my day, everything was much slower and more peaceful. We were far more content than people are today, but then we had nothing to do and nothing to hanker after. There simply wasn't anything like there is nowadays. People seem to have so much money to spend on things they don't really want yet can't seem to do without. They keep rushing around doing things that are quite unnecessary. They can't seem to sit still for long. Oh well! That's life for you, I suppose."

Maud was recovering from what the doctor had said was 'a touch of pneumonia'. He had wanted to send her into hospital, but Maud had adamantly refused to move. "I have never been that far away from my home in my whole life, and I'm not going away now. You can do what you like with my body when I'm gone, but I'm staying put if you don't mind."

So the local doctor had agreed to do his best for her at home and had sent in the district nurses to keep an eye on her. In fact they had all volunteered to pop in to see her from time to time as she was so well known and loved, despite the fact that she had never needed help ever before. So there she was, resting in bed quite contentedly, taking her time to recover. Her grandson Patrick had offered to come and stay to look after her, as had his wife Lynda.

They had made Maud's bedroom homely to sit in, having brought some comfortable chairs up from downstairs, as Patrick and Lynda loved to listen to her tales. She was so easy to chat to and they were fascinated by it all. Her grandchildren had often come to stay with her when they were young, especially during the school holidays, but she never visited them. She said, "If you want to go off and see the world, please feel free to do so, but don't expect me to follow or visit you. Here I am and here I stay, but you are welcome to visit me any time".

So it had happened for years. Maud's four surviving children had all grown up and married, each one having the obligatory two children. "Why on earth do you want only two children?" she would say. "Don't you know how much fun they can be? I wouldn't have been without the four of you for anything, sad though it be that the three young ones died so tragically, but then we didn't have antibiotics in those days like you have now". For years the grandchildren came to stay whenever they could. The village was surrounded by woods that nobody seemed to own, so the kids had a whale of a time playing in them, and no one ever thought it might be dangerous. Yes they had the odd scrape and scratches, but Maud soon sorted them out in her own way, and they never came to any harm.

So it was no surprise that Patrick and Lynda had happily volunteered to come and stay with her for a while, in fact as long as she needed. Patrick's 'job' as a writer meant that he could spare the time. Actually he was more of a reporter as he wrote various articles he sold to newspapers. He had written a novel, but it had not been very successful. Perhaps the publisher hadn't done the publicity well enough. Patrick had been married to Lynda for less than a year. She had been a staff nurse in the local hospital where she had lived further up north, having met Patrick at a conference organised by the local Area Health Authority. Patrick had thought there might be an interesting subject to write about. Since marrying Patrick, Lynda had moved away from home and hadn't tried to find a job yet, although she was sure she would find one easily enough when she started looking. So, as it happened, she was also available to accompany Patrick and stay with Maud.

Chapter 2

"Gran! Why did you say 'It's not like it used to be' just now?" Asked Patrick. "What were you thinking about? Is it something to do with your pneumonia?"

"Touch of pneumonia, the doctor said. I don't have it properly apparently, just a bit," said Maud. "Well, Yes! I was thinking of the last doctor, Dr. David James. He was quite different, a lovely man, who thought of things and treated you somehow differently. He was well trained and particularly loved delivering babies. He trained in London and apparently spent some time overseas when he first qualified. He came here quite a young man. Well, I thought so at the time. He was quite prepared to give us drugs and things if we wanted them, and knew all about them, but he tried to get us to think why we might be ill and do something to help ourselves. He loved the quote from President John F. Kennedy. He had it up in his surgery having modified it to say what he wanted to get across."

Think not what America can do for you.
Think what you can do for America - JFK
Think not what I can do for you.
Think what you can do for yourself - DPJ

"How do you know about him, Gran? You were never ill, so far as I am aware, so you never needed his help did you?" Patrick asked.

"Well, hardly ever, you're right. But there were a few occasions when I visited his surgery, although I can't remember what for. We must have talked about why I was there at the time, but I never stayed long, as there was usually a bit of a queue of people to see him. He never had an appointments system like they all have nowadays. If you needed him, you simply queued up like the rest of them. If the queue was a bit long as it sometimes was, you simply went away and came back another day. If you looked as though you needed Dr. James urgently, people would simply tell you to go in next. It was so easy. Everyone loved it, but to be fair he continued the way the doctor before him had worked, and the doctor before that. Apparently his father was in general practice, and his surgery was attached to the house and he said he had always wanted to do it the same way".

"So how do you know his story so well?" asked Patrick.

"He was just like the rest of them. He popped in to see me between visiting sick people at home and we just got chatting. People had given up asking me about my life. They soon realised there wasn't anything to tell. But everyone else seemed to have had so much more varied a life than I had had. And they kept telling me about themselves. Yet I wasn't jealous of a single one of them. Perhaps I should have been a hermit or a lighthouse keeper."

"Just think of all those people you would not have met if you had been!" offered Lynda.

"So what was so special about Dr. James?" asked Patrick.

"How long have you got?" replied Maud.

Chapter 3

David James was born the third child of four children, with a brother and two sisters. He always maintained that he was not as clever as his three siblings, all of whom qualified in medicine and became hospital specialists in their own right. He said that, as a medical student, you could tell what the male students were going to end up doing, although he wasn't sure how to apply the same process to the females.

The bright, no nonsense, forthright, positive and confident students were going to become Consultant Surgeons. Some of the same types, but who were more suave and wore a bow tie would become Consultant Obstetricians and Gynaecologists. The equally bright ones but who were more laid back and less pushy than others but could always pass their exams would become the Consultant Physicians. The lads who sat in the corner smoking a pipe, sporting a beard and a moustache, and who spat into the spittoon, would become the Consultant Pathologists. The 'also rans', who often struggled with their exams because they were not as bright as the others, but who always managed in the end because they really wanted to become doctors, would become General Practitioners. Dr. James said he fitted well into the last group. He was perfectly happy in that position, because, as he had struggled somewhat, he reckoned that made him able to understand other peoples' problems better. Such doctors, he felt, were admirably suited to General Practice.

After he qualified, Dr. James went to The Caribbean for his first year. He said he didn't want to stay in his own teaching hospital as a junior doctor, and they would never have asked him to anyway. As he explained it, it was the brightest students, the ones who had done best in their exams, the ones who had caught the eye of the tutors, who were invited to become a 'houseman', the most junior post for a newly qualified doctor, in their own teaching hospital. Such a post was considered the first rung on the ladder of hopefully an exalted medical career, ending up as a Consultant of something or other.

However, in those days, the ward sisters ruled the roost in their wards, and woe betide a junior doctor who got above his or her station. As for the Consultants who had patients in their wards, they were Gods. Even the staff nurses knew far more about medicine than the junior doctors. It was laughingly rumoured that the junior doctors were only there on sufferance as they were only capable of taking the odd pulse, blood pressure or temperature, well for the first few weeks at least, until they had been carefully moulded the way all good doctors are.

David James loved every bit of his time in The Caribbean. He had struggled with his exams, but he had absolutely no problems with the responsibilities of being a qualified doctor. The experience he had was amazing. He had to do everything, because, if he didn't do what was needed, it simply didn't get done. He was in his element being a practical person. He reckoned that he gained five or six years experience in the one year he spent overseas, during which time, because of the workload, he slept one night in four. How he survived, he never knew. He just did.

He explained it like this. Imagine a population of about two hundred and fifty thousand people in the UK. There would be about one hundred General Practitioners and two District General Hospitals, with all the support systems that go with them. Where he worked, there were no General Practitioners, two worn out Surgeons who they protected for the really difficult stuff, and seven junior doctors to do everything they were presented with. Two of the doctors did their best to cope with an unending stream of patients in the Casualty Department during the day, from 8.00 am to 6.00 pm.

He himself did a normal days work in outpatients, in the wards or in the operating theatre, then was responsible all night long for particular emergencies that effectively went on all night. The next day he carried out the usual duties appointed to him, and again was on duty for other emergencies that night, working a 'normal' day next day. It was the third night that was really hard as it was his turn to be in Casualty Department, which literally went on all night non-stop. The fourth night he was off duty!

He felt the year in The Caribbean went by all too quickly, but he admitted much of the time he must have been half asleep. His contract was only for one year, and despite the fact they were short of doctors, they didn't seem willing to extend his stay. He never found out why. Back in the UK he worked in various hospitals to obtain post-graduate qualifications, where his experiences in The Caribbean were not only of great value (he was still a junior doctor), but much appreciated by the senior staff.

Dr. James really wanted to go back to The Caribbean, but somehow it didn't work out, possibly because by then he was married with the beginnings of a family. He was a bit lost with no particular idea what direction to go in. He looked at a few General Practice positions, but felt he wasn't ready to settle down into that sort of life yet. All sorts of medical jobs are available to qualified doctors, including opportunities overseas, but he just couldn't find something that he fancied. He looked at other 'islands', assuming they might be similar to the one he loved in The Caribbean. He even considered The Falklands, until he discovered where it was!

In the end he was appointed as Medical Adviser to a Pharmaceutical Company, expecting to stay for six months or so while he sorted himself out. He stayed for seven years! He travelled to many different countries, staying at first class hotels, all at the company's expense. His job was to meet doctors in those countries and set up trials on the company's new drugs.

He said that people think that a travelling representative has a whale of a time when away from home, and possibly some people do, what with their expense accounts. But the vast majority find most aspects of such a job really quite boring. You spend most of the day travelling to your next appointment, check into the next hotel, have a meal, read a book, watch TV and wait for the next day and the next appointment. Much of the time you are either alone or in the company of someone you either don't particularly like or whose language you don't speak very well or who's English you can hardly understand.

Despite these drawbacks, he had some very interesting experiences. He found the contrast particularly fascinating between the Germans and the Americans. Remember, he was meeting doctors at the very pinnacle of their careers, many of whom were quite famous in their area of medicine. In Germany, the possession of a degree was considered very important and respectable, and they wanted you to know not only that they had a degree, but also how many they had.

He remembered being introduced to a professor at his very first visit to a teaching hospital. "May I present Herr Professor Dr. Dr. Dr. Schmidt, head of the department of so-and-so". That was to inform him that Professor Schmidt had three doctorates, presumably one in medicine, and two others, perhaps in engineering and in philosophy. The German doctor who was the local representative who went round with him, who had also been appointed to the position of local Managing Director, was referred to as Herr Dr. Davos and his wife as Frau Dr. Davos, and, had he met the professor's wife, he was duly informed that she would have been introduced as Frau Professor Dr. Dr. Dr. Schmidt.

A year after a number of visits to Germany, Dr. James went to America for the first time. In those days there were not nearly as many people travelling to the States as nowadays. He remembered arriving at the Immigration Department, to be greeted by "Good morning, David. Welcome to the United States of America. Have you brought any presents with you?"

"No, I haven't"

"Why no presents?"

"Because I don't have any friends here?

"Well, put it there, Buddy," said the Immigration Officer, extending his hand, "You have now!"

Another interesting experience involved a training course in Germany. Germany had been given to him as one of his 'territories', and the company's Main Board had decided to train a new group of representatives. He had been sent on a course to improve his schoolboy German, to be of value when travelling to Germany, but also to oversee the training course.

On the first morning, everyone gathered in the lecture room of a pleasant country hotel somewhere in Germany, for everyone to be introduced. A young psychology graduate had been given the task of teaching the new representatives, and he had translated the training brochure used in England into German, having visited England a number of times.

Herr Dr. Davos, the German Managing Director, introduced the young graduate as "Herr Psychologischer Wandermann", which indicated he had a psychology degree, and then introduced Dr. James as "Herr Dr. Med. James", indicating that he had a medical degree, which to Germans would be considered superior to a mere psychology degree. Guess who found he had to run the training course from then on? The senior man, of course, who didn't speak very good German. However it soon improved. It had to.

Another interesting experience that Dr. James had while working for the Pharmaceutical Company took place in Spain, another country he was given responsibility for. This time he travelled round with a middle management marketing executive, Simon Dodds, from the Company's London Headquarters, as they hadn't yet appointed anyone locally in Spain to run things there. The doctors in Spain seemed particularly interested in studying one of the Company's new drugs, as it was novel in its approach to a particular disease. After visiting doctors in Valladolid in the north and two different hospitals in Madrid, they travelled south to Seville and Granada ending up in Cadiz, where a young up-and-coming doctor was sent by the Professor to entertain them before visiting him in his hospital later in the day.

So he took them to Jerez, the world famous sherry centre, where a very special wine and sherry tasting spread had been prepared in one of the famous Bodegas. This lavish spread was laid out in a wonderful courtyard under ages-old grape vines that wound their way along a trellis above their heads, giving a lovely cool feel to the whole place, especially in the midday sun. The whole environment was very relaxing and his hosts, being world travellers, spoke excellent English, so his meagre Spanish was not needed.

Dr. James admitted that he had absolutely no idea about how to behave under such circumstances. Apparently, or so he discovered some days later, after having carefully sampled a selected sherry or wine, he was supposed to spit it out, have a tasty morsel of something fairly bland to settle his pallet and try the next offering. What he didn't know was that he was not supposed to swallow each sample. Being virtually teetotal, he had a very poor head for alcohol, but managed to minimise the effect of the alcohol by consuming a reasonable amount of what he thought were very tasty between-drink morsels, assuming that would also count as lunch, especially as the afternoon was creeping on.

And so the whole episode went on for about three hours from midday to about 3.00pm, Dr. James just about holding his own. Imagine his horror when his hosts then announced it was time to leave for lunch, which was planned for 4.00pm. Before they went, however, there was to be a very important signing ceremony to be carried out.

When the head of the Bodega rang a beautiful golden hand bell, a gentleman appeared from inside a nearby building wearing an outfit that Dr. James assumed was similar to what bullfighters wore. It was apparently a very old livery of that Bodega. In his white-gloved hands he carried, with great pomp and ceremony, a beautiful leather-bound book, which he carefully laid on an antique table that another liveried gentleman had brought out from the same building.

With great elegance, and in perfect English, David James and Simon Dodds were asked to step forward and examine the book. Certain pages were demonstrated on which the senior liveried gentleman proudly pointed out the famous world leaders who had visited the Bodega, one of the European Kings and a European country's President being perhaps the most prominent.

He then turned to the last page, which was most beautifully inscribed with the date of their visit, a heart-warming welcome to the Bodega and some verbose description of the apparent importance of the visit. The two visitors were then invited to sign their names in the special place provided. Under Simon Dodds' name was written "Dr. Simon Dodds, International Director of a World-Renowned Pharmaceutical Company". Under Dr. James's space was written "Dr. David James, Professor of Medicine, London University, England".

They both signed with an amused smile on their faces, and didn't say a word.

During his time with the Pharmaceutical Company, Dr James was allowed to become an honorary Clinical Assistant in a nearby hospital in a subject of his choice. He saw patients once a week if he wasn't away on company business, as he felt he wanted to keep his clinical hand in. It was as a direct result of his work in this department that he thought up an idea that the Company decided to run with. He was given £1.00 for signing over the patent to the Company. His idea made millions of pounds. He didn't feel cheated at the time, because he said he wouldn't have had the idea had he not worked for the Company, which in any case was paying him a good salary.

Dr. James said that, if he had been asked at that time where he thought his medical career would end, he would most likely have said he had no idea. Perhaps he might end up as Medical Director of a Pharmaceutical Company, as things were going quite well for him at the time, and of course the Chairman and Managing Director were very pleased with him.

When a new idea is considered, to be developed into a marketable product, the Medical Adviser involved has to find doctors in clinical practice, usually Consultants in hospitals, who are experts in the relevant medical area, and who have patients suffering from the particular disease the drug needs to be tested on. In the meantime, extensive tests are carried out on laboratory animals to check the drug's safety before it is allowed to be given to the first human beings, who are usually volunteers. Dr. James said he was often one of the first, as he felt it unreasonable to ask anyone else to take it if he wasn't prepared to take it first himself.

One of the Doctors he met, who he wanted to study the drug he had invented, was a Consultant Psychiatrist, who had written an interesting book on the subject in question, entitled 'Not All In The

Mind♥. When he met him, however, he found he was changing people's diet to see if their symptoms were caused by eating certain foods, and if those foods were avoided whether the symptoms would disappear. Some patients were so tense and agitated that they were on the waiting list for a frontal lobotomy, an operation on the brain to cut certain nerve tracts.

While the operation could achieve the desired effect, it not surprisingly had undesirable effects, especially on the person's memory and personality. This doctor found that, by getting the patient to avoid certain foods, he could take them off the operating waiting list.

Dr. James had already been interested in food allergies and had even noted the wide variety of symptoms they could cause, and he felt sure the whole area was far more relevant to medicine than was considered by most doctors at the time. So he started to study the subject in depth, even attending courses and conferences in America, instead of taking a holiday. Eventually, however, his interest in this area became so strong, and he had learned so much about it, that he decided he needed to go into General Practice to try the basic principles on his own patients. So he did a short spell in one practice followed by an eighteen month long locum in a city centre practice, before ending up in Stead Norton.

For a young man in his twenties, Dr. James thought that travelling to other countries and staying in good hotels was a real luxury. When it was decided that he needed to go somewhere, he would do all the planning with whoever was going to be involved with him, both in the UK and overseas, then simply ring up the travel department and tell them where he was going and when. He would leave all the flight and travel arrangements to them and simply pick up his travel documents as soon as they were ready.

He had become quite friendly with one of the UK Reps early on, and met him fairly regularly for lunch, just to chat about life in general. He must have been working for the company for about three

---

♥ To obtain a copy of this book, see the Appendix 2, note 1.

months and had been assigned various countries to be responsible for, as the company had a brand new drug they wanted to market all over the world. To do so, it meant encouraging hospital Specialists in each country to do a study on their particular drug and then publish the results, preferably in a local medical journal.

The countries he had been assigned to were originally Greece, Germany, Spain and France, among others. He quite fancied travelling especially to France and Greece, and lying in the sun at a 5-star hotel waiting for his next appointment. But then things changed. The management decided to take France and Greece away from him and give them to other doctors who had been appointed to the staff at roughly the same time as he was.

Shortly after that, he had lunch with his friend. He was bemoaning the fact that they had taken France and Greece away from him, but his friend put him firmly in his place but telling him that the management had taken Bristol and Birmingham away from him!

Because of the novelty of the new drug, the Company's doctors were very busy travelling all over the world setting up clinical trials, so on one occasion he had to make a trip to America. On this occasion, this time in Florida one day in June, David James was staying in a 5-Star Hotel, when the fire alarm went off in the middle of the night. When he woke up with a start, because of the different time zone from England, he was understandably confused as to what was going on and even where he was. To make things worse, a security guard unlocked the door to his room and ordered him to get up and leave immediately and not to take anything with him.

So he did as he was told and joined a throng of people in the corridor outside his room. Imagine his horror when, as he heard the door close behind him, with the key inside, he remembered that he had forgotten to pack his pyjamas. He was stark naked!

Chapter 4

"Dr. James was quite a young man when he first arrived here, or so I thought at the time," said Maud Hughes. "You would have thought he would have found it very difficult to take over from Dr. Braithwaite, who had been much loved, had worked hard for the good of his patients, and had effectively devoted himself to them. He was a staunch Roman Catholic who never married. His church was his first love. He had a morning and evening surgery Monday to Saturday every week of the year, including Christmas Day if it didn't land on a Sunday, when he would be found in church!

"He never went on holiday for all the years he was our doctor. He was a bit of a skinflint and didn't want to spend money going somewhere he probably wouldn't enjoy anyway, or so he said. Besides, a locum would have cost him money. When he was dying of lung cancer, he even saw patients from his bed. Unfortunately he had been a very heavy smoker. It was awful going into his surgery. When you walked into his consulting room, you could hardly see him sitting in his chair on the other side of the room for all the clouds of smoke. Towards the end, Dr. James came in to help with surgeries, so it was natural that he should take over the practice when Dr. Braithwaite finally gave up. He died a week later.

"There were many reasons why Dr. James became accepted so quickly. One was because quite simply he was such a lovely and friendly man. He hardly changed any of the things Dr. Braithwaite had done, although he eventually stopped surgeries on Christmas Day! However, he appeared to do a couple of miracles very early on, so his reputation soon went round.

"The first person he made a huge difference to was Ada Townsend. She used to be a dancer and had been very proud of her slim ankles. In her sixties, they had started to swell up and she became very short of breath. Dr. Braithwaite said she needed to calm down, as she was quite an excitable person, so he put her onto some sort of a tranquilliser, phenobarbitone I think it was, which he had given to so many people like Ada. He once offered it to me. I can't remember why or even why I went to him in the first place.

"Ada lived in a little cottage in Main Street, with a kitchen and small room downstairs, and two small bedrooms upstairs. Because climbing stairs made Ada even more short of breath, Dr. Braithwaite suggested she abandon the upstairs part of the cottage, and have her bed moved downstairs. I remember it well because your dad helped carry the bed down and make that little room as comfortable as possible, while the district nurses made sure Ada was able to wash adequately in her kitchen.

"Ada had lived like that for at least ten years before Dr. James arrived on the scene, and I don't believe she ever went upstairs at all. She once told me she had almost forgotten what was up there.

"Ada was on Dr. Braithwaite's list of people to visit at home every so often, so presumably Dr. James saw her for the first time soon after he took over. I met Ada in the street about two or three weeks later. I have never been so surprised in my life. Her face was a bag of smiles, having been a bit sad and depressed before that, possibly because of the effect of the drug. Her legs were all slim again and she kept showing them to anyone who cared to look. She had always thought of them as her best feature, and had mourned their grossness, as she called them.

"She hold me exactly what had happened. I remember it well. I suppose it was because it was just about the first story that started to go round about the new doctor. Ada said Dr. James seemed so interested in everything about her. He even asked her to tell him about all the dancing she had done, what shows she had been in – she had danced on the London West End stage when she was young – she was that proud of herself. She was thrilled that the new doctor was interested in her past.

"He apparently examined her very carefully, taking quite a long time over her, something she didn't remember Dr. Braithwaite ever doing. Ada said he looked into her eyes with a fancy instrument, took her blood pressure, listened very carefully to her chest and heart, and took particular interest in her legs. He showed her how he could make a dimple in the swelling in her ankles that gradually filled up when he took his fingers away. She asked him what that meant and he simply told her that her feet were waterlogged, possibly because her heart wasn't pumping as well as it should have done. He then did some sort of electrical tracing of her heart.

"What really impressed Ada was when he said to her, 'I'd like to try something quite simple. I'd like to see if we can get rid of all that water and help your heart to beat a little more strongly. I'd also like to see if your body could now manage without the tranquilliser drug you've been on for such a long time. Would you like to give it a try?'

"Ada was truly astonished that the new doctor had almost asked her opinion. She said he said it in such a simple and calm way that it gave her so much confidence to have a go. Besides, she was fed up with the extreme limitation on her life from all that shortness of breath. Dr. James warned her that she would need to go to the toilet more often for a while as it was the only way her body could get rid of all that water in her legs, and apparently also in her lungs.

"Dr. James gave her two drugs, a water tablet as he called one of them and a very old-fashioned drug for her heart. It was only later when we all became interested in everything he did that he eventually told us that that drug was basically an extract of the purple foxglove called digoxin, which had been known to stimulate the heart for centuries. He also gave her some magnesium and vitamin E tablets and something called co-enzyme Q 10, both of which he said are important for the heart. The most difficult part for Ada was when he asked her to give up her regular cups of tea and coffee and chocolate, all of which she loved, so everyone kept buying them for her, as they felt so sorry for her. He said that caffeine is too much of a stimulant to the heart of the wrong sort".

"How do you know so much of Ada's treatment?" asked Lynda. "Aren't medical details supposed to be sort of secret between doctor and patient?

"Yes they are, but Dr. James did so many wonderful things to people in such a simple way early on, that the vicar asked him if he would give a series of lectures to anyone who would like to hear him talk. He happily agreed, so he started when he had been our doctor for only about four months. It turned out that so many people wanted to hear him, that the only place big enough was the Parish Church. By then, Dr. James had struck up an amazing relationship with the vicar, the Reverend Henry Middleton, and the two of them became inseparable in their work for us all.

"The vicar would tell the doctor when someone was ill or who he felt would benefit from a visit. There were some very tough and obstinate folk around here who wouldn't think of calling out a doctor unless they were dying, and even then there were some strange stories to tell about some of them. In his turn the doctor would tell the vicar if he felt someone could benefit from some pastoral care, which the vicar was very good at.

"It was because of the talks Dr. James gave that we all learned so much about what he was doing and thinking about. Ada became virtually normal within about three weeks of starting his treatment. She was so excited and thrilled that the news went round the area like wildfire, very much helped by Ada herself. So she not only gave him permission to explain what he had done for her and why, in fact she insisted her case be the first one he described in his talks, once he started them."

Chapter 5

"You said there were two particular stories very early on that impressed people. What was the second one?" asked Patrick.

"Well it was really quite a simple story, but at the time it caused a real stir. Old man Isaac Pemberton's rather simple daughter rang the doctor because she was worried about her dad's cough. Dr. James visited him in his cottage after morning surgery and examined him very carefully saying he thought he might have 'a touch of pneumonia' just like me. He put him onto a course of antibiotics, which his daughter Janine fetched from his surgery – he dispensed his own drugs, as we are quite a way from the nearest chemist. Dr. James popped in to see how he was getting on the next day and the day after that. When he visited him about a week later, he told old man Isaac that he was so much better and his lungs appeared completely clear that he could get up and go downstairs for a few hours and gradually get back to normal over the next few days.

"What Dr. James didn't know was that two years before that Dr. Braithwaite had visited old man Isaac for much the same problem, had also given him a course of antibiotics and had told him to stay in bed. At the time the doctor was rather busy because the flu was going round and he must have forgotten to visit him again and give him the all clear. Old man Isaac had stayed in bed all that time! When Dr. James told him he could get up, it was like a miracle to everyone – the second one. You see what I mean? He only did what he thought was normal medical practice, but it was like new medicine to the folks round here".

"What did Dr. James say at the talks he gave? What was he really trying to tell people?" asked Patrick.

Chapter 6

When Dr. James gave his first talk in the Parish Church, he had set up a simple overhead projector and illustrated his talk with slides. What he put on those slides were simple statements, nothing complicated. He then talked around the subject.

Dr. James said that some aspects of medicine were absolutely brilliant, but others were not so good as far as he was concerned. The really good parts were the emergency services, where someone had had a heart attack, was injured in a car accident or a stabbing or had something like an acute appendix. Then the approach was truly excellent in his opinion, which was one of the reasons why he was glad he had worked in the Casualty Department in the hospital in The Caribbean. He also did over six months as a junior Anaesthetist when he returned to England, as he felt that being first on call to help resuscitate someone who had had a heart attack, for example, was really worth learning about. A doctor who could stop someone from dying whose heart had stopped working was really worth his weight in gold, he thought.

So he explained the value of the ambulance men and women and the Paramedics who often worked hard to stabilise a patient at the scene of an accident or in the home of a heart attack patient, before carrying them to hospital, where the full emergency teams would take over. Many was the time that the hospital staff marvelled at the professionalism of those who went out to the scene of the problem.

Where he felt medicine sort of let people down was in the long-term management of chronic illnesses like asthma, eczema, arthritis, irritable bowel syndrome and multiple sclerosis, in fact just about all illnesses rather than emergencies. When someone had had an accident or a heart attack, you knew what the problem was and you had to deal with it in a hurry. You knew what the cause of the problem was. That was the most important aspect. The doctor knew what the cause was, and therefore how to deal with it.

When a doctor sees a patient with a chronic illness, he doesn't know what the cause is, or at least medical students and doctors are not taught to consider what the cause is. They only know that such and such a drug may make the patient feel better if they are lucky, because that is what they have been told by a drug company representative or they have read it in a medical journal.

So a doctor's only main treatment options are to write out a prescription for what he considers to be an appropriate drug or recommend an operation to remove part or all of an organ if he considers it has become diseased, hoping the patient can manage without it for the rest of his or her life. There are a few miscellaneous treatment options available to him such as a visit to a physiotherapist or a psychotherapist. Treatment with a drug or an operation clearly do help a lot of people, but Dr. James's point was that there is no thought to the cause or causes.

When Dr. James worked for the Pharmaceutical Company, on three occasions he presented an idea for research to the Research Director, one of which the Main Board actually ran with and became a great financial success. With the other two he identified a disease for which there were very few drugs on the market that were of much benefit but also identified a naturally-occurring chemical that was very effective but was too toxic to be used regularly. He suggested that the company's chemists play what he called molecular roulette to see if they could produce a patentable chemical that retained all the activity of the original chemical, but one that lacked its toxicity.

In each case his ideas were rejected as he was told that that was not the way they did things. Apparently the company was working on a particular line of chemicals, and, when they found some sort of activity, that was when they looked for a disease on which it might work. The problem with that approach, thought Dr. James, was that it was the wrong way round. Also, having found some degree of activity in an animal model of a disease, the chemical might subsequently be found to work on another area of importance, and that, if it were affected, might well produce an important unwanted adverse effect, in which case the drug would have to be withdrawn, at great cost and loss to the Company's budgets.

Dr. James said he was also aware that the adverse effects some drugs produced in the long run were actually caused by the nutritional deficiencies the drug induced in the person, which was why he recommended vitamins and mineral supplements to so many of his patients. He also said that many drugs entered the market place to be used to treat specific medical conditions, only for it to be discovered in due course that the mechanism of action of the drug was completely different from what it was first thought to be. Hence you could say, he said, that doctors don't know what they are really doing. He felt that long-term drug treatment was a bit hit-and-miss. In all cases he felt the missing bit was why? Why was the person ill? The hit part would come if the underlying cause or causes could be found and dealt with or eliminated. That was what he was really trying to get at, and get across to his patients.

It was many years after he started giving these talks that he described the best possible example of a drug being introduced to treat a medical condition, the original reason why it was said to do what it apparently did being shown to have been wrong all the time. Two drugs to treat stomach and duodenal ulcers were developed by two separate Pharmaceutical Companies. When long-term studies on patients were carried out, the ulcers seemed to heal well enough, but only so long as the patients kept taking the drugs. If the patients stopped the drugs for one reason or another, the ulcer gradually came back again. This meant that the patient basically needed to remain on the drug for the rest of their life, much to the delight of the two Pharmaceutical Companies, who were destined to make a small fortune from these drugs.

In due course, an unimportant Australian researcher, Dr. Barry Marshall, suggested that these ulcers were in fact caused by a spiral-shaped organism called *Helicobacter pylori.* Doctors had seen these organisms under the microscope for years when they had taken a biopsy sample. However, they were of the opinion that no organism could possibly survive the acid of the stomach, so it had to be an artefact. Yet it was nearly always there. They were clearly wrong. Dr. James wondered why doctors were not prepared to accept what they could see. Surely, he argued, if it was there, it must be there for a reason. It was up to the doctors to explain it, which they were not willing to try to do, as it didn't fit into their current ideas of what ulcers were all about.

Dr. Marshall made himself very ill when, to prove his point, he swallowed a big dose of *Helicobacter pylori,* yet he 'cured' himself with a big dose of antibiotics. He also suggested that a two-week course of antibiotics was all that ulcer patients needed and not a life-long supply of those drugs. Dr. James wondered how it was that he wasn't run over by a bus!

Originally it had been 'established' that stomach and duodenal ulcers were caused by damage to certain specialised receptors lining that area of the intestines, which these drugs were able to 'calm down', or block. Since no one was looking for a reason why these receptors were being damaged in the first place, it was logical that ulcer patients would need to remain on one of these drugs for the rest of their lives, to prevent the ulcer from returning. In fact the drug company researcher who identified these receptors was awarded a Nobel Prize for Medicine, so important was this discovery considered to be at the time.

After Dr. Marshall's 'demonstration' on himself, it was subsequently demonstrated that the two drugs had a completely different mode of action than the one first assumed. It was shown that, instead of having a blocking effect on those specialised receptors, these drugs had a potent anti-allergic effect, blocking the stomach and duodenum's allergic reaction to the *Helicobacter pylori.* Dr. James wondered just how many other drugs were working in a completely different way from the one being advertised, which could be another reason why so many drugs had often very nasty side or adverse effects.

Dr. James later on talked about another medical problem, this time a possible cause of cancer, which he felt fell into the same category. Once again he felt the medical profession was ignoring what they could see under a microscope because it didn't fit into their current theories of cancer.

"Dr. James also felt that doctors sometimes become so entrenched in their standard way of doing things," said Maud, "that they feel uncomfortable when someone suggests another way of doing things. The establishment sometimes appears determined to get rid of a doctor who seems to be trying to break the mould. He described how he felt history has a lot of examples, not necessarily in only medicine. I well remember how Mrs Pankhurst fought and fought to get women the right to be allowed to vote. Today it seems incredible that only men were allowed to vote before then, because somehow women were considered incapable of making decisions. Before even that, only men who owned land had the right to vote.

"Dr. James described how a doctor in Austria, Dr. Semmelweiss, tried to get medical colleagues to wash their hands before they attended women in labour. An infection known as puerperal fever was very common in hospitals, where doctors did the examinations, but were far less common where midwives did all the delivering. Doctors would do post-mortem dissections on rotting, infected bodies for anatomy lectures to students, then would simply wipe their hands on a rag before going into the delivery wards, where they examined each woman in turn. They would go from one woman to another, possibly wiping their hands on the same rag, and so actually be the cause of spreading any infection. Having examined a line of women in labour, the rag would be absolutely filthy.

"However, doctors in those days talked about 'laudable pus'. I remember Dr. James using those words, because they suggested that the pus was a good thing, something laudable, which he said means to be praised. In those days, doctors said pus was there to help the healing process. I don't suppose they knew anything about germs in those days. The whole thing sounds absolutely terrifying. So many women must have died in agony and in appalling conditions, particularly if they were poor.

"When Dr. James came to see me recently shortly after he had retired from here, we somehow got round to talking about this doctor. I think I asked him if things had improved in any way, and the name of Semmelweiss just came up. He said that nowadays, of course, it is considered normal practice to wash your hands regularly, and he tried to point out how doctors do eventually change and adopt new ideas, yet are very hard on originators to begin with.

"He said he was concerned that doctors don't seem capable of learning from history. He couldn't understand why they have to be so ruthless against a new idea. Why can't they keep an open mind and let time take the new idea forward and see if it has any merit or if it fails in the long run, he would say. Yet even such a good idea to wash your hands regularly seems to have been forgotten to a degree, which is why all these nasty antibiotic resistant bugs are all over our hospitals. I wouldn't go into one if you paid me. The thought scares me to death.

"Apparently the medical profession not only totally ignored the suggestion by Dr. Semmelweiss that doctors should wash their hands in between each patient, and especially after dissecting dead bodies, but they also ostracised him and drove him mad. He died a very disillusioned man, in a mental asylum, I believe.

"Any way," said Maud. "I'm feeling a bit tired, so I think I'll go to sleep now, if you two don't mind."

Chapter 7

"Did you sleep well, Gran?" Asked Patrick when he brought Maud's breakfast up on a tray the next morning.

"Oh! How kind of you," said Maud, as she pulled herself up from under the bedclothes? "Yes thank you. I slept like a log. I've been sleeping so much better since you two came to stay. It must be all the talking I'm doing," she giggled. "I hope I'm not boring you?"

"Absolutely not," said Patrick. "Your stories are fascinating."

"Well, Dr. James was a fascinating man. In fact his fame sort of spread to such an extent that the price of houses went up as people gradually tried to move here to be on his panel, just like I'm told some people move house to get their children into a better local school. Anyway, let me eat this lovely breakfast you have so kindly made for me. Then I'll get up, have a bath and come downstairs. I'm feeling well enough to do that."

"Shouldn't you wait for the doctor to say it's ok, Gran? What do you think, Lynda?" Asked Patrick.

"Blow the doctor", said Maud before Lynda could give her opinion. "Dr. James taught us to think for ourselves, and I think I've recovered enough to come downstairs. So down I'm coming when I have had a bath. Off you go, you two. I won't be long."

"Take your time, Gran," said Patrick. "Enjoy a nice soak."

"Would you like me to scrub your back for you?" Volunteered Lynda.

"Oh how lovely. You are kind. I haven't had that done to me for a very long time. My husband Ted, God rest his soul, used to do it for me, but not towards the end when he got older. Give me a few minutes to finish my breakfast. I'll call you when I'm ready."

It was later in the day when Maud had had her back scrubbed, Patrick and Lynda had had their breakfast and washed up and the Doctor had visited Maud as he had planned to do. Two District Nurses had also visited, but found there was little to do, so they simply stayed as long as they dared, enjoying chatting to her. The

Doctor had wisely told her he thought it was ok for her to get up, but advised her not to be up for too long.

"Don't worry, Doctor," Maud said. "I'll enjoy a few hours down here, then I promise I'll go back to bed. In any case, I have my resident nurse here who will no doubt keep an eye on me." And she winked at Lynda. "Apart from which, we have a lot of catching up to do."

So as not to tire Maud out, Lynda told her of the work she had done before she married Patrick, but they were longing to hear more of Maud's fascinating stories. So in fact it was not until the next day that the subject of Dr. James came up again. It was strange how little things seemed to remind her of him. This time it was an item in the News describing how a famous actress had been rushed into hospital from a show she had been in in the West End, and they had diagnosed an ectopic pregnancy, which meant they had to operate, so she lost the baby.

"Dr. James was very good at making the correct diagnosis. When he had been here for about ten years, he must have felt he really knew people and what they were like. I remember Joe Small telling me how Dr. James had insisted he was right when Joe's wife Mavis had an ectopic pregnancy. He listened to her story very carefully then examined her properly and made a confident diagnosis. He then rang the local hospital and asked to speak to the doctor on duty for Gynaecology, saying he had an unusual situation. Joe heard him explain the symptoms, but also that her husband had had his tubes tied, but he knew the couple well enough to guarantee that there had not been any hanky-panky. Yes, he agreed, it was an unusual situation, but he was absolutely confident of the diagnosis.

"Well, he kept his calm when the junior hospital doctor refused to take Mavis in, insisting she must have an acute appendicitis or something like that, so it was a job for the emergency surgery department. Very quietly he asked to speak to the Registrar on duty in the Gynaecology Department, went through the same approach, but once again got nowhere. So he quietly asked for the name of the Consultant on duty, who not surprisingly was at home. He apologised for ringing him at home and once again he told his story and repeated how confident he was that Mavis had an ectopic pregnancy. He also explained that the two junior doctors in the hospital had felt it was not a case for them.

"Clearly the Consultant was a sensible man, because he asked Dr. James how many cases of ectopic pregnancy he had ever seen. When he said 'Well over a hundred when I was in The Caribbean' the Consultant said 'Send her in immediately. I will attend to her personally. I have only seen about twenty myself'.

"Apparently that whole episode started up a real friendship between the two, Dr. James and the Consultant Obstetrician Gynaecologist. I gather Dr. James had wanted to specialise in that whole area, hoping to go back to The Caribbean as a Registrar a year or two after he had come back to the UK, but it hadn't worked out. He gave a talk at the hospital of his experiences in The Caribbean one evening, and somehow we got to hear about it, so over a hundred of us turned up to hear him speak. They had never had such a full lecture theatre ever before. What was also rather funny was that his talk was sponsored by a Pharmaceutical Company that was providing and paying for a buffet meal, presumably for the doctors. We didn't bother to ask. We just tucked into the food.

"Another amusing aspect of the whole business was that when we were asked why we had all come we told everyone of the wonderful talks Dr. James occasionally gave in the local church. From then on sometimes a few people came from the hospital to his talks. They had asked for the dates to be advertised on the hospital notice board."

Chapter 8

Maud did as she said and didn't stay out of bed for too long, after Lynda had said, "I think that's enough for today, Maud, if you don't mind. We'd love to hear more, but you told the doctor that I would keep an eye on you, so my advice is that you go back to bed". Loving being looked after by these two, Maud willingly obliged and went upstairs to her bedroom and slept for a while, eventually coming downstairs again to have supper with Patrick and Lynda. Then all three went up to her bedroom, Maud got back into bed, which Lynda had tidied up for her, and they played cards for an hour or so.

Next morning, Maud was up before Patrick and Lynda and actually prepared breakfast for them. She said she felt so much better, which she put down to their company rather than the antibiotics the doctor had given her.

"I don't really believe in drugs, but I decided to take them just in case. I was always amused by the diagnosis 'a touch of pneumonia'. Surely you've either got it or you haven't. But then I suppose a doctor in the sticks has to make up his mind and do something, rather than send everyone to hospital for tests to prove the point.

"I really must demand to have my regular vitamin B12 injection from this new doctor. Dr. James gave it regularly to any old folk who were willing to have it, gladly continuing what Dr. Braithwaite had done before him. He said that was something he thoroughly approved of. But he also recommended tablets of vitamins and minerals to many of us, if he thought we needed them or he thought we didn't have a very good diet. I think my body is saying it needs another shot."

Dr. James had care of a few patients in local old peoples' homes. When he took over he found many of them had been put onto a cocktail of drugs by the local visiting Geriatric Specialist, some to calm them down, some to wake them up and some to help them sleep. He was aware that that was standard practice all over the country, as much as anything to help the staff run an orderly place. He had heard a Specialist justify such an approach, saying that so many old people were suffering from a degree of dementia, and that they needed to be looked after in such homes. Indeed the daughters and sons of some of these old people had found that they just couldn't cope. So the system worked that way.

Dr. James decided to try another approach, so after he had visited and examined some of these old people, he spoke to their younger relatives and agreed a plan with them, saying he did not know if it would work but he would like to try. Once he had started the idea, he was surprised how many were willing to help. He found that many of the younger relatives had felt guilty not only at not being able to cope but also because they had passed their responsibilities onto other people. He also found that they were distressed to see their parents or elderly relatives in what they could only describe as a zombie-like state, which Dr. James said might not be dementia but be side effects of some of the drugs. If there were a degree of dementia, he wondered if it could be caused by nutritional deficiencies.

Because of what he wanted to do, he had to explain everything not only to the relatives but also to the matrons in charge of the homes, because it meant a change in their diet. He even had the various patients in on the meetings although he wasn't sure if any of them could understand anything he said. He explained that it was for their benefit, so they should at least be involved as far as was reasonable.

What he wanted was for the diet to be essentially the same as he had recommended to so many people, no dairy, caffeine, alcohol, sugar, white four products or chemical additives. He wanted them to drink as much water as they could manage and have as much in the way of fruit and vegetables as possible. Because that might put a strain on the homes' food preparation systems, the younger relatives were asked to bring in some fruit and vegetables for those to eat who had adequate teeth of their own. To help with vegetables he asked them to prepare homemade soups and try to bring them in every day. In fact three or four of them worked out a rota system, so they wouldn't have to do it every day. The matrons said they could easily help by warming up the soups when it was mealtime.

Dr. James then drew up a plan to try to reduce the drugs, but first he wanted to give each patient a vitamin B12 injection and some vitamin and mineral tablets. If some of them couldn't swallow tablets, he provided a powdered preparation, but said it was not so strong so would take a bit longer to work through.

To begin with there were a few teething problems. Some of the old folk were not really aware what was going on and wanted to eat what everyone else was eating, such as chocolate cake and sweet cups of tea in the mid-afternoon. So it took quite a lot of work by the staff to calm some of them down, and, to be fair, the plan was sadly abandoned quite early on for one or two of them. Fortunately, however, they were able to get through to most of them and explain what they were trying to achieve, especially those who had originally fought every time they were given their drugs. In fact, one or two of them seemed to pick up on the programme so quickly that they refused to take any more drugs, so the drugs' gradual withdrawal programme was effectively suddenly dropped with these few.

The difference this made to some people was astonishing, to the extent that some eventually asked to go home. Dr. James said it was quite logical and he explained that many aspects of one's body wear out as we get older, which is quite to be expected. In particular he picked out the production of acid in the stomach, the production of which diminished with age, some people naturally being affected more than others.

If this happened, he explained, one's ability to break down food in the stomach was affected, apart from which older people often had poor appetites anyway, irrespective of whether they had their own teeth or not, but often also because they had gradually developed a zinc deficiency over the years. As the bones in their jaw changed with age, they often found their dentures didn't fit properly, so they didn't bother to wear them. So nutritional deficiencies were an inevitable result. Since the effect of many such deficiencies is on the brain, behavioural problems were an almost inevitable consequence.

Dr. James said that what most doctors know but don't think of most of the time is that the area of the stomach that produces acid is the same area that produces intrinsic factor, a chemical that marks vitamin B12 in the diet for absorption later down the digestive tube. No acid, no intrinsic factor, no vitamin B12 absorption. Result – behavioural problems put down as old-age dementia. Once again Dr. James felt most doctors are far too quick to prescribe a drug to modify any apparent unusual behaviour than to try to work out why the problem had occurred in the first place. Although it didn't work for all the old people, he satisfied himself that he had made a valuable point that it was important to consider nutrition all the time. After all, as he explained, our bodies are made up of what we eat and what we are able to absorb from what we eat. "Our bodies can't survive on thin air, like orchids can, so far as I'm aware", he said.

"Don't forget," Dr. James also said, "Doctors are supposed to have great respect for Hippocrates the Father of Medicine, after whose name the Hippocratic Oath is based. Hippocrates is credited with saying 'Let food be thy medicine and medicine thy food'".

Chapter 9

Later that day, in the middle of the afternoon, they sat down to a cup of tea and cake. "Were all Dr. James's experiences long and complicated?" Asked Lynda. "After all to try to get other doctors to practice this type of medicine would effectively require a complete rethink of the way medical students are taught. You could say he was a medical detective, always trying to find the cause of the problem and correcting it."

"That's exactly what Dr. James called himself once – a medical detective. He felt it really conjured up what he tried to do. He said that anyone could prescribe drugs once they had learned how to handle them, but to do what he did required a lot of thought and a deep understanding of what makes the body tick.

"He sometimes wondered what medical students got from all those lectures about how the body functioned. He said he would love to have been given a chance to teach them and get them thinking along his way of doing things, as well as continuing to teach about drugs and surgery. He thought it would probably be too difficult to try to influence doctors who had already qualified and been in practice some years. He felt many of them were too died-in-the-wool and probably couldn't or wouldn't want to change.

"Dr. James told me once that he and his fellow medical students found the basic study of anatomy and physiology rather boring, although they knew how important it all was. He said they all wanted to get into the wards to start treating sick people, patients. They felt that was where their talents lay. However, he said that, once they got amongst the patients, they were shown how to make a diagnosis and what treatment to apply to that diagnosis, either an appropriate drug to deal with the symptoms or an operation to remove the offending or damaged organ.

"Later on in his career he began to realise that nothing in their training said anything about trying to return the patient to normality. He said surely that was what doctors ought to be trying to achieve, which was why he now studied anatomy and physiology with greater interest because he wanted to be sure what the normal is so that he could try to help the patient to get back there.

"Yet sometimes his approach was very easy as far as he was concerned. I remember him telling us at one of the Church lectures that sometimes the simplest approach was the easiest. I remember this one because 10-year-old Betty Johnson's mother was also called Maud. She took Betty to his evening surgery once and asked for a tonic for her. When Dr. James asked what the problem was she explained that Betty wasn't doing very well at school. As was his way, he asked more questions, something he always told us were so important, and not to take the first statement at its face value.

"Maud Johnson then explained that Betty kept falling asleep in her lessons. Again when pushed she said she only fell asleep in the afternoons, not in the mornings. The problem wasn't with any particular teacher because it didn't matter who took the lessons. Maud was worried because Betty was falling behind the others in her class. The head teacher had suggested she ask the doctor for a tonic or otherwise they might have to call in an Educational Psychologist. That frightened the wits out of Maud Johnson at the thought of her Betty being picked out for special attention.

"'Does she fall asleep in the afternoons at weekends?' asked Dr. James. 'Now that you ask, she seems full of beans at the weekends. Perhaps the head teacher is right after all', suggested Maud Johnson. 'I'm not so sure', mused Dr. James. 'What does she have for lunch?' 'I send her to school with sandwiches. They don't have a canteen at school'.

"'Ok', said Dr. James. 'Do you think you could stop giving her anything with wheat in it for a few days? I will give you a list. Send her to school with some fruit and sticks of carrot or something like that. Let's see how she gets on. Tell your head teacher we are trying something and to speak to me if she is worried'.

"Dr. James apparently thought no more about it until he got home from visiting patients in their own homes one day about a month later, to find a scruffy piece of paper shoved through his surgery letterbox. There was no indication who it was from and all it said was

'Thanks, Doc. It wasn't the bread. It was the cheese!' Maud Johnson had obviously twigged what Dr. James was thinking and had worked it out for herself."

"Dr. James must have helped so many people in such a simple way over the years that we never heard of. I mean, to him Betty's problem was so basic. In next to no time he had sorted out a young girl. Fortunately her mother was bright. But just imagine what she might have gone through, with the Educational Psychologist getting involved and all that would have entailed. And just think of the cost, when all the girl needed to do was stop eating cheese. So simple, yet so practical and so effective. I wonder how many people there are in the world who would benefit from seeing someone like Dr. James. Imagine the savings in the cost of drugs, for example, especially when so many of them don't seem to do what they are supposed to do, or have nasty side effects. Many people have told me how grateful they were to be able to stop their drugs, once Dr. James had helped them.

"He said that was one of the reasons why he loved General Practice. He was pleased he was the first person a patient came to to have their problems sorted out. That gave him a unique opportunity to try to sort out their symptoms before they became a real problem.

"In fact I remember another person whose problem he sorted out very quickly. Jennifer Small consulted him because of a pain in her hip or lower back area. She wasn't exactly sure where it was. It didn't trouble her all the time, but sometimes it could be quite a nuisance. She was a bit of a weekend golfer. She was on a lot of local committees and helped out in the hospital, so was a very busy person, seldom having time to play golf during the week."

Jennifer consulted Dr. James one Monday morning. "It's my wretched back or hip, Doctor. I'm not really sure which, but it can make walking quite difficult, and I'm putting on a bit of weight, which I don't like. I was never a slim person, but this doesn't suit me. It also interferes with my golf swing. It's not brilliant at the best of times, but I'm sure it used to be better when I was a bit lighter and more agile. Also the pain seems to affect me at the beginning of the week, so I can only assume it's somehow caused by playing golf. After all, you swing that part of the body when you drive, although I was told by the club professional that my swing is as smooth and perfect as anyone's he has seen. I should have a better handicap, but my eye is not as good as it should be."

"How active are you during the week?" Asked Dr. James.

"Very," replied Jennifer. " I walk everywhere I can. I refuse to go in lifts, and am known as the 'stair lover' by my friends and colleagues. I also eat very sensibly. I learned a lot about good eating habits at College. It's something I have always been interested in."

"So it doesn't make sense that you are putting on weight. Do you get tired?"

"Good Lord No. No one can keep up with me. I'm a bundle of energy."

"Ok! So let's look at the unusual. One reason some women put on weight is because their thyroid gland may not be working properly, but such people usually complain of fatigue, so we can probably rule that out in you, although we could consider doing a blood test in due course. So tell me about your weekends, especially the golfing, how much you play, that sort of thing."

"Well, on Saturdays and Sundays I get up about half an hour later than in the week, so about half past six, do some house work, have breakfast, and generally potter around the house, going to the club around eleven, probably staying until six or seven, a bit later during the summer. On Sundays I go to the eight o'clock service and may not get to the club until around midday. I probably have a salad for lunch on both days and tea and sandwiches around four. I usually play a couple of rounds on both days. It's a very sociable club. Lots of my friends play golf, or I suppose it's more appropriate to say I have found my friends from among those who play golf. That's about it, so far as I can think of." Dr. James wrote something down on a piece of paper and put it in a drawer.

"I assume you are here this morning because your pain is a bit of a nuisance and is making walking a bit difficult. Do you have the problem during the week, and when does it start?"

"Well it seems to begin during Saturday night and gets a bit worse during Sunday. I'm often a bit stiff in church and have a bit of difficulty getting up and down from kneeling. It generally seems worse on Sundays, and can be quite bad on Mondays, like this morning."

"How long ago did you start getting the pain? I mean is it a recent problem or has it been going on for years?"

"I need to think about that. It's certainly been getting worse for the past year or so, but it could have started when I joined the golf club about two years ago, shortly after we moved to this area. My husband retired so we decided to join the club together. Neither of us had played golf until then. We thought it would help us make new friends, and it has."

Dr. James examined her carefully. He found one or two tender spots, but otherwise her back and hips were remarkably mobile.

"We could do some X-rays, but I have a suspicion they wouldn't show much wrong with you. Yes, a little arthritis perhaps, but that's only to be expected at your age, although your joints seem to be in remarkably good condition to me. But I don't think that would explain your pain. Have you seen an osteopath or considered seeing one?"

"Yes I have, but at the time I wasn't in any discomfort. Like you, he couldn't explain the pain either. He also said my joints are in remarkably good condition for my age. So you both agree."

"Actually I haven't yet said I can't explain your pain. All I have said is that arthritis is probably not the explanation as it could be in so many people. The reason why I asked if you had seen an osteopath is because we doctors learn our anatomy on dead bodies, whereas osteopaths learn it on living moving people. If two of us with our different approaches to learning have failed to identify the cause of the pain from a structural point of view, then I start looking for other explanations.

"In fact I have written down an idea I thought of earlier on when I was asking you some of those questions. I've put it in my drawer. You told me about your golfing weekends, but I'm sure you left out quite a lot of details, of the sort I am interested in. It is often silly little things that people forget to mention that turn out to be the most important. To be fair to you, you don't know what I know. So can you think of anything that you do at the weekends that you haven't mentioned?"

"Not really, so I suppose you'd better ask me some specific questions."

"Ok. Let's talk about what you would have eaten, in detail if possible, or, more specifically if you can think of anything that might be different between what you eat at home and what you might have at the club."

"No there's nothing that I can think of. The food there is no different from at home."

"What about drinks?"

"Oh Lord. Of course. At the club, after I have finished playing, I have a glass or two of wine with whoever I have just played with, usually white, but sometimes red. I suppose by the time I have left the club I could have had perhaps three or four glasses."

"Any nibbles?"

"Sometimes a bag of nuts and raisins or two. They sort of go together."

"Do you have alcohol during the week days, or bags of nuts and raisins, for that matter?"

"Actually I don't. My husband is effectively a teetotaller, so we don't drink alcohol at home. I don't see any point in drinking on my own at home. I see what you are getting at. Could it be the alcohol?"

"When did you start to drink alcohol?"

"I've always had the odd glass, for example if I met a friend in town for lunch, but never on a regular basis. In that case I might have one glass of wine once every month of so. I would never drink more than one glass because I would be driving home. My husband drives us to and from the club, and he doesn't drink. So I suppose my regular drinking started when we joined the golf club. My husband and I seldom finish playing at the same time, so, by the time he is through, I may have finished an hour or two before that, by which time I could have had three glasses of wine and two bags of nutty things. "What did you write down on that piece of paper?"

Dr. James took it out of his drawer. "Alcohol", read Jennifer. "What made you think of that?"

"I don't play golf myself, but isn't the club house called the nineteenth hole, basically where everyone either celebrates their win or drowns their sorrows? You never mentioned anything about drinking, so I wondered. So many people have a drink and don't think anything of it."

"Yes, some of them do drink rather heavily. They are probably not safe to drive. I wonder why the police don't hover by the gate and check everyone who leaves. They'd make a fortune in fines. They can't all claim to play golf with the Chief Constable."

"Do you always drink wine, or do you drink anything else?"

"No. Only wine. Some of my friends drink shorts, but they seem to finish a glass so quickly. At least I can make a glass of wine last quite a long time."

"Would you be willing to give up all forms of alcohol for a while, and the grape in any form so raisins and sultanas? Wine is of course made from grapes, so there is a possible connection. You may have an intolerance to the grape. Most unusual, but distinctly possible in my experience. If you do, you will be taking grape extract in a jet-propelled vehicle, the alcohol of the wine. Besides, I know a number of people, especially women, who say that alcohol is one of the worst causes of their putting on weight."

"How interesting. I have to confess one of my friends at the club has given up alcohol completely for just that reason. She has lost about a stone in about three of four months. She is absolutely delighted. She also says she feels so much better in many silly little ways. Nothing special, just somehow better. Ok. I'll give it a try. It won't be a problem for me, and I imagine my husband will be delighted. He's often hinted on Sunday evening that perhaps I had too many glasses of wine at the club. Perhaps he's right. I don't know.

A month later, a happy Jennifer paid Dr. James a visit at his surgery. "So far so god," she said. "No pain, and I have lost six pounds. I don't want to lose it any faster. Actually I did have a glass of wine that first weekend. It was a bit silly of me. Somehow I just forgot. My husband finished his round of golf earlier than usual and came and joined us. He noticed the empty glass in front of me, and, as soon as he asked me if it was mine, I realised what a silly girl I had been. Couldn't sleep that night because of the pain. In a way I'm not sorry, because it has proved something to me. I've decided to stay off alcohol for the rest of my life."

"I feel I have a duty to tell people the truth," said Dr. James. "So let me explain something to you. If you stay off alcohol for, let us say, two or three months, your sensitivity to it should diminish sufficiently for you to be able to have a small glass of wine. But if you start drinking it regularly, your sensitivity to it will eventually return, and may produce different symptoms. It's all very strange. On the other hand, very occasionally, once a person has found the cause of their problems and they stop it, they seem to become even more sensitive to it than before, and find that a small dose has an even stronger response than before. But I repeat, that is the less common situation.

"So it's up to you. I just wanted you to know the facts. Also it would be a good idea to see if eating grapes, raisins or sultanas causes any problems. To be fair to you, you might be ok with whiskey or gin or champagne."

"Don't worry, Doctor. I'm not that bothered, and, to be fair, like my friend, I also feel somehow better. I may test some grapes, but after that I am happy to join my husband as a teetotaller. He won't half be pleased."

Chapter 10

"Dr. James loved the simple things of life in the country," said Maud. "He liked the fact that so much went on that people took for granted that would never happen in a big town or city. People had simple expectations and were far less demanding in the past, although more and more people are coming to live in Stead Norton from outside, buying up new houses as large gardens are sold off for building plots.

"Can't say I am happy about some of the newcomers," said Maud. "They buy a house supposedly in a country village, but bring their city dweller attitudes with them. I even heard someone in the shop the other day saying they were going to try to have the church bells silenced as the noise – fancy calling church bells a noise – woke them up when they wanted a lie-in on Sunday mornings. Why on earth did they buy a house so close to a church if they have that attitude? At least the Vicar has assured us they haven't a chance. He says our church has a right to summon the faithful to attend on a Sunday going back hundreds of years."

Dr. James felt life was so much more peaceful in the country. When he worked in the city practice before he settled in Stead Norton people seemed so much more demanding. They seemed to know their rights and were often determined to have them satisfied.

He felt that the people in Stead Norton were the sort of people he wanted to serve. Yes there were some pushy people, but so many were old fashioned, gentle in their ways, respectful of others in a simple, non-ingratiating way and overall seemed so much more content. Perhaps Maud was an extreme case, but there were others not unlike her, although none of them had lived in Stead Norton as long as she had.

Doug Berry lived two doors away from Dr. James. He had a fairly large property. The cottage was quite small, but it was surrounded by a lot of land that Doug tended to in his own way. He was the perfect market gardener. Whenever you went past his place, you could be sure he was digging away or tending to some plant. He never stopped, unless you chose to stop by and talk to him. He was a friendly old man, well into his eighties, with incredibly gnarled hands, although they served his purposes well enough. He had been a miner until he was about fifty, when his pit closed down further up north, so he came to live with his brother, who was not too well, and his wife, although Dr. James was never quite sure of their marital status.

They had a daughter, Janice, who was not quite 'all there' as they used to say, but she seemed harmless enough. Dr. James's predecessor had sent her for assessment to the local psychiatric hospital, and the doctors seemed to have come to an arrangement with her. They would admit her for about a month every so often. Janice loved it there, possibly because she was in love with one of the doctors, or so she said. Actually he was one of the gardeners, but Janice probably didn't know the difference. They were all so kind to her.

Janice looked forward to her visits away from home. In the meantime she would wander the streets aimlessly. Stead Norton was one of those villages whose main street didn't actually go anywhere. It simply began at a turn off a B road, ending at a small road junction where Church Street went off to the right and Station Road wandered slowly back to the B road. Yes, Stead Norton used to have a train station, though not even Maud could remember anything about it. All that was left was Station House, which looked as if it could have once been a station house, but had been altered and added to so many times it was hard to tell.

Stead Norton also had had a canal running through it in the late seventeen hundreds, but it had burst its banks some miles away and flooded the surrounding land. The owners lost a lot of money compensating the farmers, so it never functioned as a working canal.

Janice and her family lived half way down Station Road. Opposite their place was a wood that, as Maud had already said, no one seemed to own, so everyone wandered into it at will. Although kids can sometimes be unkind to people with a problem, they never were to Janice. One or two may have tried, but whatever they did or said would have gone over her head, so they had probably given up even if they had ever bothered to try.

It was when Janice stopped going into the wood and started to wander down the middle of the B road that Dr. James, following his predecessor's advice, arranged for her to be admitted into hospital once again. That seemed to be the sign. Fortunately the B road was not very busy, but was becoming busier, and everyone in Stead Norton said that, if she were ever knocked down and injured or killed by a car, they would all go to court in defence of the poor driver. Somehow everyone knew her time was up, and the moment Janice started to wander down the middle of the road, someone would tell Dr. James.

On the other hand, Janice had her own way of telling Dr. James that it was time for a holiday, as she called it. She would come to his surgery and start banging her head against the wall. She was often one of the first to queue up to see Dr. James. Sometimes if someone came in after her, when it was her turn the newcomer would kindly tell her she was next, only for Janice to slap the person gently with her empty handbag in a playful sort of way. Janice always wanted to be last in, whether she arrived first or not. It was only newcomers who didn't know her strange behaviour.

Of course, by then Dr. James knew that Janice was waiting to see him, and would also have been told she was wandering again in the middle of the B road, so when it was her turn for her to enter his consulting room, he would immediately be regaled with "I need a holiday, Doc!"

"All right, Janice. I'll organise it. I'll ring them up and see if they can fit you in as soon as possible. I'll come round and let you know as soon as they have a space for you."

Janice would waddle home in her funny way of walking. She always had high heeled shoes on that didn't fit her properly. That was probably one of the reasons it was so comic seeing her struggling down the middle of the B road. As soon as she got home she would stuff some clothes into a suitcase, anything so long as the case was full, and go downstairs, sit in a chair and rock herself gently, with a distant smile on her face. She would be in a world of her own. She would hardly eat anything until an ambulance came for her, when she would suddenly brighten up. To please her, the driver would turn his siren on when he left her house, only to turn it off when they were a mile away from the village. Stead Norton would heave a sigh of relief until the next time.

One day Doug Berry came to Dr. James's surgery. "What can I do for you?" Asked Dr. James.

"My brother Walt died about two this morning," said Doug.

"Why didn't you call me out?" Asked Dr. James.

"What for?" Replied Doug. "No need to get you out of bed. He were dead. Nothing you could do. Betty and I have laid him out nice and respectful like, ready for the undertaker. We've taken his teeth out. No good to him where he's gone. We knew he was going. You told us the other day that he probably didn't have long to go. His heart just gave up."

"There were many things about Stead Norton and its surroundings that Dr. James loved so much," continued Maud. "Because he had had great difficulty finding a locum doctor to take over if he went on holiday, he and his wife Elizabeth decided not to bother, and to spend the money that would save and buy ponies for the children and horses for themselves. After all, as he would say, once you have had your holiday and spent all that money, it was all gone and you then had to save up for the next holiday. Also a locum doctor could be additionally quite expensive. If you bought ponies and horses, on the other hand, you would get pleasure from them not just during the two weeks you would otherwise have been away on holiday, but any day you wanted to ride them, so effectively all the year round.

"Dr. James had a really beautiful black horse, while his wife had a white one. I think white horses are called grey. Not sure why. Anyway, it was wonderful to see the two of them riding down the street every so often, usually when the sun was shining. I don't suppose there was any point in their riding if it was raining. The horses would get wet and dirty, and so would they. They often went riding in the afternoons before Elizabeth went to fetch the kids from school, and of course the young ones went with them during the school holidays.

"As I've already said, Dr. James had a dispensing practice, as our village was considered too far for people to have to travel into Fulton to visit a chemist. This meant Dr. James had his own supply of drugs and dispensed them himself. It was his practice not to provide more than a month's supply of drugs to anyone, so as not to waste them, so he gave them all a repeat prescription card to pop into the waiting room whenever anyone needed more. Time and time again, when he rode down the street, someone would hear his horse's hooves on the road, and would rush outside and give him their repeat prescription card. 'I'll have them ready for you by evening surgery' he would say. 'They'll be on the windowsill as usual'.

Chapter 11

"Stead Norton is also starting to become a place where people decided to live whose jobs are in different areas from each other," said Maud. "We have one of the new Consultants from the Hospital twenty miles away in Chadstowe living down the road in one of the new houses built on Wilf Jackson's ramshackle farmyard. Her husband works thirty miles in the other direction, where he runs an engineering company. I suppose she was fortunate to get a job as a consultant anywhere near her husband's factory.

"Wilf was rather lucky. Some developer offered him a lot of money for his farm and some of his land. It was in a terrible mess really, but he was happy there. He was considered a bit of a character, what with his trousers being tied up with a bit of bailing twine. His wife Betty must have been a saint to have put up with all the mess. I have to say they built some nice houses there, not that I would like to live in a new house.

"There were some amazing old people in Stead Norton, but just about all of them have sadly passed on. It was only last year when we buried Sadie Rowbottom at the age of ninety-three."

Sadie came to live in Stead Norton when she was in her late forties. Her husband Jeff had worked on an allotment for much of his life, so was lucky when Lord Weybridge needed a new man to work on his Estate. But Jeff had died about ten years ago, at the age of eighty-three. He had worked hard on the land, feeling grateful to Lord Weybridge for giving him a job. He was one of the few soldiers who survived the horrors of the trenches of the First World War. Like so many of his kind, he never talked about it, but, sometimes if you happened to be near him without his being aware of your presence, you would hear him talking to his old comrades.

"Well, Billy my lad!" He was once heard to say. "They'll be sending us over the top soon, I 'spect. Don't know what they think it'll achieve. None of it ever seems to gain anything much. Them Krauts is well and truly dug in and have a' awful lot o' guns. Why don't they come for us instead? It's their turn. Here! 'ave a roll-up.

I just made a couple. Yer can have one o' mine. Won't be long now. Make sure yer keep yer 'ead down. Don't want it blowed orf."

Jeff then lit two roll-ups, smoking one and handing the other to an imaginary person, mumbling something inaudible all the time. When he had finished he said, "Well I can't sit here all day gossiping. I got things to do. Yer silly bugger. I told yer to keep yer 'ead down. What yer git killt fer? I didn't. Not right yer being killt an' me left alive. I really miss yer, Billy. I really miss yer."

Apparently Jeff was the only one of his platoon who survived that day. There were heavy casualties on both sides, but the enemy retreated a hundred yards, only to get it back a few days later. Jeff was found wandering in no-man's land later in the day, when there was a lull in the noise from the British artillery. He had lost his rifle somewhere on the field of battle. No one could get through to him. All he would say was "All gone! All gone!"

Jeff was gently led back to base, where he was invalided back to England, being admitted to a special unit where the doctors tried to help with what was assumed to be shell shock. He was effectively in a trance, a world of his own. Like so many of them in that hospital, he had terrible nightmares to begin with, although they did eventually become less of a problem.

Sadie was one of the nurses who looked after him. She never knew how or why, but somehow she felt she was able to get through to him. When she was allowed to, she would sit for hours with him, holding his hand and letting him mumble away to himself. Sometimes he would look at her in a sad, distant sort of way, and say, "Why did Billy have to die? He was so young. It weren't fair." And before she could say anything, he would lapse back into his own world.

Jeff took five years before he recovered enough to be let out of the unit. He went to live with his sister, whose husband had been killed in the war. He had had an allotment, which by now was rather neglected, although friends had tidied it up occasionally. Gradually Jeff started to dig it over and plant things, but neighbours used to hear him talking aloud every so often. When someone asked him if he was all right, he would say it was the war and he was still trying to come to terms with all the killing and pointlessness of it all.

Jeff would often say in reply, "The generals didn't know what they were doing. They didn't seem to realise their plan was pointless, but they still sent us to our deaths. It was either be killed by the Germans or be shot by our own for cowardice in the face of the enemy. They wouldn't have done it themselves. It was such a waste. I lost so many good friends. They died, so why should I have been spared? I should have died with them. It don't make no sense." And he would wander off to be alone with his thoughts.

After a number of years in the special unit, two years after Jeff was admitted there, Sadie had moved on to be a Ward Sister in a big hospital nearby. Then one day, at least three years after Jeff had left hospital, by coincidence he was admitted to her ward as he had cut his leg badly and it needed special attention. Sadie recognised him straight away. Jeff said he was pleased to see her, although he hardly remembered the days and months he spent in the special unit. Sadie had tried to keep in touch, or at least find out how he was doing, but, when he was discharged, she wasn't allowed to be told where he had gone.

Jeff had to stay in hospital for well over a week, by which time they had had a chance to get to know each other better. Sadie had always had a soft spot for Jeff, and had wondered what he was really like behind all his sadness. She seemed to want to get to know him better. The man in the next bed teased him by saying that she fancied him, and that, if he didn't want her, he would like her for himself.

That woke Jeff up. He suddenly realised that he rather fancied her himself. He had been so deep in his thoughts for so long that he hadn't been the slightest interested in women. Sadie seemed to make him realise that perhaps there was reason to live after all. Suddenly there was a point to life. He smiled for the first time for about eight years. As he did so, Sister Sadie happened to glance at him. That night, despite all the goings-on in a busy ward, Jeff slept soundly for the first time in ages, and didn't dream or have a nightmare at all.

When Jeff was told he was to be discharged, he astonished himself by asking Sadie if she would like to go to the cinema one evening, although he hadn't been to see a film for a very long time. To his delight she said she would love to, but he made it clear that he didn't want to see a war film. Sadie understood well enough.

Their courtship was a gentle affair. Sadie had worked for so long in the special unit where she first met Jeff that she understood something of what men like him must have gone through. She knew that some of them never got over the damage at all and eventually died still in a shell of their own. Others seemed to fade away, and, if they died at an early stage, a post-mortem examination would fail to reveal anything obviously wrong with them. They had simply died because their soul couldn't take it any longer.

Jeff and Sadie were married in a quiet ceremony a few years later. Despite her obvious loving nature, Jeff had told her that he didn't want any children. He was still haunted by his experiences in the war, and, because of what he saw as the stupidity of it all, he didn't want to have any children who might have to fight in another war, as he felt that some human beings are so arrogant and selfish that another war was likely to occur. Little did he know how right he was, and, when the Second World War loomed, he new he had made the right choice.

He kept talking of Billy who was so young and had died so needlessly. He worried about Billy's mum and dad, and tried to imagine their sorrow when they were told that Billy had been killed, like so many other mums and dads. He didn't want to be like them. He didn't want any child of his to have to go to war because some despot wanted to take over the world or do something equally stupid.

He had no faith in people at the top. He felt they were far too willing to send other people to war to do their dirty work for them. Sadie understood it all. She had nursed far too many broken souls not to understand.

Jeff and Sadie lived a quiet and unexciting life, with Sadie continuing her work in the hospital and Jeff tending his allotment every day. There he met one or two other lost souls and found that, as he had gradually got over his own trauma, he was able to help others just by sitting and talking to them, or, more to the point, letting them do most of the talking. When his sister, in whose name the allotment was, sadly died when she was only in her late forties, Jeff lost the use of the allotment. At the same time, Sadie felt she wanted to give up nursing so they moved to Stead Norton. When Sadie was off duty in the past, they often just drove their car into the country, simply because it was there, and the peace of some villages made Jeff in particular feel more relaxed than anywhere else.

Of all the villages they had visited, Stead Norton was the one that they both said they would like to move to one day. And so it seemed the time was right to make a move. Sadie had saved up a reasonable amount of money from her pay and selling Jeff's sister's house gave them enough to be able to buy a small house in Stead Norton when one came up for sale.

While Jeff worked full time on Lord Weybridge's estate, cycling to work and back every day, Sadie became a District Nurse part time, helping out when one of the other nurses went on a refresher course or took a holiday. Life suited them both. Neither was interested in excitement so they simply lived the life of quiet country folk, joining in anything that the community chose to organise. They fitted in perfectly, even if Jeff was a bit quiet and retiring. All he wanted to do was get on with life and be with Sadie. Jeff said he was safely back in England and didn't ever want to leave its shores again.

But Jeff was now dead. It took quite a while for Sadie to get over her loss. But, as she said, everyone has to lose someone at some time in their life, and now it was her turn. They had been such close companions and she missed him terribly, but she reminded herself of how she had tried to console other people over the death of a loved one, telling them that time is a great healer and the pain will gradually ease. And so it did so Sadie.

Sadie had always been helpful to anyone who needed her help. Helping others had been what she had done all her life, and it was instinctive to her. That was why she had become a nurse. It was second nature to her. It was probably why she had taken such an interest in Jeff, to try to help heal his sorrows, which she felt sure she had been able to do. All her life she had had a love of hats and people gave her their hats when they had finished with one and wanted to buy a new one. She didn't mind people's cast-offs. When her sons cleared out her house after she died, they said the place was absolutely full of hats. She would never throw one away. She kept them all.

When she grew older and after Jeff died, she took it upon herself to help as many people as possible in the village. What she felt she could do was some shopping for the 'old folk', as she was still quite sprightly. But she had started to become a bit eccentric, not badly so, just a little bit unusual. People said it was something to do with her love of hats, although no one could think why hats should do that to her. Everyone decided that they simply did.

Sadie would wait at the bus stop for the bus into Fulton, 'to go shopping for the old folks', as she would say, many of who were just as old as she was. She pulled her wheeled trolley behind her, which wasn't very large, so she couldn't have got much in it for many people anyway. But she did it out of the kindness of her heart. She always caught the same bus, the same day of the week and at the same time of day. It almost became a tradition to see whose hat she had on. People would walk down the lane to somewhere near her house in anticipation of her grand exodus. If the lady whose hat she had chosen to wear happened to be in the audience, you could guarantee she would say, "She's got it on back to front! Can't she tell?"

Sadie would get onto the bus with a royal wave to her admirers and set off for Fulton. She would do her shopping and come home when she was ready. If anyone saw her get off the bus, she would be in a fluster with her hat all lopsided. Being smart and tidy on her return was more than she could manage. She didn't have a mirror to check what she looked like.

Chapter 12

"It's funny how as soon as I tell you a story about one person," said Maud, later that day, "it reminds me of someone else. It's almost as if we were all connected somehow. Now that I come to think of it, that's not surprising, because we became a very close community. Everyone seemed to want to help someone else. I suppose it was the attitude of Dr. James and the Reverend Middleton that brought us all together. It didn't matter what a person's status in life was, whether a lowly worker or a toff, we just came together. It was talking about Jeff and where he worked that made me think of our local toff, Lord Weybridge. Well you had to call him that because he was one, yet not in the slightest toff-like, if you see what I mean."

Lord Weybridge was one of the old school. He was as kind and benevolent as anyone could be. He was a distant cousin of the queen and lived in the sort of huge house that once had servants running all over the place, with an efficient butler in charge of the household. The house was enormous, more like a castle, because it had battlements and turrets, but had tall windows from ceiling to floor, so would not have been easy to defend from attackers, but it had probably never been attacked anyway. It was called Norton Castle on all ordnance maps, the name castle having probably been in the mind of some previous owner with ideas of grandeur. But then it was lived in by a Lord, so a castle was a perfectly reasonable place for a Lord to live in.

Inside the castle was amazing, if not a bit eccentric. The tall windows had curtains made of once lustrous damask, with ornate patterns of wild flowers. They were in great need of repair or should have been replaced years ago, but the cost would have been horrendous. The windows let in the cold during the winter, and there was no possibility of replacing them with double-glazing. The cost of that would have been an eye-watering sum, they were so big and there were so many of them. Their only saving grace was that they had internal shutters.

But the rooms were so big and the ceilings so tall that they were a nightmare to warm in winter. The central heating, such as existed, was not very efficient, but at least they had the sort of old-fashioned big radiators you could sit on, with big pipes leading to and from them. When the central heating was on in the winter, the whole thing grumbled and gurgled. People sleeping in some of the upstairs rooms would often be woken by strange noises coming from the walls, as some of the pipes wended their way from the boiler deep in the basement kitchen to various part of the house. Some radiators were so far from the boiler that they seldom received much heat, so that part of the house was seldom used. What was in it hardly anyone had the slightest idea. No one had seen in some of the rooms for years. They could have housed all sorts of valuable items, possibly old master paintings, that could have been sold to be used to do up parts of the property or replace old curtains.

No one had any idea how Lord Weybridge earned his living, but then it was none of their business. People assumed it was from the proceeds of land. He probably owned many acres in other parts of the country. Perhaps he was also on the board of international companies, which paid him a useful sum for his title. He was certainly a very active man and was in his fifties when Dr. James first settled in Stead Norton. By active doesn't mean he spent a lot of his time in the garden. He had a beautiful old Rolls Royce, the sort that certainly suited his position in life. He was regularly seen driving it through the village to get onto the B road and then on to the main roads to London. Norton Castle was to be found deep in the country with access to it down a narrow road that led from Stead Norton.

Lord Weybridge was much loved in the area. He was a bit eccentric by some people's standards. He was a historian of some repute and came from a long family line of Noble Lords going back to William The Conqueror. The time in history that he was most passionate about was the late fourteen hundreds. He loved the spirit of adventure of the times, the chivalry and the jousting tournaments, and was an expert in the armour and dress of the latter years of the fifteenth century.

Lord Weybridge put on lavish weekend shows twice a year, when full armour jousting was the main attraction. He would dress up himself in the most beautiful armour and get involved in the jousting tournaments. He had a team of young men and women who made up his special group called 'Les Chevaliers d'Honneur', all of who performed similar re-enactments at other Castles and Country Homes up and down the country during the summer months. Everyone's armour had been made to exactly the same style and in exactly the same way as they had been made all those centuries ago. Men and women had studied and learned how armour was made in those days and had become full-time or part-time armourers for those who could afford the many thousands of pounds a proper suit of armour cost.

The shows were attended by thousands of people, as they were held on Bank Holiday weekends. The Castle and its grounds were absolutely ideally suited for such pageants. The main house had been built at the top of a slight rise in the land, which was reached by a well-kept drive that ended at the west end of the building. The drive itself had fields of grass on either side in which wandered horses and usually sheep, sheep being the best animals to keep grass in good condition.

A road to the left off this drive, just after the grand entrance to the whole property with its lodge house, led to the farm buildings and farm manager's house, one of the farm workers being given free living at the lodge. The main drive had been spectacularly designed to compliment the whole area, being lined by beautiful old oak trees. People flocked to the events, which Lord Weybridge put on free for anyone who wanted to turn up. They were his passion. Not surprisingly his events were a great success. Everyone wanted to see this beautiful place. Nobody questioned the fact that it wasn't a real castle any longer. The original building had burned down about two hundred years ago, when mobile fire engines had not been invented. The new castle had probably been designed as a mixture of what it had once been like and what the current Lord thought was practical.

The main aspect of Norton Castle faced south, perfectly complimenting the landscape. The west, north and south sides of the

Castle were surrounded by large areas of pebbled driveway. To the west was a walled garden of extensive size. To the south, the driveway gave onto beautifully tended sweeping lawns that started by descending about five or six feet, then became an expanse of perfectly level grass of about five acres, an absolutely perfect setting for the twice yearly pageants.

The whole show was run by National Heritage of England but sponsored by Lord Weybridge. He usually managed to entice a fairly high-ranking Royal Person to open the Show and act as the Representative of the crown to whom all jousters paid homage. Even that person was dressed in an appropriate outfit of the late fourteen hundreds. After the success of the first few years, it became so popular that members of the Royal Family offered their services for years ahead.

The shows started a couple of years before Dr. James arrived at Stead Norton. As with his predecessor, Dr. James happily officiated as Medical Officer, accompanied by the St John's Ambulance Service. Most of the time there was little for him to do, although there was perhaps the odd nose bleed or minor injury usually to a couple of young lads who had bought a wooden sword from one of the stands and had tried their luck at sword-fighting.

One year Lord Weybridge invited a troop of Cavalry Lancers to demonstrate their skills. Their horses were huge, over eighteen hands tall. They were delightful creatures, wonderfully gentle when standing in a row being groomed and prepared for their performance. Yet they were immensely strong, and, apart from being useful in battle in the past, they were also so strong they could easily pull a plough, which was what they had basically been bred for since their warrior duties were no longer required.

What the Lancers demonstrated was their ability to pierce with their lance, at full gallop, either a ring suspended from a pole or a small piece of wood embedded in the turf. These had originally been invented as a form of practice for warfare, but, more recently, had been revived as a way of entertaining people.

"You have to imagine the scene," said Maud. "There were eight Lancers divided into two teams, the East and the West teams. They had brought drummers to beat out a thunderous roll as soon as a Lancer set off at full gallop. The first item was the suspended ring, only two inches in diameter, which the rider had to pierce and carry off on his lance. The crowd was asked to roar the Lancer on as he started his run, and bring their voices to a crescendo as he then attempted to spear the small piece of soft wood embedded in the turf. The accuracy required was phenomenal. Remember, they were galloping flat out, these huge animals thundering their way across the grass.

"I understand it takes a lot of strength to control a horse when it is galloping fast, and a lot of skill to be able to do so in a confined space with only one hand and a double bridle. Remember, they had a lance in their other hand. The skill of the riders was awe-inspiring, each Lancer achieving maximum points until the last rider set off. The crowd started to roar as the drums beat out their roll. The Lancer caught the ring through the middle and carried it on to the wooden peg, when disaster struck.

"As I said, the skill and accuracy required to pierce such a small piece of wood sticking only two inches out of the ground was phenomenal. Unfortunately the lancer didn't get it quite right and stuck the end of his lance in the ground. Well you can imagine what that did. It put him off balance and nearly knocked him off his horse. Fortunately he let go of the lance – well he had to as it was stuck in the ground. But by then he had lost control of his huge animal, which assumed it should continue galloping at full tilt because its rider hadn't instructed it to stop.

"Well you can imagine the chaos. The crowd standing at the end of the run suddenly realised there was a giant animal thundering towards them, apparently out of control. They started to scatter in all directions, realising that the metal-framed fence separating them from the performance area was not going to provide much protection.

"I remember the whole thing. I was there at the time, but fortunately watching from another spot. It all happened so quickly.

One minute there was a small crowd of people watching happily at the end of the run. The next minute panic. I remember seeing this huge horse flatten the fence and brush a young woman aside. A baby she had been carrying in her arms flew out of her hands up in the air, only to be caught safely by her husband who had watched the whole thing with utter horror. Fortunately it all ended happily with no one hurt, but there could have been all sorts of injuries. That made them review their safety arrangements for the following year. It had never occurred to them that anything like that could happen.

"Lord Weybridge was most apologetic. He took full responsibility for the whole incident, asking if there was anything he could do to compensate the anxious couple for their stress. I don't know how it was resolved, but I'm sure it was to everyone's satisfaction. Lord Weybridge was that sort of a man. Dr. James examined the baby and its mother very carefully, but neither was in the slightest hurt. The mother was naturally in a bit of a state, but she was a sensible young woman and soon got over it. The following year Lord Weybridge asked her, her husband and their baby to be his guests of honour at the pageant. They loved it, Lord Weybridge even giving a graphic description of the whole event. To everyone's amazement he set up a giant screen and showed the full episode. Someone had caught the whole thing on a cine camera!"

Shortly after he took over the practice from Dr. Braithwaite, Dr. James was asked by Lord Weybridge to give him a smallpox vaccination, as he needed to travel later on in the year to a part of the world where it was wise to be covered. Dr. James willingly agreed, so they arranged for Lord Weybridge to visit him at his surgery. What Lord Weybridge didn't know was that Dr. James had never been asked before to do a smallpox vaccination. Fortunately his father, who was still in his own practice about fifty miles away, had done it many times before, so was able to instruct his son. The whole process went off without a hitch. Little did Lord Weybridge know that he was Dr. James' first smallpox vaccination patient!

Chapter 13

"Do they still have those shows every year?" Asked Lynda. "They sound such fun. I've never seen a jousting show. I'd really love to. When's the next one, Aunt Maud?"

"The next one is in a couple of month's time. They have changed a bit. They are far more conscious of health and safety nowadays, but they are still great fun. Do come. You could always stay here. I'm getting a bit old for such things. I haven't been to one for many a year, although I really enjoyed them when I did go."

"Did Lord Weybridge have many friends round here," asked Patrick. Perhaps you don't know things like that."

"No, I haven't the slightest idea, but then he probably associated more with his own kind. It's only natural. He probably had many business friends. A number of people helped out at dinner parties every so often. They were really grand affairs. Lord Weybridge had a wonderful butler who came from London whenever he had an important evening do, who happily trained some of the young men and women to serve at table. They all loved it, seeing how the rich live and enjoy themselves, and there's probably many a story there, but I was seldom told about them.

"There was one lady round here who tried to befriend Lord Weybridge, but I don't think she had much luck.

Mrs Rose Weston-Carnaby had come to live in Stead Norton later on in life. Her hyphenated name was very important to her. She was a true matriarch. She had outlived her husband by twenty-two years. She insisted on people calling her Mrs Weston-Carnaby – the full name. None of this modern first name nonsense for her. Her husband had worked for the Foreign Office as an Ambassador or High Commissioner somewhere in Africa, though probably not in a very important country, until his retirement. It had constantly irked her that he had never been knighted, and had merely been given an OBE.

"Most people say it stands for 'Other Blighters Efforts'," she once said, although many people used a far more rude word than 'blighter'.

Following the correct protocol was how Mrs Weston-Carnaby had lived all her life, and the correct protocol by her standards was how she wished to live in Stead Norton. Somehow she had managed to bring with her a maid who was even older than she was. No one had any idea where she had come from.

Mrs. Weston-Carnaby had four children of her own, two boys and two girls, fifteen grandchildren and thirty-two great grandchildren. She was clearly the head of a big dynasty. They were all doing very nicely, thank you.

Mrs. Weston-Carnaby lived in a house far too big for her. She lived in it all on her own, well, with her maid, but then she didn't count. She had managed to find two other women who were prepared to come in every day to help keep the house clean and tidy. Why they stayed in her employ, no one could ever understand, but they did. Perhaps she paid them well. She was very exacting, going round with them to make sure they did the house exactly as she wanted it. She had done the same when she and her husband had lived in Africa and they had had so many servants.

The Weston-Carnabys came to live in Stead Norton very shortly after Mr. Weston-Carnaby retired from the Foreign Service. They had no concept of living in a small house, as they had been given large accommodation wherever they had been posted. So, from their point of view, it was very fortunate that the Manor House came up for sale at the right time for them. Unfortunately Mr Weston-Carnaby died three months later of a heart attack. Dr. James was called urgently, but the man was clearly dead when he arrived. Having worked in hospitals as resuscitation anaesthetist first on call, he knew there was no point in trying to revive him. Mr Weston-Carnaby had at least probably not suffered, having been found dead by his wife sitting comfortably in his favourite armchair listening to his favourite music by Beethoven.

True to her calling and organisational abilities, Mrs Weston-Carnaby had organised the funeral all by herself. She arranged for details of his death and funeral to be printed in The Times. No other Newspaper would be appropriate for her husband. The people she wanted to know about his departure would only read The Times.

Mr. And Mrs. Weston-Carnaby had few friends in the area. They had tried unsuccessfully to cultivate Lord Weybridge, by inviting him to dinner. He had accepted politely, but had not reciprocated, yet she insisted on calling him 'my friend Lord Weybridge'. As she had so many family members, after her husband died she tried to have one of her sons, daughters or grandchildren to stay at weekends, to fill up the house. As there were so many of them, the whole family organised a rota to make sure she had company every weekend. To be fair, they all loved the place so much, not having very big houses themselves, that sometimes two groups stayed there. There was certainly plenty of room for them all. The children in particular loved to run free and play games in the extensive gardens. Despite her rather stiff appearance, she was not an unfriendly person and absolutely adored having young children in the house.

Mrs. Weston-Carnaby did not want any staff members in the house at weekends as she considered she had brought up her own children so well that her visitors were perfectly capable of helping her run the place, so her living-in maid was sent away. Where she went no one had the slightest idea. She just caught the bus in the middle of Stead Norton on Friday evening and returned very late on Sunday evening, ready to take over after whoever had stayed the weekend had gone home.

The only thing that some visitors were not too happy about was her insistence that they all attend church on Sunday morning, but they went along with her wishes. No one ever complained. Mrs. Weston-Carnaby had a deep faith in her God, sure that He was guiding every aspect of her life. She had totally accepted it when her husband had died, saying he had been called for some duty somewhere else. Duty was in her husband's blood and it flowed equally strongly in hers.

Every decision of any importance she ever made was made after asking God's advice. If she had not asked His advice about something of apparent unimportance and it had not worked out the way she had hoped, she would castigate herself and apologise to God for not having asked his advice in the first place, saying that everything in life is important to God, who she firmly believed wanted to help her in every way possible. All she had to do was ask. She had taken over her husband's stocks and shares, and had asked God's advice about every transaction. That she was comfortably off she put down to her God advising her to do the right thing. She had never made what some people would call a fortune out of any of her shares, just a steady income. God would never have let her become rich, she was sure. There was no need for her to be greedy, just comfortable.

So life carried on much the same for Mrs. Weston-Carnaby for the next number of years. She was a woman of habit. It never occurred to her that her family would like to live their own lives. Even if she did, she would have said to herself that each family group only had to visit her once every two months or so. She never went away on holiday, as she didn't like to go on her own, and didn't have a friend to go with. Apart for which she had travelled extensively wherever her husband had been appointed, so why on earth would she want to travel now? No, she was perfectly content to stay in England, in fact in her home in Stead Norton. A bit like Maud Hughes, she had decided to stay put and let other people visit her.

As she got older, into her eighties, Mrs. Weston-Carnaby became a bit fragile. She refused point blank to go and live in some place where she could be looked after or some sort of sheltered accommodation where there were people on call should she need help. She had got used to her large house and liked to wander about in it, even if it took her longer to get from one room to another than it used to.

One day she tripped and fell on a step, banging her head as she went down. Her maid called Dr. James, who had visited her on a number of occasions in the past when she had needed his help. At every visit she had told him her opinion of the world, how the Lord was looking after her and keeping an eye on her every move. She had even asked her God if she should take the tablets Dr. James recommended. To his satisfaction her God always seemed to approve of his recommendations. That put Dr. James very much in her good books.

Dr. James told her he had a basic faith in God but didn't know how to explain all the miseries of life. He listened to her patiently and wanted to ask her why her God spent so much time looking after her while allowing so many children to die of starvation in Africa every day. But he didn't ask her. He didn't think it would be fair.

On one occasion, she asked him what his real attitude was, and he told her he thought everyone should live as good a life as possible, and that it didn't matter whether they believed in God or not, so long as they had been good. She said everyone had done something bad in their lives and it was important for them to repent before they died. She went on to tell him that, however bad someone had been in life, whether they had been a rapist, a murderer or a paedophile, if they repented at the last moment, they would go to heaven and sit with God. When Dr. James plucked up the courage to ask whether such a person would be more readily accepted in heaven than a person who didn't believe in God but who had lived a good life, she was adamant that the former bad person who repented would be forgiven and the person who had not repented would not. Dr. James couldn't find it in his heart to argue with her.

On this particular occasion, after Mrs. Weston-Carnaby had fallen down a step, she duly told him that, as she fell, the Lord had told her to put her hand behind her head so she wouldn't hurt herself, and amazingly she hadn't. He didn't have the heart to ask her why her God had pushed her down the step in the first place!

Chapter 14

"What with Mrs Weston-Carnaby assuming she was in the top drawer, and of course our dear Lord Weybridge, we seemed to have people living in our area from all levels of the social strata. Everyone probably has a story to tell about himself or herself, but I don't know all of them, just the ones people decided to tell me about themselves. There were a few incidents that occurred that only vaguely had anything to do with Dr. James, but he was involved in just about everyone's life in one way or another as our doctor."

Fred Blunt lived with his wife Doris and their son Elvis. The Blunts lived in one of the few council houses in a cul-de-sac off Station Road. Fred had not done a day's work for as long as anyone could remember. He was an idle so-and-so, expecting The State to provide for him. What little money he did have he spent in the local pub, always sitting with a small group of similar down-and-outs.

Fred's wife was no better. She was the most untidy person you could imagine, with long straggly unwashed bleach-blond hair falling all over the place. She was grossly overweight. Fred and Doris were smelly, as they seldom washed. In fact they didn't have anywhere to wash. Their bath and the basin in the bathroom upstairs were full of coal. Fred had apparently been a miner in the past so somehow was entitled to free coal for the rest of his life.

There was hardly a functional door in the house as they had taken most of them down and chopped them up for firewood. The house had a small garden at the front, but not a flower in sight. What greenery there was were weeds poking their way through all the rubbish they had collected, which included two cars minus wheels, with the bonnets always up as though someone was about to inspect them. They were both rusted beyond repair.

Everything about the place was a real mess. Their poor neighbours had given up trying to get them to improve their plot. "What fer?" Fred would ask. "It's not that bad." Well it was. It was awful. The council had been asked many times to re-house them somewhere else, but wherever they were put it would have been the same. They were that sort of people. They didn't care about anyone else, and, so far as anyone could tell, they didn't care about each other.

The police had been called to their house so many times, usually to separate them from their neighbours. Fred got drunk all too often, and, when he was like that, he became belligerent, paranoid, foul-mouthed and totally impossible to handle. Things tended to be resolved only when he finally fell into an alcoholic stupor. He would sleep for the next twenty-fours hours, giving everyone a short-lived peace. At the local police station they had an unwritten rota as to whose turn it was when the next call came. Fortunately Dr. James was rarely involved or called to their house, as they never seemed to be ill. No one could understand how they kept alive. Their diet must have been of nothing but junk food and booze, although Doris was not nearly as bad with the drink as Fred was. But all she ate were biscuits and crisps. Of course they both smoked heavily.

Their one and only son Elvis had been born when Doris was in her late forties and Fred was in his fifties. Wayne had not only not been particularly wanted but was totally unexpected until Doris went into labour late one night. Dr. James was called by a neighbour who had heard screams coming from next door. When he arrived, he just beat a police car with its siren blaring away. The neighbour thought that Fred was probably either beating Doris up in a not-uncommon alcoholic stupor, or he was trying to murder her. They had been heard screaming at each other all too often, and someone said he would do her in one day.

Dr. James and the policemen had a quick discussion about the situation, the policeman drawing his truncheon and entering first, as he felt was his responsibility. Fred was sitting amongst a load of rubbish on what might have been described as a chair. "She's upstairs 'owling 'er 'ead off," said Fred. "No idea why," he added.

The policeman, with Dr. James hard on his heels, ran up the stairs. "Careful, Doc. There's a step missing here. Probably used it for firewood if I know Fred."

It was not difficult to find Doris, as she was making so much noise. They both fought their way through rubbish strewn all over the place and tried to open the door to the bedroom Doris was screaming in. "Fer Gawd sake. Someone 'elp me," she shouted. "'elp!"

With a heave the policeman managed to force the door open. It wouldn't open fully because of all the soiled clothes behind it. But they managed to squeeze their way in. There was Doris, lying in a filthy bed, in a pool of blood and urine. "I'm bleeding, whoever you are. Fer Gawd sake do somefing, will yer," she shouted at them.

"I'm Dr. James. Let me take a look at you." Then after a while, "I think you're having a baby."

"I'm what?" Said Doris. "How could I?"

"Call an ambulance, will you please, and tell them what the situation is," Dr. James said to the policeman. "And tell them to bring spare face masks and gloves! We are going to need them. We'll need some help to clear some of this rubbish out of the way to get her out of here. I had no idea she was pregnant, and I don't think she did either. Still, she's a fat woman anyway."

That was how Elvis came into the world, in an absolute mess. He wasn't as bad as his parents. No one understood how he managed to make himself look reasonably respectable, coming from that pigsty. Nevertheless he did a bit better at school than anyone had given him a chance of, and he even managed to pass a few exams. That helped him to get a job in the local brick factory about ten miles away when he turned sixteen, when he was old enough to ride a small motorcycle.

Elvis was proud of his job. Again for reasons no one could understand he seemed very fond of his parents. It all seemed to be one-way traffic, because Doris and Fred couldn't seem to care less about Elvis. They treated him appallingly. As soon as he came home on a Friday evening with his pay packet, Fred would demand some of it for board and lodging. Fred would then immediately wander down to the pub and buy a round of drinks for his mates.

Fred and Doris never asked Elvis how he managed to get himself a motorcycle. It would never have occurred to them to think of such things. Perhaps they thought he had stolen it or at least stolen the money to pay for it. What they didn't know was that the Manager at the factory had taken Elvis under his wing. "Fancy calling him Elvis!" He once said. "What were they thinking of? Probably the first name that came into their sozzled heads."

The Manager knew of Fred and Doris. They were the neighbours from hell. He knew what they were like. He knew they didn't care for Elvis, even though he seemed to care for them. He knew Fred would drink Elvis's hard-earned money away every Friday evening, so he only put into Elvis's pay packet envelope enough to satisfy Fred, keeping the rest and putting it into a special fund. He told Elvis the factory needed him to work there so they would pay for a small motorcycle so that he could get to and from work. Elvis was so grateful he worked really hard.

The regular instalments for the motorcycle cost very little on a monthly basis, especially as the Manager had made special arrangements with a friend of his who owned a motorcycle shop in town. So the money that was left over was building up steadily in the local Building Society into a tidy sum. The factory paid good wages. All of this was unknown even to Elvis. The Manager felt that what Elvis didn't know he couldn't tell Fred. He was concerned that the fact that he had this little nest egg might slip out one day and Fred would demand a bigger slice of the cake.

Elvis continued to live in squalor, while Fed and Doris seemed to get even worse, if such were possible. But somehow it didn't seem to affect Elvis. He continued to have some strange sort of affection for his parents, especially his dad. But then he was their son, so everyone accepted it as not unreasonable. And so Elvis's little nest egg grew into a substantial sum. Even the Manager was surprised at how much a small sum of money could grow if it is left alone. He found that a most interesting object lesson, and encouraged his grandchildren to set up a small Building Society account, for a deposit on their own house when they grew up. That was basically why he was doing this for Elvis. He was sure that, one day, Elvis would want to move out into his own place. He assumed that no one, not even Elvis, could possibly stand the mess forever.

One day when he was in his mid-twenties, Elvis was driving home on his little motorcycle on the B road. He was so proud of it that he cleaned and polished it every weekend. People in the village wondered why Fred and Doris couldn't see what a pleasure it was to be tidy, but they couldn't have cared less. Elvis continued to work happily at the brick factory and clean his motorcycle every weekend. Little did he know that the monthly payments had stopped a long time ago, so his little nest egg was growing very nicely.

When Elvis was nearing Stead Norton and was about to turn into Station Road, a sports car came round the corner in his direction, clearly going too fast. The driver lost control and came careering onto Elvis's side of the road. Elvis tried to get out of the way, but didn't manage to completely. As the sports car went past him, it struck the back wheel of Elvis's motorcycle and sent him spinning into the gutter. He banged his head on a lump of concrete and was temporarily knocked unconscious. Fortunately he was wearing his crash helmet at the time, or the blow would probably have killed him.

As seemed to be their job, the people who lived in the house in Station Road closest to the B road rushed out of the house once again. That was the third time they had gone to help in the past month, and they seemed to enjoy the responsibility. As usual they called Dr. James, but his wife said he was out somewhere visiting patients, but she said she would try to find him. In the meantime she said she would ring the Emergency Services.

While waiting for the ambulance and police to arrive, Elvis started to come round. The couple advised him to stay where he was until help arrived. They told him he had been knocked down by a car, which was now lying upside down in a field not far away. The young man driving it had managed to crawl out from under the upturned car, none the worse for his ordeal, apart from a few unimportant bruises.

Once he came round sufficiently and realised what had happened, Elvis said, "Call my dad, would you please. Let him know what has happened to me. I'm sure he'll get here as fast as possible. If he's not at home, he might be in the Crown and Anchor."

While the woman stayed to keep an eye on Elvis, her husband went straight to the pub. He knew perfectly well it was a waste of time looking for Fred at his home. The pub was more like a home to him. And, surprise, surprise. There was Fred sitting in the corner with a couple of his mates with pints of beer in front of them.

"Fred! Elvis has been knocked off his motorcycle at the junction of Station Road and the main road and he's been injured. He's asking for you."

"Have you called the Doctor and the ambulance?" When the answer was yes, he said, "Good! They'll look after him. So there no point in me getting in the way. There's nowt I can do. Give me another pint, Dan!"

About a year later, when Fred and Doris were getting even worse, Fred becoming more and more drunk more and more often and it was obvious he was losing weight, while Doris was putting on even more, someone in the pub commented that he ought to see the doctor because he seemed to be turning yellow. As he was being sick a lot, Fred actually did go to the surgery, stinking the place out. As soon as he turned up everyone decided they could wait another day to see the Doctor so Fred was seen next. Dr. James wanted to send him straight into hospital, but Fred would have none of it, so Dr. James suggested he take a blood sample to see what the matter was. He knew perfectly well that Fred had alcoholic cirrhosis at least or probably liver cancer, and may be lung cancer as well, as he had started coughing even more violently, but he didn't say so at the time. When he left the surgery, Fred went straight to the pub and got even more drunk than usual.

How he got home, no one knows. He was almost comatose when he left the pub at closing time. He must have had a built-in compass directing him to him own pit.

Some time in the early hours of the morning, one of their neighbours was woken up by the smell of smoke. She hurried out of bed and looked out of the window. Smoke was curling past their house, possibly from next door. She woke her family, running outside shouting, "Fire! Fire!" at the top of her voice, banging saucepans together as loudly as she could to wake the neighbours.

By then it was perfectly obvious that the Blunts' council house was on fire. Being sober, Elvis managed to get out, in a sleepy state of mind. Suddenly he realised what was going on. "Mum! Dad!" He shouted. Running back towards the house, Elvis tried to fight his way in, but it was no use. He managed to get into the front door, by kicking it in, as it was so flimsy and rotten. But then he was driven back. The house was ablaze. People had to physically restrain him. They knew it was hopeless. They knew Fred would be unconscious with drink, while Doris's weight would make it impossible for her to escape without catching on fire as she did so. People hated Fred and Doris, but they had no wish for them to end their lives this way.

It wasn't long before the Fire Engine arrived. By then the house was a total ruin, a pile of ashes. There had been so much rubbish and junk in the house it had gone up in flames as though someone had poured petrol on it. When the fire was finally extinguished, the officer in charge went in to try to ascertain how the place had caught fire. He found the skeleton of a man in the so-called sitting room, surrounded by springs, which he assumed had been the chair Fred had been sitting in. Doris had been in bed upstairs, but the floorboards had given way and her body was found on the ground floor, having presumably crashed through the ceiling.

Hearing that Fred had been a heavy smoker, his report was that Fred had probably lit a cigarette, sitting downstairs, and had fallen unconscious, letting the lighted cigarette fall from his fingers, and thereby setting fire to the house. Dr. James wondered whether he had done it deliberately, as one of his drinking pals told the police that that evening Fred had said, "I'm done for. I'm a gonner".

Out of support for him, a number of people from the village and the works' manager attended Fred and Doris's funeral. It was a strange affair. Everyone had wanted to be rid of them years ago. Now they were gone. They all felt somehow guilty. As someone said, "It don't make sense, feeling guilty like that. But there you are."

Elvis wept his heart out. For a while he was inconsolable. "I loved my Mum and Dad," he said over the coffins. No one had the heart to say to him that they probably didn't love him.

Chapter 15

"When I started with this infection," said Maud, "I thought I was developing asthma, as I sort of wheezed. I thought it was strange to start having asthma at my age, but then I suppose it could occur at any time of life. Dr. James told us that just about anything could happen to anyone at any time in their life. From his experience of the many amazing things he did for people and observations he made of the way people reacted, and how they got better when they stopped whatever the cause was, he once said to me 'I have now realised that just about anything can cause just about any problem in just about anyone'. He also said he was astonished at the range of problems that people could complain of, and even more astonished at what he found to be the cause once he started looking. That certainly applied to Jayne Worthing."

Jayne and Terry Worthing were new to Stead Norton. Jayne suffered from asthma and was on quite strong drugs when they registered with Dr. James. She told him she had been admitted to hospital on a number of occasions with severe acute asthma attacks, the last one when they went on holiday to the Isle of White four months ago. Jayne told him that, in between attacks, she was never completely free of wheezing, and was short of breath much of the time. She had wanted to climb mountains when she was a child, but the shortness of breath had made that impossible. She said she could never have coped, especially as steep hills made her so much worse.

Jayne asked Dr. James for a repeat of her prescriptions. There were some tablets of steroids and two inhalers. Dr. James asked her what the cause was of her asthma.

"It's hereditary," said Jayne. "My mother and father both suffer from allergies, my mum from asthma and my dad from hay fever. The Allergy Specialist said it was inevitable I would suffer from an allergy of some sort because of my family history."

"That doesn't answer my question, though" said Dr. James. "Your family history gives you your genetic predisposition, but what causes your asthma? What triggers it?

"I asked the Specialist that question and he said it was probably stress, but I don't suffer from stress, apart from the asthma itself. So I don't know."

"Would you like to find out?" Asked Dr. James

"Would it make any difference?"

"If we could find out what is causing your asthma, and do something about it, you could be much better. You might even be able to come off your drugs. And if we were really lucky, you could get rid of your asthma all together."

"Really? The Specialist never said anything about that. He said he would like me to stay on the drugs, but that, if things became any worse, he would try stronger drugs. What would I have to do? How could we find the causes?"

"It's not really practical to do anything now, as there is a crowd of people in the waiting room. We need to organise for you to come back when we can take our time. I will need at least one-and-a-half hours, so let's see if you could come back around eleven o'clock next Wednesday. I will give you some forms to fill in and some information about my attitude to all forms of ill health. It should orientate you to start looking for causes. You would be surprised what I sometimes find in someone. It's like detective work. It's actually a lot of fun. But I will be going right back into childhood. I will be asking you a lot of questions."

Jayne and Terry came back later in the week, in the middle of the morning. Jayne gave Dr. James the forms he had asked her to complete. "Wow! You certainly do go into detail," she said. "We found it absolutely fascinating. Your reasoning why people become ill is so logical. It makes such good sense. On our own, we would never have thought of half the things you suggest, but, once we realised what you were trying to say, we found it quite easy to think of what may be causing my asthma."

"What have you thought of so far?" Asked Dr. James.

"I have ruled out stress as a main cause, but I was under some stress with exams around eighteen, doing A levels, then again each summer at University when exams came round. I took them seriously. Yes, I was a bit worse during those times, so perhaps stress does play a part."

"Let's look at that a bit closer. Let's not assume the obvious. While you were studying and were perhaps a bit anxious, did you put on weight, eating biscuits or crisps, for example, as a lot of young people do?"

"No way! I couldn't eat. I didn't have much appetite anyway, and I lost quite a lot of weight, but that was good because I was a bit overweight anyway."

"So, what did you eat? And where did you eat? I assume you were at home until you went away to University, so you ate mother's cooking until then?"

"Yes. Well Mum tried to get me to eat as good food as possible, but all I wanted to do was drink milk. I must have had a couple of pints a day. That seemed to keep me satisfied. It certainly helped me to lose weight as I've already said."

"Ah!" said Dr. James. "That could explain a lot. You might have a milk intolerance. It is such a common problem in my experience, despite everyone thinking it is a healthy food. I know of many people who have felt better in all sorts of ways when they gave up dairy products. Also all that calcium in it may block the absorption of magnesium, which everyone seems to ignore. Calcium is responsible in part for muscles contracting, while magnesium helps them to relax. So anything that goes into spasm may be because of a magnesium deficiency, like asthma, migraines, constipation, back ache and cold hands, as examples. Stress tends to reduce your body levels of magnesium, which can be difficult to replenish if you don't eat plenty of green vegetables. So a dairy intolerance combined with a magnesium deficiency may be two causes in you."

"I've never liked cabbage and things like that," said Jayne.

"I often pick up a history of too many episodes of upper respiratory tract infections, such as tonsillitis and ear problems, but you don't seem to have suffered in that way when you were a child. Incidentally, when did your asthma start?"

"I was apparently a bit wheezy when I was young, but it didn't worry me much until I started having periods at twelve years old. The periods became so painful and heavy that the doctor put me on the pill, with my parents' knowledge, of course. I had also started to suffer from pre-menstrual moodiness. I hated it, but couldn't help myself. In the end my mum asked the doctor if the pill would be worth trying, and he agreed, saying it was bad enough having asthma without adding period problems."

"There is a lot of stress on the body of a young lady when she goes through puberty. It's not the usual sort of stress, but it's stress nevertheless. Having said that I have helped very many women over the years lose all their premenstrual and menstrual symptoms by simply changing their diet in some way. Some women seem to react to one lot of foods, while others react to a different group. However, the common foods to nearly all women are dairy products and caffeine in my experience. So those items will need to go in the first instance, so let's start there and see what happens.

"Stay on your drugs as before. Do you take all three of them all the time?"

"No, I take a small dose of steroids every day, and one of my inhalers, the steroid one, four times a day on a regular basis. The Specialist said it would cut down the inflammation in my lungs. But I only use the bronchodilator when I need it, usually once or twice a day."

"If you do have inflammation in your lungs, I would ask why. What causes the inflammation? That's what we are going to find out hopefully. Anyway, I'd like you to start a diary of daily events, please, assessing how bad your asthma is four times a day, say when you wake up, after lunch, before your evening meal and finally when you go to bed. Score how you are on a ten-point system, with one as very bad and ten as symptom free or the other way round. You choose, but stick to whatever you decide upon. Don't forget to write down the drugs you use, even if you take two of them on a regular basis. Note down also how often you use your bronchodilator. You never know, things might change.

"Recall what you do on a daily basis. Be pedantic. Chart where you go as much as you can. Write down exactly what you eat as soon as you have eaten it. Don't rely on your memory. It tends not to be reliable. I will lend you a Peak Flow Meter. You probably know how to use it. I would like you to record the result of three hard outbreaths into the machine at the same time you record how you are feeling on the ten-point scale, so four times a day. Would you please keep an eye on what she records, Terry. It is so easy to forget. Try to get into a habit of recording everything. If you go out, make sure you have a pencil and some paper wherever you go; then transfer what you have written down onto your master record."

"I've just remembered," said Jayne. "I tend to wheeze more at night. I told the Specialist about that and he arranged for me to have some skin prick tests, to feathers, wool, house dust and house dust mite, I think he said, but I was negative to everything they tested."

"Tests of that sort are not one hundred per cent accurate. So that doesn't mean you don't react to any of those. The tests can give false positive and false negative results. Many years ago I did a survey of one hundred consecutive patients who presented with classical symptoms of hay fever at an Allergy Clinic I worked in. We did as big a range of skin prick tests on them as was available at the time, and about thirty per cent were totally negative. In the meantime we asked for volunteers from staff working at the hospital who had no symptoms of hay fever whatsoever. About thirty per cent of them had positive skin prick tests to grass or one of the other classical pollens, to which they were unaware of symptoms. A bit confusing, you might say. But that's science for you."

That was enough to start with. Jayne and Terry went away with lots to think about. When they next saw Dr. James about three weeks later, they were armed with lots of information. Jayne had stopped caffeine and dairy and was already generally better. After about a week, she noticed that she no longer took her bronchodilator inhaler as often as before, but she was still occasionally having mini attacks of wheezing and shortness of breath, but not enough to need to use her inhaler most of the time. She noticed that she was still a bit worse at night and also seemed to have a bit of a problem in the middle of some mornings.

"Let's look at what you had for breakfast when you felt a bit worse in the mid-mornings. Have you worked out what the common denominator is?" Asked Dr. James.

"I tried to alter my diet and eat different things on different days, as much as possible, like you suggested, and two foods could be suspicious, bread and cornflakes."

"Ok!" Said Dr. James, "it could be either or both. The simplest way in principle to see if they are relevant is to stop both at the same time, or you could stop each one separately. Stopping both completely is the quickest, but not necessarily the most convenient. It will mean stopping eating a lot of regularly eaten foods, such as bread, pasta, biscuits, cakes, most cereals, gravy mixes, etc. for wheat, and cornflakes, corn flour, corn-on-the-cob and gravy mixes, in the main."

"Don't worry. I'll stop both. There are plenty of foods left. I should lose more weight, which will be a bonus. I've already lost seven pounds. I could do with losing at least another ten pounds and then I will be satisfied.

Jayne saw Dr. James three weeks later. "Well I've lost another seven pounds so am getting near to where I want to be."

"Interesting that you mention your weight loss before telling me how your asthma is," remarked Dr. James.

"Well, her weight is important to a woman. Ok! I am better and I haven't used my bronchodilator inhaler since I last saw you. I also decided to reduce the frequency of my other drugs, so am down to my steroid inhaler only three times a day and I have reduced the steroid tablets by a third. The Specialist told me how to do that some time ago, if I was ever able to. To be fair to him, he didn't want me to take steroid tablets for longer than necessary, but I was clearly bad enough to need them. I hate the weight they have made me put on, even though it's not a big dose. At least the dietary changes I have made have compensated a bit."

"I suggest you continue to get off the steroid tablets first, staying on the inhaler steroid for now. The biggest dose of oral steroids you have taken is only five milligrams, so you could stop them immediately, so long as you keep some tablets in reserve, and ring me if you have the slightest problem. Most patients are advised to reduce their steroid dose very slowly, especially if they have been on a big dose for a long time. But you haven't, so you could stop immediately if you feel comfortable to do so. Being your doctor, I am willing to come out and treat you if stopping the steroids straight away doesn't work. Please don't travel away from here for the next two to three weeks, so that I can keep an eye on you.

"But I think you have already identified some of the causes of your asthma. By avoiding all the foods you are avoiding at present, even if avoiding all of them is not necessary, the inflammation in your lungs is diminishing, so you probably don't need too big a dose of drugs. But please be careful and sensible. I repeat, please ring me any time, day or night, if you need me."

"Talking about night time, my asthma doesn't seem to be so bad at night. In fact my charts suggest I am not having any problems during the night. So perhaps I don't have a dust mite or feather allergy after all."

"Actually you might, but your level of sensitivity may not be all that high. One of the interesting observations I have made over the years with allergies is that, if you can identify that you react to a number of things, your response to some of the lesser ones may disappear if you avoid the main culprits. So, what I'm saying is that, if dairy products are your main trigger, avoiding dairy may reduce your overall sensitivity sufficiently to stop you reacting to lesser stimulants, unless, that is, you are exposed temporarily to a large amount of one of the lesser ones. I tell you, allergies are absolutely fascinating."

Jayne stopped her steroid tablets straight away. It didn't cause her any problems at all. She was pleased to be rid of them, hopefully for ever. She continued to lose weight and reached her ideal level soon enough. When they next met, Dr. James asked her if she was willing to try some wheat or something made of corn, but she was not yet ready to experiment. She wanted to get off all her drugs before doing something like that. "Before I forget, can you tell me the name of the pharmacist where you collected your drugs from before you came here? I have a hunch. I'll let you know about that in due course. I don't want to give the game away, in case I am wrong." Jayne gave him the details.

"Do you think you could go back to when you had your last bad attack when you were on holiday in the Isle of White?" Dr. James said to Jayne when they next met. Tell me what happened. Be as precise as you can remember. I will jog your memory with questions every so often. I'm quite good at teasing out details. I've done it so many times. Start from when you left home."

"Well! Let me see now," started Jayne. "Help me, Terry. We had planned the holiday about three weeks earlier. Terry hadn't been sure whether he could take time off work, so we hadn't planned anything before that."

"Yes! My boss said he might have to travel to America, but didn't know the exact dates, so asked me if I could wait until he was sure. It didn't matter to Jayne or me when we went. You can't guess the weather in England so we were prepared to go when it suited my boss. He was very grateful. It was only when he said he had to travel suddenly and should be back within a week, that it was possible to do some planning. At that stage we had no idea where to go. We weren't particularly bothered to go overseas, so the whole country was open to us, as we were not going during school holidays. We don't have any children, yet," said Terry winking at Jayne, who blushed.

"Come on you two love birds. Let's concentrate on the matter in hand. But that's such a lovely idea for the future."

"We thought about all sorts of places," started Jayne, when she had got over her embarrassment. "In the end, we chose the Isle of White. We went into a local travel agent and saw pictures of some lovely hotels. The lady said she had been there herself, on a travel agents' special excursion, so felt she could happily recommend it. We selected a lovely hotel on the top of a cliff, with beautiful walks around it, nothing too steep, because of my asthma.

"My bad attack was on the Wednesday night after we had arrived on the Sunday. It was very severe. We had to call an ambulance. The hotel staff people were very good."

"What time did the attack begin?"

"It must have started about eleven o'clock. I started to feel a bit tight chested and wheezy before we went to bed, but I didn't think anything of it, as it had happened so many times before. I just took a dose of my bronchodilator inhaler and hoped for the best. But it didn't help much, if at all. I seemed to get gradually worse, so in the end Terry became anxious and called the emergency services. I was helped with a nebuliser before they took me into the local hospital, where they set up a steroid drip. They said I would need a bigger dose as I was already taking steroid tablets."

"What did you do during the day? Try to remember the details."

"I'm pretty sure we got up late that morning. We felt it was so luxurious to be able to snuggle down under the bedclothes and not rush down to breakfast, apart from which it was raining, so we knew we wouldn't be able to go for a walk. In the end we missed breakfast all together. It rained for much of the day, well, until teatime at least, and we played some cards with another couple we had met the day before. We had lunch, but I can't remember exactly what we had. Can you remember, Terry?"

"Sorry! I can't, well not in enough detail to be of any use."

"Having had an early lunch in the hotel, we had afternoon tea around three o'clock. We had egg-and-cress sandwiches, with the crusts cut off. They were served on beautiful plates, and tea came in a lovely silver teapot. I had a little milk and a dash of sugar. Nothing unusual in that. I felt really spoiled. It was so romantic. I remember telling Terry that I wanted his baby there and then, but I'm afraid I didn't manage to get pregnant," Jayne said with a little sigh.

"It's probably that your body is telling you it is too busy trying to deal with your asthma for you to conceive. Don't worry! Once your asthma has gone you'll conceive as easily as you want to." That really brought a huge smile to both their faces. "Go on."

"Oh yes! We went to the pictures that evening. It stopped raining about five o'clock and the sun came out. There were a few puddles around, but it dried up remarkably quickly. We saw the latest James Bond movie. It was great fun, but totally unrealistic. Those sorts of things could never happen in real life. Then we walked home. It wasn't far from the cinema to the hotel, but I remember thinking that the slight incline was more difficult than it should have been. Then I gradually became worse, and you know the rest."

"I suspect you have left something out," said Dr. James.

"I can't think of anything else," said Jayne.

"Terry?"

"I can't think of anything else either."

"Did you buy any sweets or have any pop drinks at the cinema?" Asked Dr. James.

"How silly of us," said Jayne. "We felt very indulgent. We both had a large coke and a huge carton of popcorn. I think I probably ate most of them. They were lovely and crunchy. Oh my God!" Exclaimed Jayne. "Caffeine and corn, and a big dose of both. What made you think of that?"

"I've found it in someone else before. Incidentally, I've discovered the filler in your steroid tablets was cornstarch, although that would have been a very small but regular dose on a daily basis. It occurred to me that your small dose of steroids might be making things worse."

"That's so clever. Working out such intricacies is amazing."

"It's just a matter of experience. I've been doing this for years. Have you ever asked Terry to explain exactly, and I mean exactly, how he does what he does. As an engineer he has to be very precise, accurate to a millimetre or less. He has to work it all out very carefully. The difference between what he does and what I do may seem to be worlds apart, but I can assure you it's in the detail. That is why I am not happy at simply prescribing drugs. Yes they do work, but I believe they should only be used to deal with an acute episode. After that the cause should be sought and avoided, to prevent the symptoms from returning. Mine is just another way of doing things, that's all.

"So you may not have a wheat intolerance at all. In the long run I would encourage you to try it out in due course, but the longer you stay off wheat, the less severe a reaction is likely to be. I don't want you to be avoiding a food if there is no need to. If you want to stay off wheat to help keep your weight where you want it to be, all well and good, but to have to stay off it indefinitely when there's no need to is not something I would encourage. Would you not enjoy going back to the hotel in the Isle of White, or somewhere similar, and having egg-and-cress sandwiches again?"

"Ok! Point taken. I will, but not for now."

"Incidentally, when you do, please let me know so that I can be on hand to help you if you need me. As it would be our experiment, I would like to be in charge of it."

Jayne stayed off all the foods for a while longer, then one day rang Dr. James to tell him she was going to try some wheat. He suggested as pure a form of wheat as possible to start with, such as egg-free pasta, then gradually test other forms of wheat that might be combined with some other food item, such as yeast to make bread or egg to make normal pasta. By then Jayne was totally free of asthma and off all her drugs. Her weight was exactly where she wanted it to be and she was very happy.

When Jayne had completed her testing without any problems, Dr. James reminded her that she could probably conceive as soon as she wanted to. He explained to her that, with her asthma gone, her body should now be in the right frame of mind to carry a baby. In the meantime, her husband Terry had quietly had a sperm test done to make sure that, as far as he was concerned, there was no reason why they could not start a family. Jayne told Dr. James she had deliberately avoided getting pregnant until she was sure she was as healthy as could be. "You have been a model patient," Dr. James told her. "I have never met anyone quite like you. You've done everything exactly as I suggested and it has turned out really well."

"Thank you for that compliment, Dr. James," said Jayne, "but then I consider you to be the perfect teacher. You have instructed me at every step of the way and, as you say, I have done exactly as you suggested. Somehow I felt I should trust you from the beginning and you got it all right."

"It is interesting that the word doctor comes from the Latin word 'docere' to teach. Most doctors only prescribe drugs. They don't teach anyone anything. Before I forget, I would like to see you and Terry one more time, to talk about conception. I think it is ideal to explain a few things to a couple before they start a family. Having a baby is an amazing event, and the more you know about it before conceiving the better. There are one or two nutritional supplements I would like you to consider, especially some capsule of desiccated fruits and vegetables[♥]. A most interesting pilot study has been done on them. I will give you a copy. It is being repeated at present in a more scientific way to make sure the results are genuine."

Jayne was soon pregnant. She and Terry were so excited. The pregnancy went well, and Jayne delivered a baby boy weighing seven pounds on time. She had insisted that Dr. James be allowed to deliver her baby, even though she was aware that it had become normal practice to have a first baby in hospital. She got her way. Dr. James advised her to take homoeopathic arnica as soon as she went into labour. Jayne was sure it helped the whole thing, although she didn't have a previous delivery to compare it with. She had heard that first deliveries tended to be the more difficult and prolonged, but hers wasn't.

Jayne was amazed how well things had gone with her not having dairy products during her pregnancy. Dr. James had told her he was happy for her to do so. Her baby boy was perfect in every

---

♥ See Appendix 1 for a copy of this study and Appendix 2, note 2 for further information.

way, which he felt was a satisfactory way of demonstrating that human beings don't need dairy products at all. "If a woman can conceive," he said, "have a perfect pregnancy and deliver a perfect baby on time while not consuming dairy products, I don't know what is. All we have to do now is let you breast feed for as long as you want to and watch the baby grow normally and we will have completed the task. Many women have done as well as you having followed my advice."

Jayne loved breast-feeding her baby. They called him Tim, but it soon changed to Timmy. It gave her such a wonderful feeling of motherhood. She tried to explain it to Terry, but she simply couldn't find the words. "It makes me feel so warm inside. I nurtured this baby for nine months inside me, and breast-feeding seems such a natural way of completing the cycle. I so love doing it. I can't describe the feeling. When I think of it, Terry had such a tiny part in all of this. I knew immediately I was pregnant. Yet here we are with this tiny, dependent child."

The baby grew well. Dr. James considered Jayne to be the perfect mother. The health visitor was equally impressed.

Four months later, however, Jayne started to wheeze again. It started very gradually. She still had her bronchodilator inhaler, which she hadn't used for well over a year. She wasn't sure it would still work. She was worried it might be out-of-date, but it wasn't, yet it didn't seem to be working, or, more to the point, her asthma seemed to be getting worse. She consulted Dr. James again. Jayne explained what had happened and told him that she had been gradually getting worse over the past two weeks.

"If my memory serves me right, we worked out that you reacted to caffeine, dairy products and corn. Can I assume you have stayed off those all along?"

"Absolutely," replied Jayne.

"Ok!" Said Dr. James. "We need to look a bit further afield and consider the unexpected, the unusual. I've just had a thought. The new event in your life is the baby, so it is likely to be something to do with him or the fact that he is there in your house. So go through your day with him and let's see what we can find."

"I tend to feed him as soon as he wakes up. Once he had regained his birth weight, I did as you suggested and started to feed him last thing at night that's convenient to me and first thing in the morning that suits me. Until then, if he woke up in the middle of the night, Terry volunteered to get up and give him a bottle of warm water. He soon realised that it wasn't worth asking to be fed in the early hours. Also, perhaps Terry's arms are not as soft as mine, and his heartbeat is different to mine. Timmy heard my heartbeat all the time he was inside me, and he hears it again when I am breast-feeding him.

"He's a bright baby, or so I like to think. It didn't take him long to twig. So he gave up bothering to wake until I was ready for him. Now if he wakes before I am ready, he simply lies there as good as gold, gurgling away happily to himself. It is a most beautiful sound. He is such a contented baby. He smiles all the time, but seems to smile even more when he sees me for the first time in the morning and somehow knows I am going to feed him. I'm not sure who gets the greater pleasure from breast-feeding, him or me. I love him so dearly."

"It is my experience," said Dr. James, "that babies born to women who prepare themselves physically, like you did, are much brighter and more content than the average baby that happens to come along without any particular thought. I might as well warn you now that your baby is going to need a lot of attention. He will probably want you to read to him a lot. He will be interested in what you read, and will soon learn the stories off by heart. If you make a mistake, he will correct you. He will never stop wanting to learn, so you will need to find ways of stimulating his interest. He is likely to be able to read at a very early age, and will probably learn to speak very early on. Life will be very interesting with your baby. You could be very busy, so get yourself prepared for it. Sorry! I have digressed as usual. Tell me what you do once you start breast-feeding him."

"Well I pick him up as he is and take him back to bed with me. We both get comfortable and settle down. I love the way his hands move as he is feeding from me. I can't describe the joy of personally providing his food. I've observed what you said to me that a breast-fed baby has to work at it and suck hard, because it is lying on its side. I have watched some friends bottle-feeding their children. They don't have to do anything. The milk simply flows out of the bottle by gravity. Their babies lie on their backs and hold the bottle upright. And its cow's milk. It all seems so unnatural to me. I have mentioned the difference to some of them, but they said they wouldn't want to breast-feed. They think their way is more convenient. They don't get it. I don't have to warm up a bottle and hand it to my baby. I carry the perfect milk around with me all day long.

"Anyway, once he has finished, I put him across my shoulder and wind him. Terry has watched him do that. He says he puts on an even bigger smile when his wind comes up. It's all absolutely fascinating. I then take him into the bathroom and sit him on his own potty. It was difficult finding one small enough, but he usually obliges eventually. It is interesting what you said that, in babies, you put food in one end and something comes out almost immediately the other end. You told me that somehow we lose that response as we grow up, because it is your opinion that we should open our bowels three, if not four, times a day, i.e. one meal in and one meal out, provided there is enough overall fibre.

"I have worked out a system that seems to work. I make sure the bathroom is nice and warm and I run a big bath. I put two or three layers of towels on the floor beside the bath, and then we both get in. Having already wiped him if he has done his poo, I wash him all over very gently and play with him in the water. I want him to grow up liking water and not being afraid of it. He certainly does seem to enjoy our few minutes of play.

"I then gently lay him on his tummy on the towels on the floor, and complete my own washing. I then get out and dry myself. I have a big mirror on the wall in the bathroom, and I am watching how my body is returning to its proper shape. I am determined not to let my body become loose and flabby. I will be joining a gym soon.

"When I am dry, I wrap a dry towel round myself and dry Timmy, being very careful in between the cracks and folds of his skin. I then scatter baby powder all over him…"

"Whoa! Stop there, Jayne! That's it! Those baby powders are made of fine corn powder. You have been inhaling corn, one of your intolerances, directly into your lungs ever since you have been using baby powder. Once you have avoided something and become effectively symptom-free, it may take many weeks to resurrect your intolerance to it. It seldom starts to produce symptoms immediately as soon as you expose yourself to it again, if you have avoided it for many weeks or months. In fact you stayed away from it for at least four months before you became pregnant, plus the nine months of the pregnancy itself, so well over a year."

"How simple, yet how complicated," said Jayne. "You really do know your stuff. I would never have thought of that in a million years." Jayne stopped using the baby powder and her symptoms disappeared.[♥]

♥ For more information about preparing for pregnancy, see the Appendix 2, note 3.

Chapter 16

"**W**e must remember to think of things like that when we decide to start a family, mustn't we, Patrick," said Lynda. "I often wondered why some women find it so easy to get pregnant, while other struggle to start a family."

"As we are learning so much from these stories you are telling us, Maud, it would be silly not follow much of his advice," said Patrick. "What fascinates me is the incredibly wide range of medical problems that Dr. James became involved in."

"Actually," said Maud, "he told us that our area provided him with the sort of different problems that most doctors encounter in General Practice. It was just that he sorted many of them out in a different way. He was even occasionally called to attend car accidents on the B road, as it is a bit twisty and sometimes drivers drive too fast round some of the bends. I remember one time he was called, which had an odd twist to it."

There was a particular rather tight bend close to the village where unwary drivers going too fast sometimes came to grief. Dr. James was usually called by the people who lived at the end of Station Road, because theirs was the nearest house to where most of the accidents occurred. On one particular occasion they said, "You'd better come quickly, Doctor. This looks like a bad one." And so it was.

There were two cars involved, the front one having two young women in it, the other having two young men in it. It looked as though the second car had bumped into the first, at very high speed, and shunted it off the road, as the dent in the back of the first car matched the dent in the front of the other car. Dr. James took a quick glance at the two young men, both of whom were alive but groaning. It was quite a different picture with the other car. It had struck a tree head on. The front end was partially wrapped round the tree, and was in a terrible mess. None of the occupants in either car had been wearing seat belts. It probably wouldn't have made the slightest difference to the girls. They were hardly recognisable as human beings. Their bodies were in a shocking mess. It didn't need a doctor to say they were both dead. No human frame could possibly have survived such an accident. Dr. James returned to the other car to attend the two young men, and did his best for them.

It was not long before the ambulance and police car sirens were heard coming from Fulton. The road was quickly blocked off and diversions set up. The normal procedures following such an accident were set in place.

That same morning, the police had rung Dr. James, while he was doing his morning surgery, to ask him if he was the owner of a particular car. When they gave the registration number, he said yes it was his car. "What's happened to it?" He asked, worried about the answer.

"Should the car be being driven by a young man with another young man and two young women as passengers?"

"Not that I am aware." Replied Dr. James. "My wife drove it into Fulton this morning, leaving here after the rush hour was finished. I think she said she was going to park in the big supermarket behind the Town Hall. Is there a problem?"

"We received a report from a lady shopper in that supermarket, to say she saw four young people looking a bit suspicious, wandering around in the car park laughing and giggling. She thought they were up to no good, so she watched them. She thought they were trying door handles of various cars to see if any of them had been left unlocked, but her eyesight is not very good, so she didn't challenge them. She sounded a bit of a timid lady on the phone, so she was probably sensible to leave them alone and report what she saw to us. Then she thought she saw one of the young men bend down and open the door to a small car. They all piled in. She put her shopping down on the pavement and got out her glasses, putting them on in time to take down the number of the car as it swept past her. As you know, there is only one entrance and exit to that shop. The number she gave us seems to have been your car. It looks as if it has been stolen. I'm sorry, sir!"

"It's good of you to ring, Officer. I was afraid you were going to tell me my wife had been in an accident. It's the sort of phone call we all dread."

"Fortunately not, Sir!" Said the policeman. "We've put the details out, so all officers will be on the lookout for your car, Sir. We'll let you know when we find it. It's bound to turn up. They always do, but not always in a good condition, I'm afraid. They were obviously joy riding, if the description the lady gave us is anything to go by. Good Day to you, Sir." And with that he put the phone down.

Dr. James rang the supermarket to let them know what had happened. He asked them to let his wife know when she couldn't find her car.

In the meantime, Elizabeth James had been to have her hair cut. When she was finished, she went into the supermarket and did her shopping. That must have taken an hour-and-a-half in total. She left the shop and went to get into her car. It wasn't where she thought she had parked it. "I'm sure I parked it here," she said to herself. So she wandered round looking for it. There were only certain places she ever parked, so she checked them all.

In the end she couldn't find her car so wandered back into the supermarket and went up to the Assistance Counter. "Can I help you?" A pleasant middle-aged lady said to her.

"I can't find my car," said Mrs. James. "I think it may have been stolen."

"Are you Mrs. Elizabeth James?"

"Yes. I am," replied Elizabeth.

"It has been stolen, I'm afraid. Your husband rang to say the police had had a call from one of our shoppers to say she thought she saw it being driven away suspiciously. They are looking for it, but it could be a while before it is found. Would you like me to ring your husband for you? He said he would come and fetch you when you rang."

"That would be very kind of you. Thank you." And with that, she rang Dr. James who drove into Fulton to fetch his wife.

Later that day, they received a phone call from the Police to say that their car had been found abandoned in a cattle market in the middle of a town thirty miles away. They had been alerted because a patrolling Police car, sitting quietly in a side road, had seen the car flash by on the main road at probably sixty miles an hour in a thirty mile an hour speed limit, overtaking several cars and sounding the horn as they did so. They tried to give chase, but the car was far too far ahead for them to have any chance. Once it had been found, they called out the AA to check the car over. It appeared to be all right, but it was being driven over to Stead Norton.

When the car arrived about an hour later, they had a word with the AA man and gave him a cup of tea. He told them that, when he arrived, the car had smelled strongly as though it had been raced along the road between where it had been stolen and where it had been abandoned. He said that was the normal way joy riders did things. They were just out for what they thought was a bit of fun, at other people's expense. By the time the car had been brought back to Stead Norton, the engine had cooled down, so seemed none the worse for wear, but they said they would have it checked out at the local garage as soon as possible.

The next day they had another phone call from the same Policeman, who asked them if they had had the car sorted out in any way. When they said they hadn't got round to doing anything about it yet, the Policeman asked if they could come and fetch it as they may need to take some forensic evidence from it. Apparently, once they had abandoned the car, they stole two more cars, the young men getting into one, the young ladies into the other. They had raced along country roads at tremendous speed and were reported by a number of people who gave a description of the two cars, with some details of their occupants.

"Unfortunately the two young ladies were involved in a horrendous accident and both of them were killed," said the Officer.

"I have an awful feeling I attended to them yesterday morning. Was the accident just outside Stead Norton?"

"Yes, Sir. It was. What a strange coincidence. The ambulance people said you had done a good job with the young men by the time they arrived. Strange it was one of those young men who stole your car in the first place. Now that's what I call poetic justice."

Chapter 17

"Doctors get used to death," said Maud, "especially if the person involved is not someone they know. But, even still, that episode upset Dr. James. He felt it was such a waste of two young lives, all for the sake of what they thought was fun. He apparently visited those two young men in hospital, where he found them very contrite and chastened. He was strangely impressed by the way they both apologised for stealing his wife's car."

In the end, the elder of the two, Jeremy, admitted he stole the cars so took the rap for the others. He also admitted that he was driving the car that bashed into the back of the car the girls were driving, pushing them off the road at high speed to crash fatally into the tree. He was given a six-month prison sentence, basically for causing the death of the two girls, and banned from driving for two years after he completed his sentence.

When he came out, he was a totally changed person. He was absolutely gutted at the death of the two girls, which he accepted he had caused, albeit not deliberately. He used his time in prison in two particular ways. First he found he could talk to the chaplain and spent as much time with him as he could, and, before he left prison, he was baptised and confirmed. Fortunately he shared a cell with an older man who had a long sentence to complete, who told Jeremy it was his fourth sentence and that he realised how he had wasted his life. He somehow got Jeremy to open his eyes and start using his talents, although at the time he had no idea what they were.

The second thing Jeremy did was to start a course on computers and found he had a real gift for it. At school he had been described as bright but not willing to put his mind to anything, but suddenly he had changed.

Five years later, Dr. James was just about to finish his morning surgery, when in walked Jeremy with a most attractive young lady.

"Good Morning, Dr. James. Do you recognise me?"

"Could you be Jeremy?" Asked Dr. James.

"Now that's most impressive, Doctor. I really didn't expect you to remember me. How come you do?"

"Despite the tragedy around our first meeting, I knew there was something about you. I couldn't put my finger on it, but it was there. I lost contact with you once you left hospital, but the local papers were full of your trial. I was most impressed by your attitude, and I suspect the judge was also, otherwise you might have received a longer sentence."

"I can assure you it was long enough. I hated it, but my cellmate kept me sane to begin with, but it was meeting the Padre that changed things."

"Good. I thought it might," said Dr. James.

"Do I have reason to suspect your hand in it?"

"Actually yes. I asked our Vicar here, the Reverend Henry Middleton, to contact the prison Padre if he could, and ask him to make contact with you. I thought he might be able to help you. I remember your attitude while you were in hospital, and you seemed to be a changed man by the time you were in court. What the papers reported you said when you were convicted and given the custodial sentence gave me hope for your future."

"I can't thank you enough for that. That was very good of you, but I had no idea the suggestion came from you."

"To be fair the Padre would have got round to seeing you in due course, I would imagine, but perhaps our intervention made him seek you out sooner than he might otherwise have done. I felt you were in great need of pastoral care, and it would appear I was right."

"You've no idea how much he helped me. I was in a bad way by then. The death of those two girls will be on my conscience for the rest of my life, and I intend to make amends one way or another. As it happened, I spent all the rest of my time learning about computers. A man came into the prison every so often and showed us all about them. By the time I left, I had learned an astonishing amount, and studied everything I could get my hands on. I had so much time on my hands as I was banned from driving for two years. Within a year I started up my own business. The one thing about computers is that, if you have a good idea, you don't need a lot of start-up money.

"I have been very successful and am already making a lot of money, but I will tell you more about that in a minute. The other thing that has changed in my life is that I now sing in the choir of our local church, which is where I met Anita, who is also in the choir. We have just become engaged."

"How absolutely wonderful. My congratulations to you both. When's the happy day?"

"That's part of the reason why we are here today. We both have an unhappy background, having both been in care as youngsters. I was particularly troublesome and difficult, and rather rebellious. I couldn't understand what life was all about. There didn't seem to be any point to it all, but the one thing I didn't do was drugs and alcohol. Nor did I smoke. There didn't seem to be any point in those either. I tell you. I was in a real mess. That's why I did those silly things. That was the first time I had been caught, but not the first time I had stolen a car. I assumed I would get away with it forever. It had never occurred to me that racing along country roads would end up killing two girls. I still have nightmares about it all, but they are gradually fading, especially since I met Anita.

"Anita told me she was brought up by her grandparents as her own parents couldn't cope. Her real mum and dad died when she was in her teens, but her grandparents were old and very strict, so she rebelled a bit and ran away from them two or three times, always being taken back to them when she was found. Once she was sixteen, she left them for good, but strangely wandered into the local church, where the priest was very kind to her and found her somewhere to stay. He discovered she had a lovely singing voice and suggested she join the choir, and she has not looked back since.

"Jeremy told me all about his accident," said Anita. "I felt a compulsion to see where it had all happened. It was a very harrowing experience for him to see the spot again. He actually cried. More to the point, however, we wandered round Stead Norton and fell in love with it. We have bought a house in Main Street, well it's a large cottage really."

"Ivy Cottage?"

"That's the one," said Anita. "If all goes to plan we should take possession of it in about two months time. That's also partly why we are here. My grandparents both died in the past two years, and I don't have any family members left that I am aware of. Because you were so good to Jeremy despite the fact that he stole your car, I would like to ask you if you would kindly give me away at our wedding, whenever that is."

"I would be most honoured," said Dr. James. "So what are your plans?"

"Well we don't have any just yet, but the first hurdle is over, asking you to give Anita away. Thank you so very much. We would naturally have been married in the church where we sing in the choir – yes I have also joined the choir. I had no idea I could sing in tune. Anita encouraged me to try – but the priest has been appointed to another parish rather a long way away, and a new priest has not been appointed yet, so we are in a bit of limbo."

"Hang on a minute, let me telephone someone." And with that Dr. James picked up the phone and dialled a number. "Henry. It's David James. Are you free? You are? Good. Could you please come down to the surgery, and bring your diary with you? See you in a bit."

A few minutes later there was a knock on the door.

"Come in Henry. May I introduce you to Anita and Jeremy? Anita and Jeremy. This is the Reverend Henry Middleton, our esteemed vicar. They want to get married and don't know where to go. Can you help?"

"Are you the Jeremy who…?"

"I most probably am," replied Jeremy, before anything more was said.

"I would be delighted to see when I can fit you in, and I do mean delighted," said Henry Middleton. "The prison Padre told me such nice things about you. Now let's have a look."

"Dr. James has agreed to give me away," said Anita with a broad smile on her face. "Once we have decided on a date, all we'll need is somewhere to have a party."

"Leave that to me," said Dr. James. I have an idea."

"I wonder if you are thinking of what I am thinking," said Henry Middleton. Need my help?"

"Could be. I'll tell you about it later."

"Three months later," said Maud, "on a beautiful sunny summer's day, Jeremy and Anita were married in the church where Dr. James had given so many of his talks. The bride and groom had given up asking where the reception was to be held. All they knew was that they could arrange to go on honeymoon the next day, having been advised not to go away that evening. Jeremy was invited to dress at the vicarage, while Anita was fussed over by Elizabeth James at their house.

"I don't know what it was, but Dr. James really did see something special in that young man. The church was packed with people from Stead Norton. When the ushers asked people whether they were friends of the bride or groom, so they could advise them which side to sit in the church, nearly everyone said 'both of them', so the ushers gave up and told people to sit where they wanted. I had never seen so many happy people at a wedding. Everyone was smiling all the time. It was as though they had taken to the two young people who were about to move into the village.

"When the ceremony was over, the happy couple walked arm-in-arm down the aisle in the middle of the church, smiling at everyone. When they reached the outside and walked into broad daylight, they couldn't believe their eyes. Glinting in the sunshine was a guard of honour, eight mounted knights in full armour, four one side, four the other – Lord Weybridge's Chevaliers d'Honneur. The two young newly-weds were met by Lord Weybridge himself, in fully resplendent armour of the late fourteen hundreds, the time of chivalry. They were led to a waiting coach, this time of a more modern vintage, as His Lordship didn't think the coaches of near the end of the fifteenth century were good enough for these two special young people. Four of the most beautiful black horses were harnessed at the front of the coach.

"The procession wound its way through the village, the coach being escorted on either side by the Chevaliers d'Honneur, all the way to Stead Castle. The entire congregation walked happily behind the procession, except for those who couldn't walk that far. Lord Weybridge had laid on additional coaches for them. I decided to join them and take a lift," said Maud.

"Somehow Dr. James and the Reverend Henry Middleton had arranged it all, people in the village being willing to help out with all the catering. The young people who had been trained by Lord Weybridge's butler from London willingly served the guests. It was the most memorable wedding you could possibly imagine."

Two weeks later, Jeremy and Anita, who were back from a romantic honeymoon somewhere in the sun, came to see Dr. James after his morning surgery, accompanied by Henry Middleton.

"I've no idea why I am here," said Henry, "but I was asked to come. So here I am."

"Do you remember when I first came in to see you with Anita, and she asked you to give her away at our wedding? Although that was the most important reason for our visit, I said at the time that I had made a lot of money since starting my company, and I had intended to talk about that, but you managed to sidetrack us into making our arrangements for the wedding.

"As I said, I have made a lot of money, and am likely to make a lot more, but we really don't want much for ourselves. Anita and I never had much money when we were young, and we don't have the slightest desire to live expensive lives now. We have bought our cottage in Main Street outright, and it's certainly big enough for when we start a family. So we have all we can possibly spend money on, but it doesn't really interest us. As I said before, I am determined to make amends for the mistakes I made in the past, and Anita and I have given a lot of thought about what to do, although I had already come up with an idea before I met her.

"There are hundreds of young people much like me, who are lost in this world, not having a clue what to do with their lives, probably stealing cars out of boredom, like I did. To be fair to Anita, she wasn't anything like as bad as I was, although she ran away from her home a number of times. Otherwise she didn't get into any trouble, but she certainly met many boys and girls who did.

"I want to do something for such young people. I have already set up a charity with my accountant's and my solicitor's advice, and I want some help. Will you two please help me? I have already started the charity with four million pounds. There'll be more where that came from."

"I'm almost speechless," said Dr. James.

"So am I," said Henry Middleton. "That's an enormous sum, but I'm sure we will be able to put it to good use."

"I've already got some ideas," said Jeremy, "which I would like to discuss with you whenever convenient."

"To be fair," said Maud, "I don't suppose Dr. James had any idea that one of the young men he patched up on the side of the road was the person who had stolen his wife's car earlier on in the day. In any case, it wouldn't have made any difference. He would still have done his best. Jeremy's charity made such a difference to so many young people, but then he knew what it was like to be one of those youngsters. He had been there himself. No one could have been better able to understand the mind of lost young souls.

"When the policeman was told that Dr. James had looked after the victims of the original crash, he had said 'that's what I call poetic justice'. Justice sometimes has a way of turning to face the truth," said Maud. "Jeremy couldn't undo the damage he had done. He would have to live with having killed two young girls for the rest of his life. He knew that, but he found a way of making some sort of recompense."

Chapter 18

"I suppose Jeremy and Anita soon started a family," said Lynda.

"Oh yes! They had four children in six years," replied Maud. They were a really gorgeous family. They became fully involved in the local community, especially the church. Jeremy continued to make a lot of money and was very generous supporting almost anything we wanted. He told everyone to ask for money if they had an idea. He really meant it. He insisted that he and his family had more money than they could spend, but he couldn't stop making it.

"As for his charity, it became a national institution, helping so many young people to find something of value to do with their lives. Jeremy was regularly to be seen wandering the streets of towns and cities looking for ways to help young people. I wouldn't be surprised if he is eventually knighted for services to the community.

"In a way Dr. James was partially responsible for his life changes, because he visited him a number of times in hospital and somehow got through to him. At that stage, however, he was still badly affected by his involvement in the deaths of those two young women. What he felt made things even worse was that he didn't even know them. The girls were apparently looking for a car to steal from the same car park at the same time as Jeremy and his mate, and, when they realised what they were all up to they sort of joined up."

"What happened to the young man who was in the car with Jeremy?"

"He was given a suspended prison sentence for about two years, I think it was. He wasn't as badly affected as Jeremy by the deaths and joined the Army. I gather he is doing very well, and is also a changed person. Pity the girls died. I wonder what would have happened to the four of them if their escapade hadn't ended so tragically?

"Incidentally, Dr. James delivered all four of Anita's babies at home, which reminds me of another story.

Because of his love of Obstetrics, Dr. James delivered as many babies at home as he was able to. He had two excellent District Midwives, both of whom were as keen as he was to have home deliveries. One of the first, when he had only been in Stead Norton for about a year, was Jane Davidson, the fairly new wife of John Davidson who had taken over his father's farm when his dad had a small stroke. They had a lovely farm of many hundreds of acres, with cows and sheep and lots of wheat and barley. John's dad had run a very orderly farm, John finishing his course at University just in time to take over.

There was no surprise about his taking over. John had loved working on the farm with his dad all his life, and had spent every minute amongst the animals, running home from school as fast as he could. He loved every bit of it and was a real natural to take over from his dad, who soon recovered when Dr. James got him back from hospital. But that's another story.

Jane Davidson was not surprisingly a farmer's daughter, so was most comfortable around farming folk and farming things. She had also helped her own father deliver many a cow and sheep, so the thought of her own labour didn't worry her in the slightest. The house was nice and cosy so there was no reason why she couldn't have her baby at home from that point of view, except that it was her first baby and she was twenty-eight years old, so what the hospital called 'an elderly primip'.

Jane, Dr. James and both midwives did everything they could to convince the hospital Specialist to let her have her baby at home, and so it was arranged.

As Dr. James said to her, she was born to have babies. She was the ideal shape in every way and he predicted a large family if she wanted it, which fortunately she did. Mind you, she was also a most attractive young lady and John felt he was really lucky that she had chosen him.

The pregnancy went perfectly throughout, Jane attending all her antenatal appointments when they were due. She never missed a one. She was such a model patient that she was presented to some visiting medical students who were on secondment to the local hospital to learn outside a big teaching hospital. She was examined by some of them carefully and by the Specialist, of course, who pronounced that he was quite happy for her to have a home delivery.

Towards the end of the pregnancy she was seen by Dr. James and one of the midwives every week and everything was declared fine. Everyone was looking forward to the day of the delivery, which Jane hoped would be the same as her granny's birthday. Dr. James and both midwives guessed the weight of the baby, varying from seven pounds to seven-and-a-half pounds, which they all considered was just about the perfect weight.

On granny's birthday, Jane went into labour exactly on cue, starting just after breakfast after she had finished washing up. Trust Jane to wait until then, when the house was spick-and-span. The two midwives were called and they agreed that one of them would sit at home with her for the first two hours, the other taking over then. They both wanted to help with the delivery, but it was agreed that whoever was 'on duty' at the special time would take charge. After all, it was her first baby so no one knew how long the labour would be.

As instructed Jane took a dose of homoeopathic arnica every hour as soon as her labour started. Dr. James was notified and asked to be kept informed of her progress. He said he would pop in after morning surgery and would not go out in the meantime. He had full confidence in the two midwives. Sooner than the midwives thought, but roughly when Dr. James had guessed, John telephoned him to say they thought she was ready to deliver. So Dr. James drove to the farm, which was only a couple of miles from his surgery.

Everything was going according to plan. Jane was having contraction almost every two minutes by the time Dr. James arrived, soon after which the midwife in charge told Jane she could push with her next contraction. Within five minutes of pushing the baby was born and was quickly cleaned and wrapped up. He had cried immediately. He weighed a healthy seven pounds.

As the baby tore her slightly during the delivery, Dr. James went into the bathroom next door to wash his hands before applying a few simple stitches. He had hardly dried his hands when there was a cry of alarm from the bedroom as a second baby started to come out, foot first. Calmly Dr. James took over and delivered the second baby safely, which also weighed seven pounds when they eventually got round to weighing him. Everybody, the Specialist at the hospital included, had missed that she was having twins. They hadn't started doing scans routinely yet in those days. So the weight of 'the baby' turned out not to be somewhere around seven pounds but fourteen pounds! Dr. James's final comment before leaving a very happy family was "I told you you were born to have babies and lots of them, but I didn't expect you to have so many so quickly!"

Chapter 19

"Over the years we have had just about every sort of person living here," said Maud. "I got on so well with Dr. James and he visited me quite a lot, almost as if he felt I needed the company. I never did, mind you, but it was always grand to see him. He was such a friendly, likeable fellow. He just seemed to pop in every now and then, possibly when he was passing, or had a bit of time on his hands. So he told me the odd story or two, although he never divulged who he was talking about. I think he modified the stories a bit to keep the identity of the person a secret.

"He told me of the time his wife Elizabeth said the first thing that came into her head when a patient rang up in a bit of a state. He said most people seemed to assume a GP's wife knows all about them, assuming that all they talk about at home is the patients. People also possibly assume that doctors marry a nurse. Oh Lord! That's a lot of 'assuming'. In fact Dr. James married a PE teacher. I remember the Rector saying much the same. Because he was in the 'caring' business, people assumed that his wife was also as concerned about them as he was. Apparently it was even worse for a bishop's wife.

"Anyway, apparently a bloke rang up early one evening saying he was depressed and asked to speak to the doctor urgently. Dr. James's wife said the doctor was out on an emergency visit and might not be back for an hour or two. When the man then said he was going to commit suicide, his wife said the first thing that came to mind. 'Do you think you could wait until he comes back around 8 o'clock?' To which the man replied, 'No I can't. I'm going out then!'

"It was only when Elizabeth put the phone down that she fully realised what she had said, and worried what her husband would say. She also realised she hadn't asked the patient his name. Apparently Dr. James roared with laughter, saying he knew exactly who the call was from. He said he was a depressive, alcoholic homosexual, quite a mixture, who was particularly depressed at the moment because the local council wouldn't provide him with a flat to share with his boyfriend!

Chapter 20

"One of the saddest stories Dr. James ever told us in one of his talks in the Church was about a lady who asked to see him from somewhere up North. Although Dr. James worked for The National Health Service effectively full time, he was allowed to see private patients in his spare time if he wanted to, and somehow this woman had heard of him through a relative. He used this story to illustrate basic causes of diseases.

"This woman came with her husband and told him all about the cancer in her oesophagus – that's the gullet you see; I learned a lot of fancy names of parts of the body from Dr. James. The hospital had recommended an operation to push a tube inside her throat so that she would be able to swallow and that she had radiotherapy. She didn't like the sound of any of it and hoped Dr. James would be able to help her.

"He asked her a lot of basic questions to begin with, then got round to a question he thought was important to ask. He asked her if she had any idea what the cause was. He said patients often had ideas of their own, but the medical profession has such fixed ideas that they seldom ask such a question, or, if the patient dares to suggest an idea, it is immediately brushed aside.

"That was when her husband immediately jumped in and said, 'Oh! I know what has caused all this. It's all that scalding hot tea she has drunk all her life. I don't know how she does it. It is straight out of the teapot, no milk or sugar, but straight down her throat. She must have burned it years ago!'

"Dr. James considered this for a while, then asked her if she agreed. She said she accepted it was a possibility. However, as I have said before, Dr. James said he seldom accepted the first thoughts, often finding there was something else that could be involved, if he looked for it. So he simply said to her what he had said to so many cancer patients before. 'Have you been under any stress for perhaps the past few years?' He had found so many cancer patients had had a significant degree of stress in their lives shortly before cancer was diagnosed. He had read an article by a German Doctor who was convinced that cancer was the result of complete exhaustion of the adrenal system, which in turn damaged the immune system so that it no longer did its job of killing off rogue cells before they had time to develop into a tumour.

"'That question did it', Dr. James said. 'It opened the floodgates. It happened so often that I had boxes of tissues always ready, and this lady was about to let go. Her story was so sad.'

"Apparently her own mother had suffered from a particularly awkward form of Alzheimer's Disease, to such an extent that no care home was able to cope with her. Being a dutiful daughter she decided to keep her mother at home and do her best, which she did for a few years. She said it absolutely exhausted her.

"Unfortunately her mother also suffered from diabetes, which gradually got out of control. When gangrene developed in her legs, the surgeon said the only thing for it was to amputate both of them. Because of her mother's Alzheimer's, she was unable to make decisions for herself. So her daughter, the patient with cancer now in front of Dr. James, had been given legal responsibility for her mother, who was made a ward of court. It was the old lady's daughter, the cancer patient, who had to sign the hospital papers agreeing to the amputations.

"That was bad enough, but unfortunately, although the operations were a success in surgical terms, her mother died twenty-four hours later. Apparently she never recovered from the general anaesthetic. She blamed herself for her mother's death. She accused herself of killing her mother. She just couldn't forgive herself; she was so full of remorse.

"Dr. James said he had met a few patients who just couldn't find it in their hearts to forgive themselves for something they had done. He knew it was a waste of time telling her that she had clearly made the correct decision. He could see in her husband's face that he had tried that approach many times but to no avail, so he tried another approach.

"'I think it is likely that drinking all that tea for so long may have scalded your throat – made it a target for all that stress. I'm sure you didn't feed yourself well while looking after your mother'.

"'There wasn't time for food', she sobbed. 'I was rushing around so much looking after mum twenty-four hours a day. I lost four stone in weight over the last two years. But her death was my fault'.

"Dr. James admitted it was hard for him to go through his normal approach of explaining underlying mechanisms, but he did his best. Yet all along he felt he was not likely to get anywhere until she had somehow come to terms with her guilt. He could see no way she had any chance of improving her immune system and giving her body a chance to deal with the cancer while she felt like this. So he completed her history and did his usual examination.

"'I seldom rush into any particular advice to begin with, but I would like you to read a book I will give you. When a patient first gave it to me, I found it so fascinating that I stayed up all night until I had finished it. I think it could be the best way for you to start and I will see you again in a couple of week's time.

"Dr. James decided not to tell her what the book was about, hoping that she would read it. The book was called 'The Journey' by Brandon Bays♥. 'Unless you have read it, it is a little difficult to explain', he said. 'Yet the book explains why some people develop cancer because of some problem in their lives. Half the time they don't even remember what the problem is, as it may have been buried so deep in their soul. Brandon Bays gives some fascinating examples of how the various problems were uncovered and how that helped the patient recover.

"'In one part she takes the patient through an imaginary situation where he or she is 'confronted' by the person or situation that underlies the problem, sitting round a camp fire in the person's mind. I know it sounds a little weird', he said, 'But you have to read the book to understand what I am explaining rather badly. Anyway, I

♥ To obtain a copy this book, see Appendix 2, note 4.

hoped this lady would 'meet her mother' and have the opportunity to talk to her about her having signed the form for her mother to have both legs amputated. I felt sure her mother would have told her she did the right thing and that she wanted to die anyway, or something like that'.

"Dr. James said he never saw that lady again. She did not come back to see him. He thought perhaps he should have rung her to see how she was, but he didn't. He felt it was up to her anyway. She wasn't an NHS patient of his, so he didn't have the usual responsibility for her care. In many respects he wished she had been, as he really wanted to help her after all she had been through.

"Perhaps she read the book and it solved part or all of her problems. Perhaps she thought he was going to wave a magic wand over her and cure her. Perhaps she never read the book at all, but he said he would never know. He hoped she at least found peace somehow. She deserved it after all she had done for her mother."

Chapter 21

"Actually Dr. James told me of an even sadder story, although this one was mixed with some amusing episodes".

When he was a medical student in London, he moved around the Capital, living in different flats. He couldn't remember why he kept moving. Possibly the lease was up or something. It was never because he hadn't paid the rent. He earned enough money to pay for things like that by driving mini cabs in the evenings and early hours of the morning.

There was a time when he shared a basement flat with a most interesting character, Sam Jackson by name, but, again, he couldn't remember where he met him. Anyway Sam was a bit older than he was, possibly in his mid-thirties, and had been around a bit, as they say. He was forever bringing attractive women back to the flat. He certainly was a good-looking fellow himself and knew how to attract members of the opposite sex.

Anyway, David James came home one day to find the flat had clearly been broken into by very skilled operators, because there was no sign of a break-in. At first glance he thought the place looked in a terrible mess with things strewn all over the place. However, when he looked more closely, mainly to see what of his own things had been taken, he found to his surprise that nothing of his had been disturbed.

So he looked more carefully and wondered what the purpose of the break-in was for. He wasn't aware that Sam was up to any mischief or had anything of value to steal. It was then that he noticed that all Sam's clothes had been pulled out of their drawers and scattered everywhere, but all his trousers, both short and long, and all his underwear had had the crutch cut out of them! That was when he realised what this was all about – revenge or a warning. He never found out which because he never saw Sam again. He received a telephone call from him about two weeks later apologising for the awkward situation he had put him in, but assuring him that they were only after him, Sam, and that he, David, was in no danger. Sam admitted he had 'plucked' one young lady too many, or more to the point, he had plucked the wrong one. He needed to hide, possibly once again.

His friend Sam was clearly living a bit close to the mark. He had a beautiful sports car and was regularly stopped for speeding, but apparently was never fined even though he went to court a number of times. He had three Christian names, the first being Sam, the second and third being Hamilton and Middleton, having been named after his two grandfathers. Whenever he was stopped by the police – they didn't have speed traps in those days – he would give his full names but deliberately say Middleton before Hamilton. When he was asked in court if his name were Sam Middleton Hamilton Jackson, he would say that was not his name and the case was immediately dismissed on a technicality.

Before the parting of the waves, they had had many an escapade in London. Although David James was hardly a drinker, his friend Sam was, and knew many interesting 'watering holes', as he put it. David often kept Sam company and met many interesting and famous people. When they visited a particular club for the third time he asked Sam why everybody kept buying drinks for a thin man who clearly was permanently drunk.

That was when he was told the saddest story you could possibly imagine. This bloke was an ordinary chap going about a normal life, contented with his job, happily married with three lovely children. One day his wife and three children were standing at a bus stop when a drunk driver swung round the corner, far too fast and out of control, mounted the pavement and wiped all four of them out. David James wondered how anyone could get over something as awful as that.

"Hang on." said Sam, "That's not the whole story".

Somehow this chap survived and managed to pick up his life again. He met someone else, married her and they had three children. They all lived in a third floor flat. By then this bloke had got himself a better-paid job as a night watchman, and he was happy again. Horror of horrors, during one night the man in the ground floor flat fell asleep smoking a cigarette and his bedroom caught fire. He was a bit old and doddery and only just managed to get himself out of the door into the night, but by then, the whole building was ablaze. The fire brigade came as fast as they could and did everything possible, but everyone in the building apart from the old man died that night.

"That's unbelievable", said David.

"Hang on." Said Sam. "I told you this is the saddest story you could possibly imagine, because it's not over yet".

To everyone's total amazement, this chap managed to survive yet again but he kept his past history to himself. Sensibly he moved to another part of the country where no one knew him. He met a new woman, married her and had two children, and decided enough was enough. Imagine his horror when she told him with great joy that she was pregnant again. He was in a panic. He just didn't know what to do. So he decided to leave the country and go overseas.

Halfway through the pregnancy he, with his wife and their two young children, packed their bags and went to Africa to work on a farm as a handy man. The baby was born in due course and he felt his luck had changed. But fate of fates. He had moved to a part of Africa where an uprising had started. His wife and three children were captured, chained to a tree and butchered before his very eyes. He was let go.

"I'd like to buy him a drink," said David. "I agree he deserves to be kept in a permanently drunk state".

Chapter 22

Dr. James always said he did many things differently from most other doctors, even if he did many things the same way everyone else did. He felt it was the job of a General Practitioner to do everything possible within the area they lived. He tried very hard not to send a patient into hospital if there was a reasonable chance he and they could manage at home. He said he was blessed to have a group of really dedicated district nurses to help him. He felt they also thoroughly enjoyed working with him, and, when one left either to go to another job or to move to another part of the country, there was quite a list of nurses who applied for the job. They all felt that they did what they were trained to do, that was to look after people.

George Mason's wife Rebecca rang Dr. James in the early hours of one morning saying her husband had woken up frightened, short of breath and felt as though someone was sitting on his chest. Dr. James knew it was likely George had had a heart attack, as the description was classical and they tended to occur at that time of the morning anyway. So he rushed to the farm cottage where they lived and examined George very carefully.

Dr. James had visited a number of patients over the years, or they had queued up at one of his surgeries to see him, who had had heart attacks, but none of them had been too bad, and, in any case, he had learned to give an immediate intravenous injection of magnesium to calm the heart down, something he had learned from doctors in America. Apparently the heart is very sensitive to magnesium. Despite the magnesium settling things down, he felt that George's condition was sufficiently severe and unstable for him to need to be monitored for at least the next twenty-four hours, during which time he was aware a person could have another heart attack.

It is the normal custom, when sending a patient into hospital, for the attending General Practitioner to send a short note in an envelope with the patient to explain the situation and to indicate any treatment given. Dr. James not only did the usual but ended up with something that no other doctor had ever done before, so long as anyone in the hospital could remember. He put "Please may I have Mr George Mason back into my care as soon as possible".

Two days later Rebecca fetched George home, as the hospital doctors said his heart had settled down remarkably quickly, far more quickly than they would have expected, given the state of his heart when he arrived. So Dr. James immediately visited him at home to try to get him to consider ways of healing his heart. He said the sooner you start the better chance you have.

"What I want you to do is to consider a change in your diet. I know farming is in your blood, but I want you to consider my advice. I never bully people. I merely advise what I think would be best for a person, although I admit my advice is very similar whatever the problem. I'm happy for you to argue with me so long as you can justify your point of view.

"The first thing I would like you to avoid totally is all dairy products, milk, cream, cheese, especially cheese, yoghurt and butter, for the first month, although I may allow butter and cream in moderation later on. I'll explain my reasons in a minute. I also want you to avoid all forms of caffeine, so that means stopping drinking cups of tea and coffee and not drinking or eating any chocolate. Oh, and all cola drinks. Please cut out all sugar, white flour products and any food with chemical additives in them. I know lots of people eat ready-prepared foods that can be bought in most shops nowadays, but I want you to eat home cooked food. You probably do anyway. Also I want you to eat as much in the way of fresh fruit, vegetables and salad items."

"Most of what you suggest won't be a problem, will it Rebecca?" Said George.

"No. It all sounds fine to me," agreed Rebecca.

"But why no dairy products?" Asked George. "You started by mentioning my farming background, so you were aware that cutting that out might come as a bit of a shock to someone like me who has been producing it all his life."

"Well," replied Dr. James, "I could start by asking why you had that heart attack. Did you ask them in the hospital? No? If you had they might have said something about your cholesterol level, but in fact yours wasn't at all high. The chances are that they just accept that it happens to some people and that it is their bad luck, or something like that. Personally I believe that there is always an explanation for every illness and it is my job to help you find it if we can. They have sent you home on a couple of drugs, but they are basically to keep your heart nice and settled, and I am perfectly happy about them so long as they suit you and you don't develop any side effects.

"So, I come back to my question. Why did you have a heart attack, especially at the age of fifty-six? My answer would be that you might have been doing something for a long time that doesn't agree with you, and the one thing you do every day is eat and drink. So if you have been eating and drinking something all your life that somehow isn't right for you but you aren't aware of it, it just might gradually damage some of your blood vessels, especially some of the ones to your heart. In other people it might give them arthritis or asthma or eczema, depending upon your genetic make-up, I suppose."

"That's very interesting," said Rebecca, turning to George. "Because I remember your mother telling me that you used to hate milk as a child. No one could understand it. All farming folk love milk, or so they say, but you were different. You got into a lot of trouble bribing someone at school to drink your milk. Don't you remember, George?"

"Now you mention it I remember the walloping I got from a teacher when she found me out. Yes, it used to make me sick. I hated drinking it," said George.

"So there you are. But how come you have it now?" asked Dr. James, knowing perfectly well what the answer was going to be.

"Well I suppose I gradually started having a little in cups of tea. It's funny, now I come to think of it. When I went to Agricultural College in the evenings after I left school, everyone was drinking coffee with milk and sugar. I hated it at first, but there was nothing else to drink so I suppose I gradually got used to it."

"What all this is really telling you, George," said Dr. James, "Is that your body was trying to tell you that these things didn't agree with you, but you ignored the warnings, so your body adapted to the insult. It's rather like the way a tree adapts to the insult of having a nail hammered into it. If it could speak, it might ask you to take the nail out. But it can't speak so it adapts. Ok, so the nail doesn't give the tree a heart attack, but there is some degree of similarity between the two situations.

"All right. Point taken," said George. "I'll give it a go. What else?"

"Well let's finish off my reasons for asking you to give up caffeine, now that we have dealt with the dairy side of things. Tea may have been ok for you in moderation with its fairly low caffeine content, but you possibly blew things by starting to drink coffee at College. Unfortunately caffeine lowers your body's levels of magnesium, which in turn makes your heart sensitive to the stimulating effects of caffeine. So I will recommend you take at least 500mg magnesium per day, possibly more to begin with. Incidentally, calcium competes with magnesium for absorption, so cutting out the high calcium intake of dairy products will improve your absorption of magnesium.

"As a digression, there are certain drugs on the market prescribed for high blood pressure called calcium channel blockers. Although I have never asked anyone from a drug company, I suspect they know that calcium, possibly too much of it, can cause high blood pressure in some people. They must have known that magnesium is an effective calcium blocker, but they couldn't patent magnesium being a natural product.

"I also want you to take at least 400IU vitamin E per day. There were two Canadian Cardiologist brothers, Drs Shute, who did a lot of research on vitamin E and found it to benefit the heart. I would also like you to take about 1g vitamin C per day, which incidentally works well with vitamin E, as vitamin C is very important for the integrity of collagen, which is the basic material that binds tissues together. It worries me that a lot of people may be deficient in vitamin C, and probably many other nutrients. Oh yes, and vitamin D.

"The final supplement I want you to take is 100mg Co-Enzyme Q10 per day, which is possibly the heart's most important energy chemical. So, a considerable change in your diet plus supplements of Co-Enzyme Q10, magnesium, Vitamin C, vitamin E and vitamin D, which I will arrange for you to have. That'll make a new man of you."

George did as Dr. James recommended. To begin with he found it a bit hard. In particular he found he missed – no he admitted he craved – certain foods, especially sugar and coffee, but Dr. James told him how to manage that, mainly by taking regular doses of sodium bicarbonate after meals for about a week.

Six weeks after his heart attack, Rebecca drove George to the hospital for a follow-up appointment with the heart Specialist. Because there was a long list of people to be seen in the Outpatient Department, he was first seen by a Registrar who asked him how he was, examined him and arranged for him the have an ECG, an electrical tracing of the heart. The doctor reminded him that he had had quite a bad heart attack so he wanted to see how things were.

Later on in the morning when all the tests had been done, he was called back into the Registrar's office, where, to his surprise, he was asked to repeat his name and address and give his age again. When he had given the information, the Registrar left the room. A few minutes later, a nurse popped into the room and asked him to go into the Specialist's room, so he followed her, wondering what that was all about.

"There's nothing to worry about," said the Specialist. "We needed to check your details as we thought we might have someone else's notes by mistake. But I'd just like to examine you myself, if you don't mind." So George got suitably undressed once again and lay on the couch.

When he had finished, the Specialist apologised to George for taking so much of his time, then said, "I have seen a considerable number of people, mostly men, six weeks after as bad a heart attack as you had, and I have never, ever not been able to find plenty of evidence that the person had had a heart attack. There's always something to find. In your case, however, we have not found any evidence of your heart attack. It is almost as if you never had a heart attack in the first place."

The Registrar reminded the Specialist of the letter that had been sent with George when he was admitted early that morning six weeks ago, asking for the patient to be returned home as soon as possible. "Oh yes. I remember seeing it. It amused us all, but we did as your doctor requested, possibly sending you home earlier than is our usual practice. But I must say your heart seemed to settle down quicker than usual, so we felt it was probably ok to let you go. Why did your doctor want you home so quickly anyway?" asked the Specialist.

"He said he wanted to start healing my heart and the sooner he started the better," replied George. "He recommended considerable changes to my diet and put me on some vitamins and things," George added.

"Who's your General Practitioner, Mr. Mason?"

"Dr. James," replied George.

"Hm! Oh him!" Said the Specialist. "He does seem to do things differently."

"George Mason stuck to Dr. James's advice and did very well," said Maud. "He later admitted that, despite having had a heart attack, he started to feel better than he had felt for quite a while. He said that for a long time before the attack he had felt tired much of the time but had simply put it down to getting older and working hard. He started talking to a number of his farming friends and convinced some of them to do the same, although many said they weren't all that worried, so didn't bother.

"Dr. James told him not to crusade. He said a lot of people want to be able to do what they want, expecting the doctor to fix them up if something went wrong. He felt far too many people were of the opinion that, if things went wrong, that was when you involved the doctor, and not before. In any case, he said, if you went to the average doctor to ask what to do to remain healthy, you would probably be told to go away and only come back if something went wrong. In his opinion, however, people ought to take some responsibility for their own health and try to prevent things from going wrong in the first place if possible. He kept saying that at his lectures. He tried to get us all to think for ourselves and not rely on others if we could help it.

"That experience with George Mason and his follow-up appointment at the hospital, and one or two other stories, upset Dr. James. He had hoped to get through to other doctors, especially in the hospital, that there was another way of thinking of things. George told Dr. James that the Heart Specialist seemed to acknowledge that the dietary changes and supplements might have helped to heal his heart so quickly, but, so far as they were aware, didn't take it any further.

"When he became our General Practitioner," said Maud, "Dr. James found there were more than thirty patients with nasty leg ulcers, some because of bad varicose veins, others because of their diabetes. He said the normal situation was for them all to attend the Skin Department at the local hospital at regular intervals, where the doctors saw them, advised what ointments to put on them and asked the nurses to do the treatment and arrange for their next appointment in three months time.

"Sometimes some of the patients were asked if they would be willing to be involved in some research on leg ulcers, as a Drug Company had produced a new product that the Skin Specialist had been asked to test. Sometimes a new drug would help a bit, but, as far as Dr. James could see, none of them was ever much good. He was sure that somehow the Drug Company would be able to produce enough evidence to convince doctors that the new drug was worth prescribing. He was a bit cynical, was our Dr. James.

"Well, in his usual way, Dr. James said that, while it was certainly important to treat the ulcer itself, in his opinion it was most unlikely to heal if you didn't take care of the inner workings of the body. He said it was most important to improve the circulation in the limb, especially where the ulcer was, and to help the body do its job of healing. 'You can't expect the body to heal itself properly if you don't give it the right ingredients.' So once again, he recommended patients think about changing their diets and take certain supplements. Although there were many similarities, he tried to tailor-make each person's approach.

"After about six months, some of the patients said that the nurses started to say that things were looking better, and an occasional doctor agreed. The trouble was that there were so many patients attending the Skin Out-Patient Department that each person was rushed in and out as quickly as possible. Also, that department was used as a bit of a training ground for younger doctors, who therefore tended to change round, so patients seldom saw the same doctor more than once. However, the nurses didn't seem to change departments much so were in a far better position to notice any improvements.

"In fact the Departmental Sister and one or two regular senior staff nurses took a great interest in any patient whose leg ulcer improved, wrote their own observations in the patient's notes, and insisted on seeing the patient themselves whenever they attended. To begin with they would ask the patient who their General Practitioner was, but, as it became obvious that some patients were clearly improving, they began to assume that Dr. James was their GP, and how right they were. Within five years of taking over from Dr. Braithwaite, every leg ulcer was healed.

"What distressed Dr. James was that the Skin Specialist just wasn't interested in the few patients whose legs had healed. One of his District Nurses had a friend who was a nurse in the Skin Department, who told her that, although the nurses tried to bring up the subject at one of their periodic departmental meetings, the Specialist said he didn't think patients would be willing to change their eating habits, so the matter got no further.

Chapter 23

"Dr. James surely didn't cure everyone, did he?" Asked Patrick.

"No, of course not," said Maud, "apart from which not everyone was willing to make changes to the lifestyle and diet they were accustomed to. So he continued to prescribe drugs like all doctors to those that wanted them. That's why he kept up-to-date with the latest information, and attended lectures in the local Post-Graduate Centre, but he felt it was important to give people a choice. He was concerned that far too many people attended their doctor with the attitude 'I've got a problem, doctor. Will you please sort it out for me'.

"In any case, people also died around here just like everywhere else. He accepted that readily enough. It was just that he wanted people to be as well as possible, rather than to struggle with ill health. Talking about death, I remember one person who died in Stead Norton who had been very much a local character.

The death of any person can be a sad event, although not always. Even if someone dies on Christmas Day, it doesn't need to be sad, largely depending upon the attitude of the relatives who are left behind. And so it was with Howard Gregson who did die on a Christmas Day. But then he was born on a Christmas Day, so his family thought it was totally appropriate.

Everyone had loved Howard. He was such a friendly person, full of fascinating stories. He had been a pilot in The First World War and, if tales they told and old films are anything to go by, flyers in both World Wars were characters, some almost larger than life.

Howard was crippled with arthritis, especially in his hips and knees, and had been for years, long before Dr. James started his medical practice in Stead Norton. Howard never went to his surgery. He said a little suffering was good for the soul. He never complained, even though you could tell he was often in a lot of pain. He never took anything for the pain and he wasn't prepared to try anything that

Dr. James might have suggested. He simply got on with life, doing things that most people wouldn't have tried, let alone if they had arthritis as badly as he did.

Dr. James gradually discovered who the awkward people were, or, more to the point, who the people were he felt he ought to try to help, but who never sought his advice. So he would simply pop in to see them when he was passing by, usually having visited someone else nearby. He would just chat to them about anything, but never brought up the subject of their health. Howard Gregson was one of those people. He loved them all. He thought they were the salt of the earth, Howard being the best of a remarkable bunch in his opinion.

Howard said he had flown very basic planes in The First World War. He had learned how to repair them when they needed repairing, helping the mechanics when he wasn't up in the air. He found their simplicity fascinating and sometimes wondered how they stayed up in the air. After The War he became an engineer and worked in one of the aircraft manufacturing companies for over forty years, finally having to be retired because people couldn't bear to see him working despite his obvious arthritis.

Many was the time, when Dr. James just 'popped by', that Howard was under a sports car, or bending over the bonnet trying to fix something. On one occasion, while chatting to him under the car, Dr. James thought he had been there rather a long time so decided to ask him if everything was ok. To his amusement there was a giggle from under the car and Howard admitted he couldn't move. He had bent his left knee to reach something and it had got stuck, and, because of his arthritis, he was unable to get it free.

Dr. James took his coat off and got down on one knee to see if he could help. "My wretched left knee has been giving me some trouble lately and it seems to have locked. I shouldn't have tried to reach for that wrench over there. It's just out of my reach, but there's no point in having it now. I wouldn't be able to use it properly in this position."

"What can I do to help?" Asked Dr. James.

"I'm not sure," said Howard. "I'm not sure why my knee has locked anyway."

"You probably have quite a few odd pieces of loose calcium in your knee and one of them has become stuck in an awkward place at a rather unfortunate time. I don't think there's any chance of my doing anything about it where you are. So we'll have to think how to get you out from under there."

For the next fifteen minutes or so they discussed any options they could think of. By then quite a group of people had gathered, so many suggestions were made, but none got him out of his predicament. Howard always worked on his car out in the street, but as it was a cul-de-sac, there was no passing traffic to worry about. Also his neighbours were quite used to his goings on, half the time not sure what he was doing. They often thought he took his car to pieces just to put it back again. When he had got it working he would struggle to get into the car, taking ages to squeeze his long arthritic limbs into it. It was a low-slung sports car of some ancient vintage. It was probably as old as some of the aeroplanes he used to fly. He would then take it out presumably on a test drive and bring it back with a smile on his face. What confused people was that within a week he would take it all to pieces again.

In the end Dr. James said he thought the only thing was for someone to ring the local garage and ask if someone would kindly come out and lift the car off Howard. Fortunately someone was available so they brought a large breakdown truck, put some heavy lifting gear under the front end of the car and lifted it up high enough to get Howard out safely. Even then he had become so stiff that they couldn't get him out easily, so they had to slip a flat trolley, the sort of thing mechanics lie on to slide under a vehicle, under him. As by now he didn't have the strength to lift himself up, it took four strong men, two either side of him, to lift him sufficiently to be able to slip the trolley under him and pull him out from under the car, to clapping and cheering from the gathered crowd.

"That's what I love about this place," said Dr. James. "Everyone trying to help in good spirit. It's a good thing it wasn't raining though," he added.

"I wouldn't have been working on the car if it had," responded Howard.

Now Howard was dead. His daughter said he had had a full life, possibly the sort of life many people would have envied, without the arthritis, of course. She was very matter-of-fact. "Dad said he was bound to die one day, but it wasn't up to him when the event actually happened. That was someone else's job, or so he assumed. He said so many of his friends had died when he was young and he had tried to work out why they were picked out for death and not those who survived. As he was one of the survivors, he said he could only assume there was a greater power that made such choices, so he stopped bothering about it and simply got on with whatever life handed out to him. He even said his arthritis was part of the great scheme of things and there wasn't anything you could do about it, so stop complaining and do your best - well, that's what he said to himself.

"Although he spoke like that most of the time," his daughter said, "he would occasionally smile his naughty smile and say 'Mind you, there were times when I decided that we wouldn't simply leave things as they were. It's all very well if you are in the hands of an Almighty power, but my friends and I weren't prepared to go because some stupid person made the wrong decision. Our First World War planes were as basic as you could imagine a plane to be. We couldn't fly very far to begin with because we didn't carry enough petrol. Then some idiot came up with the wonderful idea of putting in an extra fuel tank. Well, perhaps that part of the idea wasn't so stupid, but it was where they put it that was stupid. They put it on supports above our heads, as there was nowhere else to fit it.

"'Even the mechanics thought it was a silly idea, but they were given their orders so that was where the spare fuel tanks were put. Can you imagine flying with a tank load of petrol above your head? One bullet and you would be doused with burning petrol. Not a good idea. But we were smarter than they were and read the mechanics' orders and came up with our own answer. The orders had forgotten to tell the mechanics to fill the tanks with petrol, so we had them filled with water. If we did catch fire, we had a natural fire extinguisher!'"

Chapter 24

"Tell us more about Dr. James' talks in the church. How often did he give them?"

"Well there was no particular pattern. He simply decided to give a talk, often because someone pushed him into telling his or her story. A notice would go up that he was talking at such-and-such a time on such-and-such a date, and we would all turn up. Everyone in the village would let everyone know when one was due, as that was all we talked about for a while, wondering whose story he was going to illustrate. Once we arrived in the church, it became obvious because of who was sitting up front."

Dr. James's lectures in the church were so popular people actually asked him to describe how he had helped them. They would proudly sit in the front pew in seats reserved for special guests. Two very happy ladies sat in those seats at one of his talks, nodding to each other when he got to a particular part that they especially remembered. Their stories were at least a year apart, but were so similar in principle that they were almost the same story.

One lady was called Mavis Jenkins, the other Natalie Brown. Both were married at the time, although Natalie only moved into the area when Dr. James had been the local GP for about three years. When a new doctor takes over, it takes time for him to get to know everyone. Mavis had been on anti-depressants in the past, but had given them up as a waste of time. In fact she felt they made her even more depressed, so she didn't see any point in taking them. So Dr. James had not met her early on.

Something about his talks stimulated Mavis to visit him in his surgery one morning. Dr. James remembered hearing murmured voices in the waiting room, but had thought nothing of it. Apparently Mavis had arrived fairly early, but kept telling late arrivals to go in before her. Dr. James didn't have an appointment system. He felt a person should be able to see their doctor as soon as they wanted, and not have to wait for the next available appointment. He didn't understand how any doctor could keep to an appointment system of five or ten minutes per slot, so why have an appointments system in the first place? If someone came and there were rather a lot of people already there, they could either wait their turn or come back another day if their problem wasn't urgent.

Eventually Mavis was the last person to go into his surgery that morning. Dr. James had never met her before so welcomed her in his usual courteous manner. She told him she was the last one, so hoped he had a few minutes to spare.

"I have all the time you need," he assured her. "How can I help you?"

"It's my weight," started Mavis. "Just look at me. It's awful. I just can't lose it. I've tried so hard. It just won't come off."

"Why don't you start from the beginning?" Encouraged Dr. James.

"I'm not sure where to begin," said Mavis. "I must have been this weight for at least fifteen years."

"I never ask people how old they are," said Dr. James, "I prefer to ask people what their age is?"

"I'm fifty-six, so I must have started to get really fat around the age of forty, although I was never what you could describe as slim."

"Have you gone through the change of life?" Asked Dr. James.

"Yes," replied Mavis. "About five years ago, and I still suffer from the wretched sweats. It's not fair being a woman. Between puberty and the menopause you have those annoying monthly periods with all that tummy pain. As if that wasn't bad enough, your boobs become swollen and sore for a week beforehand, you feel pretty bad-tempered and you put on all those pounds, even if you do lose most of them when your period starts. I was so looking forward to my periods stopping, only for them to be changed into these ghastly hot flushes and palpitations. When will it all stop? I suppose only when I die, but I don't want to die yet. I have so much I want to do. I have two beautiful grandchildren I want to play with and have stay with us for weekends, but I just don't feel I could cope. I tried hormone replacement therapy as so many of my friends said it had helped them, but it only made things worse. It also made my blood pressure shoot up, so Dr. Braithwaite told me never to try them again. He said he didn't have anything else to offer, so I would just have to put up with it and hope they would eventually stop. But they haven't. I'm at the end of my tether. I can't go on any longer like this. I'm at my wits end. I've got arthritis in my knees, ankles and hips, which I can understand because I'm so grossly overweight, but I can't understand why I have it in my fingers, wrists and elbows. Ok I talk a lot so it makes sense I have it in my jaw. I have a headache most days. Some days I feel as if the top of my head is going to blow off. I'm so tired all the time, yet I can't sleep because of those wretched hot sweats. I've had to move into the spare bedroom to let my husband get a good night's sleep. There's no point in us both not sleeping. I'm constipated. I only open my bowels once every two weeks, and then it's a real effort and I make myself bleed. It never used to be like that. I'm so depressed. And to cap it all I think I might be diabetic!" And with that Mavis broke into tears, and sobbed her heart out, blowing her nose loudly on the tissues Dr. James offered her.

It took a whole five minutes before Mavis could bring herself under control and stop weeping. Even then her eyes were all red and blotchy. Dr. James gently took one of her hands. "Can you spare this one?" He asked her. "You can have it back if you need to blow your nose again," he said in a soft tone of voice.

"I must look a sight," declared Mavis. "I haven't had such a good cry in ages. I just couldn't help it. It all just came out. Thank you, Doctor. I feel better for it."

"You had a lot of pent-up anxiety to get off your chest. I'm so glad you let go. It tells a doctor how bad the problem is. Do you think you could answer a few questions now?" Asked Dr. James.

"Fire away," replied Mavis. "I'm ready for anything now."

"There are many questions I could ask about your past, but first I would like you to tell me what you have done to try to lose weight. Don't say 'Oh! This and that!' I want details, please.

Incidentally, what is your current weight? Don't be embarrassed. Just give me a figure."

"I think I am 18½ stone," sighed Mavis. "I suppose I started to try to lose weight about fifteen years ago by simply watching what I ate. I tried cutting out potatoes, chips and white bread, and only had one of two slices of wholemeal bread a day. But it didn't make any difference. The weight seemed to go on up. I joined one or two weight-losing clubs and listened carefully to what they said and followed their advice."

"What was their basic message?" Asked Dr. James.

"It was quite simple really. Although they wrapped it up slightly differently, the basic principle was that you need to know how many calories you use up in twenty-four hours and to make sure you consume less calories in that time. For example, if you only used up 2000 calories, you must take in no more than 1800 calories. That way you will burn off the extra 200 calories."

"Did it work?" Asked Dr. James.

"No. Not in the slightest. I kept being held up for ridicule, to show people what happens when you don't follow the rules. I assured them that I was doing exactly as they said, but their method didn't work on me. It seemed to work on a lot of people, but there were others in whom it didn't work. I assume they followed the plan like I did."

"What happened then? Did you give up and stop going?"

"No. I asked them if they had plan B. They said there wasn't one, but I could try a 500-calorie diet if I liked, which was bound to help me lose weight. In fact six of us agreed to try it as their plan A hadn't worked for them either. We were all very keen, in fact almost desperate, to lose weight, so we were willing to try virtually anything if there was a chance it might work."

"Did that work?" Asked Dr. James.

"No it did not. In fact it did exactly the opposite for all of us. We all put on weight! It was terrible. The lady taking the classes said she had never heard of such a thing. She said it was absolutely impossible to put on weight on a 500-calorie diet, even if you were to lie still all day long, as even doing that would use up about 500 calories in a day. I agree with her. It's crazy. It doesn't make sense."

"Oh yes it does," said Dr. James.

"Really? It actually makes sense to you? You can explain it all to me?" she said.

"Indeed I can, and I know exactly what to suggest you do. What's your husband's attitude to your attempts to lose weight? Is he on your side? Will he help you?"

"Most certainly he will. He can see how hard I've tried. In fact he came with me to the club meetings to bear witness to the fact that I had always done as I was told."

"That's very helpful, because you will need support with what I am going to suggest. It won't be easy, but I can guarantee it will work. I need to have enough time to explain it to you both, so I would like you to come back with your husband at a time suitable to all three of us."

"I'm so excited," said Mavis. "I was afraid I was going to have to live with all this awful weight."

About a week later, Mavis came to Dr. James's surgery with her husband Alex. "This is so good of you, Doctor," said Alex. "Mavis has tried so hard to lose weight. I have watched her come home with enthusiasm about trying something, but nothing has worked, however hard she has tried. Did Mavis hear you right? Did you say that you could guarantee your method would work?"

"Yes. She did hear me correctly, although I said it would not be easy, as I will now explain to you both. When I have finished, you will see that the whole process could be very difficult for some people, so I need to make that clear right from the start. Ok?" Both of them nodded, showing their willingness to at least listen to what Dr. James had to say.

"Mavis has explained to me what methods she tried and how they not only didn't work, but had the opposite effect. To me there is a very simple explanation for that, which I will explain in due course. Having said that, for many overweight people, the problem is that they genuinely consume more calories in a day than they use up. In simple terms, they eat too much. When they reduce their intake below their output, the weight falls off. Most people have no idea just how much they are eating. It can be a real eye-opener to show some people just how much they eat if you lay their total weekly input, rather than their daily intake, on a table. I've done it for some people, but I have also seen it shown on TV. Then it is particularly fascinating to see the face of the 'client' when their total weekly intake is demonstrated.

"Many theories have been put forward over the years to explain why so many people are overweight. Each theory seems to suggest that other theories are wrong and that theirs is the only correct one. As people are all different, it is logical to me that the reason why one person puts on weight has a different explanation from another person's reason. If we are different people, we have different reasons for things. That's why I wanted to hear what you have tried and what effect each method had on you. I needed to identify what your personal reason was for gaining weight, and I'm sure I know.

"Governments and doctors have talked endlessly about cutting out fat. Yet many really gross Americans are on a virtually fat-free diet. So either they aren't or the theory they are following is wrong. Interestingly enough, the doctor who was the main stimulus to my interest in this whole area of medicine published a book in 1957 entitled 'Eat Fat And Grow Slim'♥. A point he makes is that carbohydrates slow your metabolism down while fat speeds it up. If this is true, pure calorie counting is not the full answer, although it is to many individuals, especially if the calories they cut out are carbohydrates and in particular if those carbohydrates are white flour products.

"So, Mrs Jenkins, I assume you have been through all of that."

"Indeed she has," replied her husband. "I have been following and monitoring everything Mavis has done for so many years. I have brought a log book of her attempts for you to see." And

---

♥ To obtain a copy this book, see Appendix 2, note 5.

with that he passed a large notebook over to Dr. James who quickly scanned its pages.

"I will keep this for now, if I may," Dr. James said. "I will study it in more detail another time, but I doubt it will tell me anything you haven't told me already. But you never know. It might reveal something of value. On the other hand your detailed way of making notes will come in very handy for your wife over the next few weeks, if she decides to follow my recommendations."

"Oh I will, I can assure you," Mavis said.

"I hope you will," said Dr. James, "But let's wait until after I have explained it all to you and told you what the hard bits are."

Dr. James then explained the fact that he was sure she had a food intolerance, or probably more than one. He explained that there was a difference between a food intolerance and a food allergy. Food allergies, he explained, were obvious. You ate them and you quickly produced symptoms. A classical one was a peanut allergy, which could close up a person's throat very quickly and actually kill them from asphyxia. Some people reacted to eggs, which might give them itchy hives or a skin rash. Other people might develop diarrhoea and vomiting with shellfish. The point was that their reaction was soon after consuming the food and the reaction was pretty obvious. Although some people were born with the problem, most of the time they developed during life, sometimes suddenly, by which time the culprit was fairly obvious.

A food intolerance, on the other hand, he explained, was a reaction that gradually developed without it being obvious, largely because the symptoms were not 'classical' in the medical sense, i.e. the symptoms were not what doctors recognised as reactions, but the effect was to cause mild inflammation in susceptible tissues. In Mavis's case the target organs for that inflammation were almost all of them because her symptoms were so many and varied. Also, whereas blood and skin prick tests could identify and confirm food allergies, there was no acceptably scientific way of confirming food intolerances. As a result most members of the medical profession refused to accept that they existed.

"Although there are some blood tests that can sometimes help, the only real way to identify a food intolerance is a process of avoidance and challenge," explained Dr. James, "But it can be a rather tedious process, although the patient learns a lot during the process. So here comes the first piece of bad news. Although there are various ways of starting, I want you to start the whole process by going on a total fast of five whole days. Nothing to eat at all, with only bottled water for five days!" ♥

There was a stunned silence from Mavis and her husband.

"Nothing to eat at all for five days?" queried Mavis.

"Nothing to eat at all for five days," repeated Dr. James.

"Isn't that dangerous?" Asked Mavis's husband. "Won't that make her ill?"

"It's not dangerous," said Dr. James, "but yes. I accept it most probably will make you ill. In fact you may well feel worse than usual for the first few days, suffering from what we call 'withdrawal symptoms', withdrawing from the culprits of your former symptoms. But I will keep an eye on you. If you develop a really severe headache, for example, and it becomes intolerable which it might, I will be available to give you an injection. Unfortunately you are not allowed to swallow any painkillers, as they might contain something you might react to, so that would spoil the process of the five-day fast. In any case they don't work. The first thing I suggest you try is a cold water bottle or a really cold flannel on your head. I would prefer you to grin and bear it if you can, remembering that, to a degree, the worse the withdrawal symptoms, the better you will feel when they clear, and the greater the proof that your problems have all along been one or more food intolerances. Just think of the awful symptoms someone suffers from when they give up smoking or alcohol or crack cocaine and go cold turkey.

"Your withdrawal symptoms can be minimised by taking half a teaspoonful of pure sodium bicarbonate, which I will give you, on a

---

♥ Described fully in the book 'Conquering Cystitis', by Dr. Patrick Kingsley. To obtain a copy, see the Appendix 2, note 6.

regular basis. Also the more bottled water you drink the better to clear your body of toxins. Please only use still water from glass bottles, not plastic ones. Withdrawal symptoms are likely to be at their worst on day three, but you should wake the next morning feeling a totally different person."

Dr. James then showed them how to make a chart of symptoms, and grade them in a simple way, suggesting 0 to mean no symptoms, grade 5 to indicate very severe, and for her to make as long a list as she wanted of all the symptoms she had suffered from, such as headache, joint pains, depression, insomnia, constipation, lethargy, fatigue, etc. Mavis was also to weigh herself completely naked on a fixed set of scales first thing in the morning at a set time after going to the toilet, and again before going to bed. If she got up during the night to go to the toilet, that was all well and good. She was to do this basic information gathering for about five days to set her standard before starting the five-day fast, and to prepare herself and get in adequate supplies of glass-bottled still water. They arranged when all this was to take place, Mavis basically wanting to start straight away.

"Ideally I would like to see you the day before you start the fast," said Dr. James, "basically to check your charts and see if you have done them properly. I would then like you to ring me every day during the fast just to let me know how you are progressing. However, you must ring me, or your husband must, day or night, if you are worried about anything. I absolutely insist upon this. Ok?"

"Don't worry," said Mr. Jenkins, "I will be with her all the time. She has tried so hard up to now. We both so much want this method to work. She deserves it to."

So the five 'run-in' days were completed. Dr. James looked at her charts and was astonished at the variety and severity of her symptoms.

"Has this been going on for so many years?" He asked.

"I'm afraid so," answered Mavis. "Life really has been a struggle."

"I'm sure it has. All I can say is that there is no doubt in my mind that you will soon be a new woman. What I'm intrigued to find out, however, is what has been causing all this misery for so long. From the information you have given me, I have made some sort of a guess. I have written it down on a piece of paper and put it in this envelope, which I have sealed. Would you care to sign across the seal so that you don't accuse me of cheating when we open it?" Mavis duly obliged, with a conspiratorial wink to her husband.

"I can't wait to find out myself," she exclaimed.

Mavis spoke to Dr. James every day during the fast, except for the third day, when her husband spoke for her. It was around midday.

"I was about to ring you, but I've just managed to get her to sleep. I have been massaging her head and neck to try to ease her pain. I've done that so many times before, but I thought it wasn't going to work this time. But I persevered and she has at last dropped off. She had put a maximum points score against many of her symptoms, but I'm afraid we have had to put an even higher score against a few of them, especially her headaches and her joint aches. She said she didn't think it was possible for things to hurt so much. I offered to ring you a number of times, but she said she felt things were going to plan, especially as she was thrilled when she got on the scales this morning to find she had lost a total of ten pounds so far – in three days. She said she couldn't imagine what the total will be by the morning of day six when we have the next meeting."

"While you are about it," said Dr. James, "I would like you to make sure you have a number of particular foods in the house, for your wife to start testing on day six, depending on what she tends to eat on a regular basis." So they discussed her regular eating habits and Dr. James made some suggestions.

"I will pop out tomorrow when I hope she will be feeling a bit better. I have one or two things I need to do, so I have arranged for her sister to baby-sit her. I don't want her to be left on her own for a minute for now."

"I think that is very wise," said Dr. James.

And so day six arrived. Their appointment was for eleven o'clock, when Dr. James hoped his morning surgery should have finished, which it had. To his delight, in sailed a happy, smiling Mavis Jenkins, full of bounce and energy.

"Look at my charts." She announced. "I have not only lost all my nasty symptoms, especially my headaches, but also not one of my joints aches. And to cap it all I have lost a magnificent eighteen pounds! Eighteen pounds!" She repeated. "That's unheard of. It's an absolute miracle. I can't believe it. I feel so fantastic. I haven't felt this well for absolutely ages. You're an absolute marvel. You guaranteed I would lose weight and you were absolutely right. Oh Lord! That's an awful lot of absolutely's."

Dr. James let her finish. Mavis and her husband were clearly delighted.

"Things went as I expected. You were bad enough before you started the fast, but things got even worse during the fast itself. The worst day was day three, as I was sure it would be. You had a classic reaction to the fast, and I knew you would lose tons of weight. Now you have to go through a slow process of reintroducing foods one by one to begin with, although you may combine some foods in due course."

"Actually I don't want to eat ever again, I feel so well, if eating can make you that ill, but I suppose I will have to. It's amazing. I don't feel at all hungry. If you had told me I wouldn't feel hungry after fasting for five days, I wouldn't have believed you. In the past I would feel headachy and light-headed if I didn't have regular meals, so I assumed that meant I ought to eat regularly."

"Actually it's a sign of your blood sugar plummeting, possibly having risen too high from the last thing or things you had eaten. But that's another story. I don't want to burden you with too much science."

"Ok. So what do we do now?" Asked Mavis.

Dr. James then explained how to introduce one food at a time, testing her pulse before eating the food and twenty, forty, sixty, ninety and one hundred and twenty minutes after eating it, and what changes in her pulse to look for as an early sign of an impending reaction. She could 'test' three foods a day. She was also to keep filling in her chart of any symptoms, but this time to note if any developed within a few hours of eating each food. She was also to continue to weigh herself twice a day at the same times she had previously weighed herself. He gave her a list of about twenty or so foods to test, and said he would see her again in two weeks time or sooner if she got through the list that quickly. He also told her what to do if she had a 'reaction' to a tested food.

About two weeks later, Mavis was back in Dr. James's surgery with her husband. She was still smiling and looking and feeling well.

"You'll never believe what happened!" Said Mavis. "I sailed through the first three foods you recommended I start off with on the first day, but the next day was astonishing. I had no problems with what I tested for breakfast and lunch, but, oh my God! When I tested carrots that evening I swelled up, all my joints hurt me like crazy and I had the devil of a headache. But worse than that I put on seven pounds over night! I couldn't believe it. How could I possibly do that?" She wailed.

"What else did you notice you did that evening and during the night, or possibly did not do?" Asked Dr. James.

"What a strange question," said Mavis. "I'm not sure what you're getting at."

"Any ideas, Mr Jenkins? You're an engineer. Did you notice anything unusual that could explain her weight gain?"

"I'm afraid I was so concerned that she was starting to feel unwell again, I wasn't concentrating."

"Did you make notes of everything she did?"

"Yes. I did," he replied.

"Let me see your notes, please, if you have them with you," which he did.

Dr. James then took a few minutes to read through Mr. Jenkins's notes.

"It's all here," Dr. James said. "Your notes say it all very clearly. You really have been most diligent. I'm looking at your wife's water intake. During the run-in period she drank an average of three litres of water a day. During the fast her water intake went right down. Any ideas why?" He asked.

"I strangely didn't feel thirsty during the five days of the fast," Mavis said. "Oh now I understand your question. When I swelled up and all those nasty symptoms returned when I ate carrots, I became incredibly thirsty. Let me look at Alex's notes. Oh golly! Did I really drink six litres of water that evening and through the night? Oh, and I can't believe it, I didn't pass water once! So that's why I swelled up so badly and had put on so much weight by the morning. I had retained all that water in my tissues!"

"Exactly!" said Dr. James. "There you have it in a nutshell. You have been waterlogged all these years and that water in your tissues has caused all those symptoms."

"I also reacted to cabbage a few days later, but not so dramatically. I only put on four pounds and my symptoms weren't nearly so bad. Let's open that envelope, may we?" asked Mavis. And so they did.

"You wrote down 'one or more vegetables'. How on earth did you know?"

"I couldn't know exactly which one or ones, but it had to be at least one vegetable. I asked your husband whether he had made notes of what you ate when you followed a 500- calorie diet and actually put on weight. He had. Not surprisingly you ate plenty of vegetables during that time, not unreasonably, of course, as vegetables tend to be low in calories. That really was the clue you gave me when you told me what you had gone through at the various stages. It's just a matter of thinking logically. If your husband had also made a note of how much you drank while on the 500-calorie diet, he might also have noticed your intake also went up then."

"But I love carrots and cabbage," wailed Mavis. "They're my favourite foods. Aren't they supposed to be very healthy?

"Yes they are, for most people. But you aren't most people. You're you. You're an individual. You may love carrots and cabbage, but they don't love you. You possibly ate them too often, so your body started to react to them. You may have strangely become addicted to them. It's one of the points I keep trying to get across to people, namely our individuality. So many people react to a food item they consume regularly, without being the slightest aware it is doing them harm. As you suggested a few minutes ago, the foods you reacted to are considered healthy foods, and they are to most people, but not for you. For many people, and especially many doctors, it is a very difficult concept to grasp. But I can assure you it is very real, as you have been fortunate to find out."

Mavis was given another list of foods to test, one or two of which produced mild reactions. Over the next few months she strictly avoided those foods she reacted to on testing. Her weight fell wonderfully and, within six months, she had lost a total of five stones and was down to thirteen-and-a-half stones, taking another six months to get down to the ten stone area she was aiming for.

To her surprise, Dr. James had advised her not to start exercising to begin with, saying that there was a scientific reason for his advice. He told her that once she was effectively free of her old symptoms for about two weeks, that would be a sign that she had successfully eliminated the inflammation that had caused all her symptoms. At that stage he examined her carefully, did an electrical tracing of her heart to make sure it hadn't been harmed by her problems, and only then advised her to start on a sensible regime of exercises. She chose a local gymnasium and Dr. James had a word with a trainer and explained how he wanted him to work with her.

The end result was truly remarkable. Mavis refused to buy any new clothes until she had reached her target weight, taking in old ones when necessary, or making some for herself in the meantime. Gradually her body became trim and neat, and she felt so proud of herself. Finally her husband took her on a shopping trip to London, Paris and Rome to buy her a totally new wardrobe. As he said to her "You have never been this size in all the thirty years we have been married and nothing fits you any more, so I want you to give all your old clothes away and start again."

"That's quite an extraordinary story," said Maud to Patrick and Lynda, "but it doesn't end there. Shortly after Mavis and her husband returned from the shopping trip, Natalie Brown moved into the area and quite by chance met Mavis, who I suspect took one look at her and felt pity on her."

Natalie was 19½ stones, so a stone heavier than Mavis was when she first consulted Dr. James. Mavis invited her to tea and gradually befriended her. In the end Natalie confided in Mavis all about her weight and its problems and how it had caused her husband to ask for a divorce. Apparently he couldn't put up with her being ill all the time and her mood swings.

One morning Mavis said to her, "Come with me. We're going to sort you out once and for all." And with that she drove Natalie to Dr. James's surgery and presented her to him.

"Here's another one for you, Doctor, only worse than me if it is possible. She doesn't have a husband for now so I'm going to look after her. After all, I know the ropes, don't I?"

"What do mean you know the ropes?" Asked Natalie.

"I was 18½ stone just over two years ago and in a right mess, but Dr. James sorted me out. It wasn't easy, I can tell you, but I'm going to see you all the way through to the end. If necessary you can move in with my husband Alex and me. I'm on a crusade, my aim being to get you your husband back, with you looking as great as I look and feel."

Natalie was putty in Mavis's kind hands. Like Mavis, she hated how she looked and felt, so she went through the whole approach that Mavis had gone through. The extraordinary thing was that, whereas Mavis lost eighteen pounds during the fast, Natalie lost a staggering twenty-one pounds, and, of course, all her awful symptoms. When she tested foods, she put on a huge ten pounds overnight the first time she reacted, and this was strangely also to carrots, like Mavis. But instead of reacting to cabbage, she reacted to cauliflower. Their stories were remarkably similar. The chance of two people doing such similar things must be very rare indeed.

"It also took Natalie over a couple of years to get down to around ten stones," said Maud. "The wonderful ending to this story was that, when Dr. James gave his talk about them in the church, Mavis and Natalie were sitting in the front pew reserved for special guests, with Natalie's husband sitting next to her holding her hand."

Chapter 25

Maud was in full flow now. "You've really got me going. There are so many stories to tell you, but you have reminded me of an amazing story of another GP in the area asking for his help, when his wife was pregnant for the second time. Dr. James must have started to have an interesting reputation by then, somehow sort of different. I tell you, his attitude was that there had to be a reason for every problem, if only you could find it."

This doctor's wife, her name was Judy, was somewhere in the second half of her second pregnancy, and all the signs were that something was wrong. After the baby had started to do its usual kicking, the kicks seemed to stop. She was admitted into hospital where they did all the appropriate tests and said they thought the baby may have died in her womb, and the only chance that things could sort themselves out was if she was sedated and kept in bed in the hospital until whatever happened happened. The sad thing was that this is exactly what happened in the first pregnancy three years earlier and the baby had died in the womb. She eventually had to deliver a dead baby three weeks later.

"I can't imagine what that must have done to the poor woman," said Maud. "She apparently needed to take antidepressants for the next year or so."

Somehow Judy must have got over her sadness and allowed herself to become pregnant again, "Though what must have gone through the poor lass's mind during the early stages of the pregnancy I can't imagine," said Maud. "Then, there it was again. The same situation. She must have been in a right panic, and I wouldn't have blamed her". Her GP husband must have been a very brave man, because he discharged her from hospital into his own care, sure that the same treatment of sedation and bed rest was unlikely to save this baby. He was probably right. The baby would probably have died, just like the first one.

Anyway, he rang up Dr. James and begged him to see his wife as soon as possible, driving her there as quickly but as safely as possible. Of course Dr. James said he would see her at once. In any case he had just finished his morning surgery. He asked some simple questions to begin with and then examined Judy very carefully. He listened for any heart sounds and said he thought he was able to hear something but couldn't be sure. Then he simply laid his hands gently on the lump of Judy's tummy, keeping them there for over twenty minutes. People said he had healing hands.

During all this time he asked them both a lot of questions in a quiet voice, asking them to reply in an unhurried, quiet, non-agitated way, almost as if they were having an afternoon chat. Of course he picked up the anxiety that Judy had suffered up to then because of the tragedy of her first pregnancy, telling her how often problems occurred in a subsequent pregnancy if an earlier one had somehow gone wrong. As he put it, "If you don't explain and sort out why the previous one went wrong, it is even more likely that the next one will go wrong as well, especially when you add the effects of all that stress". As he then explained, "Stress strips your body of many nutrients, especially magnesium, zinc, vitamin C and the B vitamins, in particular vitamin B5 (pantothenic acid)".

What he also found out was that Judy had been very sick during the first three months, although she had rejected taking any drugs for fear of what it might do to the baby. Unfortunately she had found that she could reduce the sickness by drinking copious amounts of sweet milky tea. Dr. James also identified that she had eaten hardly anything of nutritional value throughout the whole of the pregnancy, exactly the same as in her first pregnancy, as by now she had become addicted to her sweet milky tea and rubbish diet. As he said in a very quiet matter-of-fact way, "How can you possibly expect to produce a healthy baby if you don't feed it and yourself properly?"

Dr. James asked his wife to prepare a nutritious drink of a whole range of fruits and vegetables, something he apparently loved making for himself. In it she put watermelon as a liquid base, then apple, orange, grape, pear and banana, plus some broccoli and water. They had a powerful liquidiser he had brought home from a conference in America some years earlier. Then he set up an intravenous infusion and slowly gave Judy a cocktail of essential vitamins and minerals over the next two hours. Wanting to keep an eye on her, they carried her up to the spare bedroom and put her to bed, with a jug of the nutritious drink by her bedside.

"I will give you a lot more advice later on", Dr. James said to them, "But for now I want you to have a cup of this nutritious drink every hour, and a glass of water every half-an-hour in between. Yes this may mean you need to get up to pass water, but somehow I suspect you are thoroughly dehydrated because of all that tea you have been drinking".

Once Judy was tucked up in bed with the drip of nutrients running in slowly, Dr. James brought up some soft soothing music, pulled the curtains closed, and told her to relax and breathe easily but not too deeply, through her diaphragm if possible. He thought this might gently rock or massage the baby. Judy thought this was a wonderful idea, because it was something she herself could do. She said it would be almost as if she had the baby in her arms and it started giving her hope. He told her to think pleasant thoughts and to will her baby to come back to life. He also told her GP husband to place his hands gently on her tummy over the bedclothes and send loving, soothing, healing thoughts to the baby. He then left them on their own, saying he would be back soon.

When Dr. James popped in to see them a couple of hours later, the drip had stopped and they were both sound asleep. Judy's husband had taken his coat and shoes off and was lying on the bed beside her. Dr. James decided not to disturb them as he felt he had done all he could for now. He had discovered that Judy's husband had been up all the previous night attending to an unusual range of emergencies in his own practice, so was likely to be exhausted anyway.

That whole event took place in December, so, by the time Dr. James finished doing other things, it was already dark. He had popped into the kitchen to have a cup of tea with his wife when there was a shout from the spare bedroom. Not sure what to expect, he rushed upstairs to find the lights on and Judy sitting up in bed with a huge grin on her face and clutching her tummy. She and her husband were laughing with joy.

"The baby has just given me one hell of a kick – pardon the language," said Judy. "Feel. There goes anther one."

"Yes. I can feel it too," said her husband. "There's another one. The baby is very active at present."

"Well it has a lot of catching up to do," suggested Dr. James. "I'm sure it will settle down to a normal rhythm in due course," he added, carefully examining Judy's tummy and placing a simple instrument in the right place to listen to the baby's heart beat. He offered for her husband to listen, which he did with great satisfaction.

"I agree," he said, "It sounds perfectly normal to me."

"The baby can kick me as much as it likes," sobbed Judy. "I will never again complain however hard it kicks me". Then Dr. James took Judy's blood pressure and pronounced it fine, as it had been when he first examined her.

Judy's husband came round the bed and hugged Dr. James, much to his embarrassment. "I can't thank you enough for what you have done. You have been absolutely marvellous."

"We still have some work to do to ensure everything works out properly, but for now I want you, Judy, to stay here tonight, so that I can keep an eye on you. You, Gregory, are welcome to stay if you like. The bed's big enough for the three of you. But no doubt you need to contact one of your partners to make sure the practice is covered for the night".

So arrangements were made. Judy's husband went home to sort out a few problems in his practice and came back with a few things for them both. They all had a good night's sleep, except for Judy who couldn't get over her good fortune. She happily dozed every now and then, otherwise keeping her hands on her tummy, marvelling at the miracle inside her.

In the morning, Dr. James' wife gave Judy more of the nutritious drink, offering a cooked breakfast to her husband Gregory, who politely refused, saying he would far rather feast on the magic potion.

"Judy. Will you please come to see me around eleven tomorrow morning. I should have finished surgery by then. In the meantime I want you to remember what I said last night. Since you were in a state of shock and agitation, I doubt if you can remember much, so I will repeat myself.

"I always try to find a logical reason why something has happened. There has to be a reason why things went wrong with your first pregnancy, and, if the reasons were not resolved, then it was entirely logical to me that some sort of tragedy would occur again. And so it did. Apart from telling me about the loss of your first baby, I didn't want to spend time on that episode, preferring to get a decent history of what had gone wrong this time. It didn't take long for me to know exactly what the problem was – malnutrition.

"It was inevitable that you would be under a lot of stress, especially to accept to try for another baby. That took a lot of courage in itself. What you didn't know was that stress strips your body of many essential nutrients, especially magnesium, zinc, vitamin C and most of the B vitamins. Where do you get those nutrients? From your diet, of course. What was your diet like? Atrocious, unfortunately, at the very time when it needed to be excellent to feed two of you. Yet that was understandable in the circumstances of your morning sickness. What you were also not aware of was that low levels of magnesium and B vitamins is often one of the causes of morning sickness. And so you compounded the situation, making a tragic outcome almost inevitable.

"So, I am going to advise you on the diet I would like you to follow, from now, from today. In particular I would like you to give up dairy products completely, which I know is a contentious issue, as well as sugar and all forms of caffeine, so all those cups of tea plus chocolate and cola drinks, and alcohol of course. Keep your animal protein fairly low, but you may have eggs and oily fish. Use only whole grain products, and have as much in the way of fruits, vegetables and salad items as you can comfortably manage, all organic if you can get it. Try to eat your vegetables raw if you can, otherwise make tasty soups, and please drink at least eight glasses of water a day, preferably filtered. Make water your only drink if you can. It is my favourite drink. I will write all this down for you."

When he had finished, her GP husband said he thought that surely dairy was good for people, especially pregnant women and babies, for all that calcium, until Dr. James said, "No animal on God's Earth has milk or milk products after weaning", which was something Judy's husband hadn't thought of. "Also most of the world's largest animals are vegans. However, I admit most doctors and dieticians will tell you that dairy is good for you. It's just that I don't agree with them and there are many doctors who agree with me," said Dr. James.

"In any case, I have put many a woman on this regime, starting before the next pregnancy, if she has already had some sort of pregnancy mishap. They all had no dairy products throughout the pregnancy, and no calcium supplements, and had an easy birth of a perfectly formed baby, some mothers breast-feeding for more than two years. If that isn't an indication that the human species can do well without dairy products, I don't know what is?

"As for calcium, women are being encouraged to take 1600mg calcium plus 400IU vitamin D per day, yet studies are showing that it doesn't prevent osteoporosis at all. Why should women be encouraged to take so much calcium when an elephant only takes in 2000mg calcium per day, and it doesn't suffer from osteoporosis? The real need is not for lots of calcium but for more magnesium, without which your body cannot use calcium properly. You get most of your magnesium from green leafy vegetables, but who eats those properly nowadays? Then, as I have already said, stress strips your body of magnesium. It's not surprising your baby struggled to survive".

The next day Dr. James sat on the bed by Judy and talked to her gently. He acknowledged that men have absolutely no idea what a woman goes through in relation to having a baby. He basically asked to be forgiven for not being able to understand what reproduction means to a woman.

"We just can't feel what you feel. We can't share your joys and pains. We can only wonder at the miracle of the whole thing.

I've seen so many women go through their pain of childbirth, only to start thinking immediately of having another one! Obstetrics was my real love and I wanted to specialise in it, but it just didn't work out that way unfortunately.

"I just wanted to have a quiet word with you, Judy. Not because your husband isn't here, but because you are. After what you went through with your first pregnancy, you were very brave to have tried again".

"Gregory so wanted us to have a child", replied Judy. "He loves me so very much and he felt that a baby between us would bring us even closer together, prove our love for each other, even though there is no doubt about it. I'm really worried what must be going through his mind now. He convinced me to try again, never for one minute thinking the same thing could happen a second time, and that we might lose a second one. He must be in an agony at present wondering what would have happened to me if this baby had died like the first one."

"I am a great believer that some things are sent for a purpose", said Dr. James. "Often, of course, we are not in a position to do anything about it. Gregory was very brave to discharge you from the hospital. How did that go?"

"They thought he was totally mad and told him so, but I looked into his eyes and knew that he had something in mind. For some unknown reason, at that moment I totally trusted him. It was as though he felt he had got us into this mess and it was his responsibility to get us out of it. To be fair to the Specialist, he had to agree when Gregory said that following their advice hadn't worked the first time, so why should it this time? He told me last night that he had quietly done some research once he knew I was pregnant, and found out that when problems like mine occur, sedation and bed rest, although what everyone recommends, seldom succeeds at all. So he didn't see any point in trying it again.

"He told me he has never panicked so much in his life when the baby seemed to stop kicking. All his research had told him of the very worst possible outcome. He hadn't a clue what to do, although he appeared outwardly calm and organised for me to be admitted for some tests to be done to see what the situation was.

"I remembered later that while I was being helped into bed by a kindly West Indian midwife, Gregory left us to it for a while. Apparently he wandered aimlessly, without a thought as to any direction, and found himself in the hospital chapel. As luck would have it, the Reverend Henry Middleton had just finished taking a service. I gather he is the Rector here in Stead Norton. He immediately saw Gregory's agony and asked him what was wrong.

"After Gregory had poured out his soul to him and had told him that the only treatment that would be recommended had failed so abysmally the first time, the Reverend Middleton said 'Then why not try something else?' 'But what else is there to try?' begged Gregory. 'Perhaps I shouldn't say this but why don't you ring Dr. James and see if he can help', said the Reverend. 'What on Earth can he do?' Asked Gregory. 'I have no idea, but I have nothing else to suggest'".

"Looking back over those few hours, now it's all over, I remember Gregory eventually coming back into the ward to be with me. Somehow he seemed calm and in control. By then all the tests had been carried out and the Specialist told us what he thought – the awful truth that perhaps the placenta had ruptured and that the baby was not getting the blood it needed, and that to stop the placenta from tearing away completely, the only hope was for me to be sedated and to stay in bed at complete rest.

"Strangely enough, looking at Gregory at that moment, he seemed totally at ease. He thanked the Specialist for his opinion and then quietly said he was going to take me away into his own care. He simply asked me to agree to sign a form of discharge from the hospital. I don't know why, but I didn't hesitate. It was as if Gregory was in total charge and knew what he was doing. I didn't panic. In fact a wave of calm came over me, even though I had just been given the worst possible news. I had complete faith in him. It was a strange sensation. So here I am".

"Please don't blame Gregory for any of this. It is normal practice to suggest that a woman try again after she has had a problem of some sort, the most common being a miscarriage, which in some way might be even more distressing to some women than what you went through, as there is no baby to bury, no coffin to weep over. At least you had that when your first baby died. And no one takes any notice of the father. He has to keep a stiff upper lip. No thought for his tears. He is not allowed to cry. It isn't manly. On two occasions I have extracted such a situation from a thoroughly depressed man and helped him to weep and release years of pent-up agony.

"As I said to you both, it is essential to work out why something went wrong, not just throw up your hands and say it is just one of those things. There has to be an explanation every time, even if it is hard to find, sometimes impossible. It never occurred to either of you that malnutrition was the cause, which was so obvious to me. Doctors are not given any training in nutrition. They are only taught about drugs, some of which are really effective, to be fair, but unfortunately can have such awful side effects, many of those side effects being caused by the nutritional deficiencies they induce. I'm fortunate. I have had training in nutrition, which I use a lot in my practice.

"So, please follow my recommendations for now. I want to give you another nutrient infusion in a few days time. We'll sort out when in due course.

"Don't worry. I will be as good as gold. You have worked absolute magic on my baby and me. I will follow your instructions to the letter. You have completely opened Gregory's eyes. I don't think he will ever be the same again. Thank you so much for all you have done".

So Judy went home. Gregory came for her that afternoon and they took all their belongings with them. "I think even Dr. James was astonished at what he had done", said Maud. "In a moment of weakness some years later he told me that he hadn't expected to be able to help much when Gregory first contacted him about the situation, but he thought he might as well try. After all, they were both expecting the worst, so he couldn't do any worse than that, could he?

"Apparently he had been involved in an incident when he was a junior Anaesthetist and, keeping his cool, things had turned out all right. But I'll tell you about that another time.

"There's not much more to tell you about Judy and Gregory's baby. Judy went to full term, although by then everyone had heard what Dr. James had done. There was no way you could keep a story like that a secret. What upset Dr. James was that the hospital Specialist continued to do what he had always done when a similar circumstance cropped up some other time. He apparently just couldn't believe that it wasn't all simple coincidence, and that the baby would have come round after all if Judy had followed his recommendations in the first place. He was of the old school and didn't believe in nutrition.

"When Judy went into labour, Dr. James advised her to take a homoeopathic preparation, arnica, which he gave her, telling her it would enormously help the delivery. Because hers was 'a precious baby' in Obstetric terms, Judy had the baby in hospital so they could monitor everything and have the special baby team on hand. In the end the delivery was straightforward and uncomplicated. I gather the placenta, the afterbirth, had all the evidence of when things went wrong, but, to everyone's astonishment, Judy seemed almost to have grown a second one. Nobody had heard of such a thing before, but then I don't suppose anyone had done anything like that before.

"The baby was a boy, and surprise, surprise, they immediately decided to call him David after Dr. James, and he also became the baby's Godfather. That David has grown up and is studying medicine somewhere in London. So a happy ending all round."

Chapter 26

"**D**r. James clearly had had a very interesting life," said Maud, "especially before he qualified, and even as a qualified doctor. He told us so many stories from the pulpit in the church. He almost had the Rev. Middleton feeling jealous. He certainly had more people attending his talks in the church than went to Sunday worship.

"What was so fascinating was that he so warmed to his audiences that he felt he could say almost anything to us. I remember two stories, one an experience he had shortly after he arrived in The Caribbean just after he qualified. The second was a joke he had heard someone tell and he thought it might make us all laugh, especially as it had a slightly religious theme, though only mildly so. Now that I come to think of it he told us a number of jokes, so I will have to try to remember some of them.

"Anyway, the first story was just after he arrived in The Caribbean when he was a young man. He said he was hoping to have a few days rest and lie in the sun, but the Hospital had other ideas. A doctor in the island not seeing patients? No way. He was far too valuable an asset, so he had to start straight away. He had told us how hard he worked, being on overnight Casualty the third night he was there, by then having hardly slept the two previous nights. He said he remembered seeing a wizened old lady almost staggering into Casualty around two in the morning, moaning away and clutching her tummy. She was followed by what he assumed were her daughters, granddaughters and great granddaughters.

A short while later Dr. James was asked by one of the nurses to see the lady who they had put in a cubicle round the corner. So when he had finished what he was doing, he went into her room and started to ask her some simple questions, such as, "Hello, my dear! How are you feeling?" "De belly she ache" was her reply. "And how long has it been hurting you?" "De belly she ache". "Can you put a finger on the worst spot?" "De belly she ache" came the simple answer. "Are you feeling sick or have you been sick?" "De belly she ache". "They don't teach you how to deal with this sort of situation in Medical School," thought Dr. James to himself.

So, deciding the only thing to do was to examine her to see what the matter was, he pulled back the sheet covering her, and there was a baby's head being born there and then! This little wizened old lady, as he thought she was, was 23 years old. A lesson learned.

"Dr. James told me that he stopped guessing women's ages from that day on," said Maud.

"Now that I come to think of it, one joke I can remember was about two Roman Catholic Priests who went to Hawaii for an ecumenical conference," began Maud.

They had booked their hotel for a week, but the conference finished a couple of days early, so they had to think of something to do. As they had come from a cold place in America to the lovely environment of Hawaii, they decided to do a bit of sunbathing. So they went shopping and bought the most outlandish shirts and hats they could find and settled down on the beach, sure no one would know who they were.

A few minutes later a most beautiful girl in a really sexy bikini, with long flowing golden hair halfway down her back came up to them and said, "Good morning, Father. Good morning, Father", and wandered on down the beach. Both of the priests were dumbfounded. They couldn't imagine how anyone could possibly recognise them dressed the way they were. However, the rest of the day was uneventful.

Then next day they decided to buy even more colourful Hawaiian outfits and big sunglasses to hide behind, and settled themselves comfortably somewhere on the beach again, confident no one could possibly recognise them this time. But to their total surprise, the same girl, in an even more sexy bikini, with her hair flowing gorgeously in the wind, came up to them again and said, "Good morning, Father. Good morning, Father."

One of the priests couldn't contain his curiosity any longer, so said to her, "Excuse me, but how do you know who we are?" To which she replied, "Why, Father. Don't you recognise me? I'm Sister Kathleen."

"Oh yes. I now remember another joke Dr. James told. In fact once he got to know us all, he started his talks with a joke, just to make sure we were awake. He said that, if we didn't laugh, we were probably all asleep, and he felt the message he wanted to get across was far too important for us not to hear. This one went something like this: -

"A voice came over the radio to a group of ships sailing somewhere in the Atlantic off the coast of The British Isles. 'Suggest you change course north-north-west to prevent collision'. 'Suggest **you** change course south-south-east to prevent collision,' came the stern reply. 'We repeat our advice that you change course north-north-west to avoid collision.' 'We are the largest Aircraft Carrier in the fleet of a friendly nation, accompanied by a whole flotilla of fighting ships. Suggest you, repeat you, change your course south-south-east to avoid not only a collision but also an international incident.' 'Sorry, old chap. No can do. We are a lighthouse!'

Chapter 27

Later that day, Maud said she was feeling so much better. "It looks quite nice outside and not at all cold. I'd like to go for a short walk. We won't be long. Are you two coming with me?" So they all put on coats and wrapped Maud up well just to be sure. Neighbours popped out to greet her as they went by.

"I hear you've not been too well," called Esther, her next-door neighbour, out of her sitting room window.

"I see you've still got your hair in curlers, Esther," called back Maud. "Going out somewhere nice tonight, are you?

"No. Just the local. I hear there's to be a bit of a singsong later on. I do love a singsong. Why don't you join us and bring those two with you, Maud?"

"Might just do that. See how I feel, but I may not be up to it yet. Got to do as my living-in nurse tells me. I'll see what she says. I might even send them out. They must be fed up with me by now".

"Honestly, Gran. How could you say such a thing?" Said Patrick. We're having a wonderful time. It's a real holiday for us, isn't it, Lynda?"

"I haven't enjoyed myself so much in ages," replied Lynda. "Nor have I laughed or cried so much. You should be on the stage. A lady of your age would go down a bomb. You'd have the audience eating out of your hands. Some of your stories are so funny, some so sad, but I've never heard so many."

Maud, Patrick and Lynda wandered aimlessly down the road, past the duck pond in the middle of the village. They strolled over the little Roman bridge under which water flowed to keep the duck pond full. The water came from the stream called the Stead, after which the village was called. Where the second half came from no one knew. It was presumably the name of some important person, centuries ago, who decided to settle there. Their path took them past the church. It was a beautiful building with a tall spire. It almost brought tears to Maud's eyes. "The talks Dr. James gave us were absolutely wonderful, so full of humour, but so meaningful and so heartfelt. We all craved more every time he spoke. He always finished with a prayer if Rev. Henry Middleton was not able to attend. In fact I think his talks helped fill the church on Sundays. Those two, the Vicar and the Doctor, were such healers. Apart from the fact that the church was the largest place to hold so many people who wanted to hear Dr. James speak, it seemed logical that we should also use the church for what it was there for – worship. We were so lucky to have them here for so long, but such good things cannot last forever. Let's get back home, shall we?"

A couple of hours later it was dark and Maud and the two young ones were sitting downstairs drinking an early evening sherry, at Maud's insistence.

"Every time Dr. James told us a particular personal story, it was always with the permission of the patient. In fact patients insisted on his telling their story, so grateful were they for what he had done. They had the special seat in the front row. He said that he hoped his telling the facts would stimulate people into thinking for themselves. He said every tale had a particular message, perhaps the most important message being that we are all different and we all have our own genetic influences, so we all react and behave in different ways. That's why he said he listened to his patients so carefully. They were trying to tell him something of importance to their particular problems. However, he told us a few experiences he had had when he was doing locums with other practices, before he settled here in Stead Norton. I'm sure he invented the names he used to keep the identity of the person a secret. In fact I remember one such story."

Jeff Chater was in his mid-fifties. He was fairly tall, about six foot two inches, of a slim build. He was one of those people who just couldn't cope on his own. He was always ringing the surgery with some complaint or another. Everyone had tried to help him as best they could. It was just that his main problem was that he was lonely. His wife has sadly died in a car accident many years ago before they had been able to start a family. It seemed he didn't have any relatives that anyone could find, or if he did they hid well away from him so as not to be drawn into his problems.

The main problem with Jeff was that he was given a drug as a teenager for some minor psychological problem that had produced terrible side effects in him. It was a new experimental drug that was soon taken off the market. It had apparently caused hundreds of people to suffer like Jeff. He was given quite a handsome payout by the makers of the drug, but that was hardly compensation for what he suffered.

He found he just couldn't keep still. He couldn't control a whole variety of facial grimaces and he made strange gyrating movements with his arms. When he walked he said he looked either drunk or like an idiot. He just couldn't walk in a straight line, but the strange thing was that he could run fairly easily and normally, but he obviously couldn't be running all the time.

Jeff had moved up from the coast when he received the large payout, but he said he had become worse away from the sea. Somehow the sea air, possibly the ozone or the clean air, had had some sort of dampening effect upon his movements, but, for some unknown reason, he wasn't prepared to move back down to be near the sea. Clearly he wasn't willing to try any drugs for fear they might make him worse, so his management was quite a problem for his doctors. Unfortunately no one had any idea what the damage was inside his brain. All tests had drawn a blank.

Another problem was that Jeff found he couldn't cope with life. Everything seemed to cause him stress, which made him worse. Any little thing seemed to upset him so easily, such as bills to pay, which he could well afford. Firework night was sheer torture for him.

Despite all these problems, he was a likeable chap and local people helped him as much as they could, but whatever they did, it was never enough. He simply wasn't satisfied. He felt he needed someone to look after him.

Dr. James did a locum for about six months in the town where Jeff lived and had his fair share of trying to help him, but it took many visits to the surgery to prise a reasonable medical history out of him, but most of the time it seemed he would never be satisfied until he had someone to look after him. That seemed to be the crux of the matter, certainly in Jeff's mind.

One part of Jeff's background that Dr. James eventually managed to extract out of him was that about ten years ago, when he was not in too bad a condition down by the sea, he had found that he could play tennis, which he had always been quite good at; and despite his obvious problems, he was somehow accepted into the local tennis club. There he met a lady who he described as perfect for him and that he had hoped to marry her so that she could look after him.

Presumably she didn't have the same feelings for him, so nothing ever came of it. However, once he had mentioned the young lady to Dr. James, she became a bit of an obsession with Jeff and he kept on asking why she couldn't have married him.

So Dr. James set him a simple problem to think about, as he was fascinated to see what answer he would give.

"I'd like to ask you to think about something," said Dr. James one day, "And I want you to think about it overnight and come back tomorrow with your answer. Imagine you had married this lady from the tennis club and she was looking after you as well as you wanted, but, as happened to your first wife, she also sadly died. How would you cope? I repeat, don't answer me now, but come back tomorrow and let me know of your answer."

The next day, as requested, Jeff arrived at the surgery.

"Well, Jeff. Have you thought about the problem I set you yesterday?"

"Yes I have," replied Jeff, quite seriously. "I think I should have two wives."

The story doesn't quite end there, because Dr. James had spent a lot of time listening to Jeff's story. As he said, all the tests had totally failed to explain what damage had been caused in his brain by the drug he had taken so long ago. Two facts made Dr. James think of something that might improve his symptoms. The first was that he said he was better by the sea and the second was that he became worse under stress. So Dr. James arranged for him to have some treatments at the local hyperbaric oxygen centre normally used by patients with multiple sclerosis. The second was that he tried some magnesium supplements plus some B and C vitamins, as he was aware that these nutrients seem to be stripped from the body under stress.

Jeff clearly improved, but only so long as he continued the treatments on a regular basis, which he was quite willing to do. However, he still felt two wives would be useful!

Chapter 28

"It didn't matter where Dr. James was he seems to have had interesting experiences. I suppose his approach was so different to other people's it's not surprising he had so many stories to tell. He had a totally open mind to what might cause people to become unwell. He also felt that some people let things happen to them unnecessarily, even when it was clear it was having a bad effect upon them. He illustrated that point with three separate events, all, strangely enough, involving patients with multiple sclerosis. He had a particular interest in that condition and apparently always asked for any such patients to be referred to him, wherever he practised. He felt that, as always, no one was seeking an explanation for the condition," said Maud much later in the evening.

"Once he showed an interest in patients with multiple sclerosis, all the doctors in the practice where he was doing the locum were only too happy to suggest any of their MS patients see Dr. James, as they hadn't been able to help in any way. So it's not surprising he had stories to tell about patients with MS. Apparently he stayed with that practice for about eighteen months as, one by one, most of the doctors in that practice either went off sick themselves or took as long a holiday as they were entitled to. There were eight partners and they were all getting towards retirement age. They asked Dr. James to stay on permanently, but he said he wanted to practise in a small rural area, not a big city one where people came and went all too quickly. We were so lucky he chose Stead Norton."

Jenny Shackleton was a gentle twenty-eight year old lady who lived with her accountant husband John and their two children. When Jenny and her husband first met Dr. James, they were astonished at the number and variety of questions he asked her. The hospital Specialist certainly didn't ask anything like as many questions, and didn't spend nearly as much time with her as did Dr. James. The thing that really amazed her about Dr. James's examination of her was not so much the usual tapping and sensation tests, but his observing the way she walked with her stick.

By then it was clearly obvious that she had problems almost entirely on her left side, there being nothing wrong with her right side at all. Dr. James asked Jenny to walk as well as she could with her stick up and down the surgery corridor, asking John to observe her carefully. It was obvious that she had a one-sided limp. He then asked if he could look in her mouth, asking her to open then close it. He then gently prised her lips apart with his fingers with her teeth closed, and a satisfied smile appeared on his face as he said, "Aha! Aha!"

"What's all that about?" Enquired Jenny.

Dr. James then asked her husband to have a look at what he had found, a big overlap of her top teeth on her bottom set, but the midline of her upper jaw was not immediately above the midline of her lower jaw. He pointed out that her upper and lower jaws were not perfectly aligned.

"Is that important?" Asked John.

"Well I have looked in the mouths of a number of MS patients with one-sided problems like Jenny has, and you all seem to have this problem. Whether it is a cause of your MS or a result I have no idea. It is just an observation I have made."

"Does it make any difference?" Asked John. "Can it help Jenny to walk better?"

"Well! Let's see," said Dr. James.

With that he picked up a wooden spatula and carefully placed it between Jenny's teeth so as to line them up perfectly, midline top exactly over midline bottom with no overlap at all.

"Keep the piece of wood exactly where it is and see how you can walk now," encouraged Dr. James.

Jenny picked up her walking stick as usual and set off back down the corridor again, but before she was half way there, to John's total amazement, she dropped her stick and kept walking. When she reached the reception area, the staff behind the desk, who must have known what was going on, started clapping. Jenny's smile was as wide as she could manage with the spatula still in her mouth.

Coming out of his consulting room, closely followed by John, Dr. James took the spatula out of Jenny's mouth and asked her to walk back into his room, which she managed, but had to steady herself against the walls of the corridor, as she was no longer as confident as she had been with the spatula between her teeth.

"Please put it back in," implored Jenny. "That was astonishing. I almost walked normally". So Dr. James obliged and Jenny walked almost normally again.

"So what happens now?" Asked Jenny.

"Before we go any further, just think about what we have demonstrated. By correcting your bite you were immediately able to walk much better. What does that say to you?" Asked Dr. James.

"I'm not sure what you are getting at," said Jenny.

"Well just think about it. The simple fact that you were able to walk so much better with your teeth lined up correctly means that you don't have permanent irreversible damage. So if we can do some more detective work we might be able to find other things that are causing your symptoms, which, if you were to do something about, might equally make a difference."

"I am absolutely astonished," said John. "You have me hooked on your approach. Do you feel the same as me?" John asked Jenny.

"I can't wait to find out what else you are going to think of," replied Jenny. Where do we go from here?

"I need to ask you a few more questions," said Dr. James, "but I already have a lot of information to be getting on with. Let's talk about your smoking habits."

"I don't smoke much, and not every day either, and probably only five or six a day at most."

"What time of day do you tend to smoke?" Asked Dr. James.

"Mostly in the evenings," replied Jenny.

"Does your walking vary at all during the day?"

"Well I tend to be better in the mornings, but it can vary. Some mornings I wake up very stiff, but usually manage to get going after I have done some exercises they showed me in the Physiotherapy Department."

"Have you looked at what you do or eat to see if you can identify any coincidences? Could your ability to walk or not walk be affected by how many cigarettes you smoked the night before, for example?" Asked Dr. James.

"Hang on a second," said John. "I see what you're getting at. In fact I noticed something I thought was strange last Friday, but didn't take too much notice of it. Now that I think about it, you were quite good during the day on Friday. Do you remember, Jenny, I had taken the day off work to be with you. We went to the zoo before picking the kids up from school, and you didn't use your stick at all."

"Yes. But I hung on to your arm all the time," said Jenny.

"I know you did, but I thought you didn't hang on nearly as much as you usually do. I'm sure you walked more easily. And especially when we went to the pub in the evening, when your mum baby-sat the kids. Do you remember? I commented on how well you were walking, but you really struggled on the way home. I almost had to leave you there and fetch the car, but you persevered and we eventually made it."

"Yes. You are right, John. There was quite a difference that day. As we walked to the pub, I noticed it myself and thought how wonderful it would be if I could always walk so easily, but it had all gone wrong on the way home, so I just assumed that was a normal part of MS. Others at the hospital say their symptoms vary quite a bit."

"What a tragedy!" Said Dr. James. "So much information and no one interested in what it might mean. So, back to last Friday evening. Tell me what you did, in great detail, from the moment you arrived at the pub until going home."

"Well we had a couple of drinks and some nibbles to start with," said John.

"I said in detail please. The details are very important. What did you drink, Jenny? Water?"

"No way," giggled Jenny. "I had two vodka and orange drinks and ate some crisps. John had a pint of bitter."

"What else?" Asked Dr. James.

"Nothing that I can think of," said Jenny. "Later on I had another vodka and orange, so about three in all. We met up with some friends and had a lovely time. One of them is Irish and he tells the best jokes I have ever heard. He had us in fits of laughter."

Dr. James wrote something on a piece of paper and folded it up. "You're surely forgetting something very important. I've written it down here," he said.

John stretched for the piece of paper. "May I?" He asked.

"By all means."

"Cigarettes!" Exclaimed John. "How could we forget?"

"It would appear some people light up a cigarette without even thinking about it. It's like an automatic reaction," said Dr. James.

"Two of our group were smoking when we joined them, so I suppose I just lit up without thinking about it. What's so important about that?" Asked Jenny.

"What I am trying to teach you is that, if you do something and something happens, it is logical to assume there may be a connection. Not is a connection, but may be. If you have arthritis and I prescribe an anti-inflammatory drug and in two weeks you are feeling better and are in less pain, you assume the drug has helped. Yes it may be something else you did, but start by assuming there is a connection.

"So back to you, Jenny, and what you did that evening. In my way of thinking of things, what you did clearly had quite a bad effect upon you. So what was it? What you are not aware of is that the Deadly Nightshade group of plants includes potatoes, tomatoes, aubergines, peppers and tobacco. You ate crisps, so potato, and you smoked, so tobacco. If we look at what your vodka is made of, it may well be potato, although to be fair, some vodkas are based on grains. Real quality Russian vodka is usually distilled from potato, so, if that is the case, you had potato in a jet-propelled vehicle, namely alcohol.

To me there is every reason why you had such difficulty walking home when you had walked to the pub so well. So for now, as an experiment, I want you to give up smoking if you can, and not be exposed to it, so you will need to tell your friends. Also I want you to stop eating potatoes, tomatoes, aubergines and all peppers. There are one or two other things I want you to give up which I will explain in a minute."

"Give up tomatoes?" Wailed Jenny. "They're my favourites."

John and Jenny were open-mouthed. The whole story was so simple yet so logical.

"When I asked the hospital Specialist if diet made any difference, he said there were no studies that he was aware of that showed that what an MS patient ate was important. So he told me to eat whatever I wanted."

"Well we haven't proved that avoiding those foods is important. It's up to you now to put my ideas into effect and see whether it makes any difference."

"Oh, I will," said Jenny. "Is there something else you want me to give up?"

"Yes," said Dr. James. "All alcohol, as at the best of times it can make someone unsteady, and all dairy products, so milk, cream, butter, yoghurt, cheese, and you will need to read packets to make sure there are no dairy products included. Also sugar and what we all call 'junk food'. The best way not to make a mistake is to go back to old-fashioned cooking and buy basic ingredients and put them together yourself."

"That won't be a problem," said John. "I tend to do the cooking so will take over completely for now to make sure Jenny gets it right. But why no dairy products? I thought all that calcium is important, especially for women."

"Jenny's history of all those episodes of tonsillitis as a child, with the attempt to put in grommets, is a very strong indicator of a milk intolerance, but more to the point, human beings are the only creatures on God's Earth that consume dairy products after weaning. No other animal does. Yes I accept this is a controversial matter, but for now I would like you to give them up please, if you will. I could suggest that milk is a food to produce an animal with a small brain and big horns!"

"Actually, I don't like milk at all. I couldn't drink a glass of it to save my life, but I love cheese."

"Enough to admit you may be addicted to it?" Asked Dr. James.

"Now that you mention it, possibly yes, and tomatoes. I almost must have some every day. In fact my need for cheese is probably stronger that my need for a cigarette."

"Do you think you will have any difficulty with your friends and their smoking habits?"

"Actually they have all been talking about giving up, and there has been a petition for the pub to become a 'no smoking' pub. Strangely enough, they are some of the people who want a ban. Everyone has agreed they will still come to the pub if it goes smoke free, and I suspect many more will use it if it does."

"Be aware you may suffer from withdrawal symptoms for the first few days. If you do, take a drink of water with a level teaspoonful of sodium bicarbonate in it. Alkalinising your body should help neutralise the acidity that withdrawal symptoms seem to cause."

"Oh! I don't think I will have any difficulty giving up smoking. I'm sure it is merely a silly habit and I'm not addicted to it," said Jenny.

"It's not the cigarette smoking I'm worried about," said Dr. James. "It's the cheese and tomatoes!"

Jenny did exactly as she was told. She had no problems giving up cigarettes, but really craved cheese and tomatoes. She wasn't bothered about peppers or aubergines as she rarely ate them anyway. As she said, peppers gave her indigestion. She thought she would miss potatoes, being particularly fond of crisps. Strangely enough, she didn't mind the food cravings as Dr. James had said to her that withdrawal symptoms, which don't always occur, are a sign that you will feel better once you have got over them. She refused to take any sodium bicarbonate, almost revelling in how she felt. Dr. James's demonstration of how much better she could walk when her teeth were lined up correctly had so impressed her that she knew the changes in her diet that he had recommended were going to make quite a difference to her MS.

And so that was exactly what happened. It took about a week before she noticed she was less stiff. When she went to the hospital Physiotherapy Department for her monthly treatment, by coincidence her special Physiotherapist happened to be by the reception desk. She was absolutely astonished to see Jenny walking in without her stick, walking with only the slightest limp, and that was only three weeks after she had made all those changes.

Jenny continued to improve slowly. Dr. James told her it might take quite a long time to eliminate all the inflammation from her central nervous system, apart from which there may be other things that she needed to do before she became totally symptom free. Unfortunately Dr. James left that practice, where he had been doing a locum while one of the other doctors had a major operation, shortly after that, but Jenny wrote to him to let him know how she was getting on. She said she had virtually become symptom free, but not quite, and felt there was probably something else she needed to do to become completely well. However, as she said, 'When you have felt so useless and not been able to walk on your own, you revel in being virtually normal once again, so I am quite content to stay as I am for now. I may seek your help again one day, so please keep in touch and don't move too far away!'

"The story doesn't end there for Jenny," said Maud. "Dr. James said he couldn't be sure that all of the things he had asked Jenny to avoid were responsible for her MS. So he suggested that she consider reintroducing some of the foods she was avoiding to see if any of them made her symptoms come back. Jenny said she was totally happy to stay off them for the rest of her life, and had no need to put them back into her regular diet. From what Dr. James had explained to her she totally accepted his explanations as they had made so much sense to her. She had demonstrated to herself that her walking would become worse if she gritted her teeth. The only slightly annoying part was walking with her mouth slightly open!

"But once again, the story doesn't even end there," said Maud. Shortly after this, they met some new people, Josh and Sue Johnston in the pub and become really very friendly, so they planned to invite each other round for meals every so often. Jenny explained her dietary problems and asked them to make sure there was nothing in their food that could upset her, and they said they were happy to oblige. To be fair John had thought they were sceptical of anything as simple as a food being able to cause any medical condition, let alone MS, but they seldom discussed the topic.

On one occasion when John and Jenny went round to their new friends' house, soup was served up for the first course. Jenny asked if there was anything in it that she wanted to stay off, in case they had forgotten her problems. They assured her that they had thickened the soup with flour, so Jenny ate it and thoroughly enjoyed it.

The meal lasted quite a long time and they were all having a good time, but, afterwards, John said he noticed that Jenny had become quieter than usual and that something was wrong with her, but he didn't say anything. At about eleven o'clock John said he thought it was time to go home and thanked their friends for such a wonderful evening. They all got up from their chairs to say their goodbyes. Except Jenny.

"Are you coming Jenny?" Said John.

"I can't!" Cried Jenny. "I can't move. My legs won't work. I'm stuck. I don't know what to do," she wailed. "Are you sure you didn't put some potato in the soup?"

"Oh no!" Said Sue. "I don't believe it. We didn't think your story made any sense at all. We couldn't see how eating potatoes could possibly have anything to do with MS, but for the sake of our friendship we went along with it. We really are sorry. It's all our fault. We had someone make the soup for us, as we were both so busy out at work. We asked her not to put potato in it, but she forgot, so, as we didn't believe it could possibly do any harm, we told a lie, I'm afraid. We really are incredibly sorry. There must be something we can do to make amends. What can we do?"

"I really haven't a clue," said John. "This is not a situation we have had to deal with before. I hope Jenny is not paralysed for life. I wonder what Dr. James would advise?"

"Ring him please, John. I'm frantic with worry. I want my legs back again. I have worked so hard to become well. I can't bear the thought of not being able to walk again. I can't move my legs at all. I'm going to need a wheel chair to get around. Just think how that will affect our lives, John!" Jenny wailed.

"May I please use your telephone?" John asked, then rang home to speak to Jenny's mother who was baby-sitting the kids.

"Angela! We have an emergency here and need to contact Dr. James urgently. Could you please go into the kitchen where you will find a pile of letters by the kettle. Somewhere there you should be able to find a letter from Dr. James. We urgently need his telephone number. I'll hang on while you look for it please."

They all waited for what seemed like an eternity, but it didn't take Jenny's mother long to find the number, which she gave him. Thanking her he hung up and rang Dr. James's number, hoping he was at home, which he was.

"Dr. James. This is John Shackleton. I'm sorry to ring you at this time of night, but Jenny has suddenly lost the use of her legs. It has happened so suddenly. She is totally paralysed and utterly distraught. She can't move at all. She's really worried."

"Ok. John. Now calm down and tell me all about it. There's bound to be an explanation. As usual start from the beginning'" And so John told Dr. James what had happened.

"Remember what I have always said to you. There must be a reason. Are you sure it is potato in the soup that has caused this?"

"Well I can't think of any other reason. Jenny has been doing so well. It must be the potato, although she never had the courage to test the idea by eating some."

"All right, John. Calmly tell Jenny we will soon have her feeling so much better, and we will prove once and for all that she needs to stay off potatoes for the rest of her life. So I want you to boil a small potato. It would be ideal if it could be exactly the same make of potato put in the soup. Is that possible?"

"Please hang on, Dr. James," said John. "I won't be long." With that he asked where the person lived who had prepared the soup earlier in the day. Fortunately she only lived a few doors away.

"Would you be willing to ask her if she has any more potato of the sort she used for the soup?" John asked Josh.

"No problem!" said he. "I would drive all night if that would help. I feel so guilty."

"Dr. James. Are you still there?" Asked John. When he said yes John said, "We are going to fetch some potato now. What then?"

"As soon as you have it, boil it as you would normally do, until it is soft enough to be eaten. Then ring me again. All that could take an hour. I will wait up for you. I'm too far away to visit you. In any case I am on duty here tonight. Tell Jenny we'll soon have her back to normal. While you are waiting, arrange four or five clean dry cups or eggcups on the kitchen surface and place by each one a teaspoon, all the same size if possible. And you will need some straws. Place separate teaspoons and straws by each eggcup, and for simplicity mark them number one, two, three, etc. Have a glass with some water in it by each cup, using preferably filtered or bottled in glass, but don't use plastic bottled water. I will await your next call."

Josh ran to their neighbour and knocked urgently on the door. Fortunately the lights were still on in the house. An anxious man asked if she had any potato of the sort used in the soup. One can imagine the response, so he had to explain as best he could, but it was not an easy thing to do. Anyway she gave him a potato and he raced back home, where they put it in a saucepan and boiled it. When it was ready they rang Dr. James again.

"That didn't take long," said Dr. James. "Is it now edible? Good. Now this is what I want you to do. Please write this down as I say it."

"Hang on a second, while I fetch pen and paper." Then to their friends, "I need to take down Dr. James's instructions."

"I'll do that," said Sue. "I can do shorthand. Give me the phone. Let me speak to Dr. James."

"Hello! Dr. James," said Sue, taking the phone from John. "I'm Sue Johnston, a so-called friend of Jenny's, who is partly responsible for the state she is now in. We really are so sorry for this mess. We had no idea how important it was for her to stay off potatoes."

"Don't chastise yourself. To be fair to you, it is such a difficult thing to get your head around. I am happy to explain it all to you another time if you like, but let's not waste time. Jenny must be really worried."

"She is. Anyway, I can do shorthand so please give me instructions at your own speed."

"Ok! Take a level teaspoonful of cooked potato and put it in the first cup or eggcup. Using the same spoon, put in four spoonsful of water into the same cup. Mix thoroughly so that you have a liquid potato mix. Call that number one mixture. Put the spoon you have just used by the side of the cup. Using a clean teaspoon, take a teaspoonful of that number one potato mix and put it into your second cup, and with that same spoon take four spoonsful of water from the next glass of water and mix together, so you have one spoonful of mixture one plus four spoonsful of water. Call this mixture number two.

"Now this is the tricky bit. As a test run, dip one of the straws into that number two mixture, put your finger over the end and lift it out. Angle the straw about 45 degrees and take your finger gently off the end and try to let one drop fall back into the cup. Practise doing this so you can do it easily. When ready, you need to do the same in Jenny's mouth, under her tongue. To repeat, put one drop of potato mix number two under Jenny's tongue. Try to put only one drop, but don't panic if two drop by mistake. Start a clock and wait about ten minutes. The exact time is not crucial, but ten minutes is about right.

"The chances are that nothing much may happen with that drop. There is even a possibility that she may feel a bit worse, but I doubt if she would notice that. It doesn't matter anyway. In about ten minutes, ask Jenny to try to get up and see how she is. As I say, don't worry if nothing happens at this stage.

"When the ten minutes are up and Jenny has tried to see what she can do, using a clean teaspoon, put one teaspoonful of mixture number two into the next cup and again add four teaspoonsful of fresh water. This is now mixture number three. Using a fresh straw, put one drop of mixture number three under Jenny's tongue and wait about ten minutes. Once again ask her to try to move. Repeat the same diluting procedure to make mixture number four, and number five if necessary, each time using clean utensils and straws, i.e. so you don't mix the strengths. As before, put one drop of mixture four under Jenny's tongue and wait ten minutes. It is this dilution that may well achieve success.

"Now please repeat that back to me, and ring me if anything happens or you are worried about anything, but in any case, please ring me ten minutes or so after you have put a drop from mixture number four under Jenny's tongue. Do not proceed to a drop from mixture number five without speaking to me first. Is that clear?"

"Absolutely." Said Sue, who then read back her shorthand notes to Dr. James, with her husband Josh listening intently as he was an engineer, and quickly twigged what Dr. James wanted them to do.

It was well after midnight when the phone rang again in Dr. James's house. "Dr. James speaking".

"Hello Dr. James! It's Jenny calling you this time."

"Hello Jenny! How are you feeling now?"

"You are an absolute miracle worker. An absolute angel," wept Jenny. "I can't thank you enough. I'm now virtually back to my normal not quite perfect self. I was able to walk over to the telephone to ring you myself, without any help. I was so frightened. I hope we haven't kept you out of bed."

"Don't worry about that, Jenny. I'm so glad I was able to help. I'm sure someone else will ring before the night is out. Before I forget, put the various dilutions in the fridge over night and keep them carefully marked. You may need another treatment in a few hours. If you do, use the same dilution that worked on you just now. Was it dilution number four?"

"Yes it was", said Jenny.

"I thought so," replied Dr. James. "It usually is. If you are only very slightly worse in the morning, don't worry. You should soon improve. You could take a level teaspoonful of sodium bicarbonate in water, which should do the trick. In any case I want you to ring me mid-morning at my surgery. You should have the number. It's on my letterhead. Good night and sleep well."

Chapter 29

"The second story of an MS patient that Dr. James told us about had a different point to make," said Maud. "This one was about a young lady in her late twenties, much like Jenny. Her MS symptoms were about as bad as Jenny's, except that both her legs were about equally affected."

Sally Beckwith knew Jenny, and, as soon as Jenny started doing what Dr. James had recommended, and noticed what a difference it made to her, she made an appointment to see Dr. James. Sally and Jenny found some causes in common, and Sally also started to improve, but not as quickly as Jenny had. She had never smoked, although stopping tomatoes made quite a difference. Although she also gave up eating potatoes, aubergines and peppers, she decided to put them back in as an experiment and found that she was fine eating them, so far as she could tell. Tomatoes definitely had a bad effect upon her, but she said she probably wouldn't have risked experimenting had Jenny had her bad experience with potatoes before she had tried them. Dr. James said that, to be fair, Jenny's reaction was surprisingly bad and that most people would merely have a simple reminder that such-and-such a food was not good for the person. However, the method of 'turning off' the reaction could be used with anything, so long as you knew what the reaction was caused by.

Despite Dr. James's best attempts, Sally seemed unable to improve as much as Jenny had, but, when they talked, she acknowledged that her symptoms could be better on some days than on others, and in fact could be better at some times of day than at others.

"There must be something you haven't told me," said Dr. James at one of their regular meetings. "How are you today?"

"Not too bad, actually. The kids are at home for a week off school for the Whitsun break. My husband, Damien, tries to take part of his annual holiday at this time, so he's looking after them while I'm here. I thought I might be worse with the kids off school, as they always seem to want me to do something, to read to them, to cook with them, to make something or to go somewhere. To my surprise I seem better when they are around."

"So when are they not around?" Asked Dr. James. "Do they ever stay away from home, such as stay with your mother, for example?"

"Oh no! They can never do that," said Sally.

"That was said with a certain degree of meaning," said Dr. James. "What's all that about?"

"My kids can never stay with my mother. Nor can she ever baby-sit for us. My elder sister has her completely under her thumb. It's so unfair!"

"Come on, Sally. Open up. There's a lot to this. Something's upsetting you."

Sally was eighteen when her sister Wendy, two years older than she was, got married. Wendy had always been top dog. She had bossed Sally around all her life. She was incredibly self-centred. Everything had to revolve around her. She was the most important person in the whole world. Everything she wanted had to be done exactly as she wanted. Her father had totally doted on her. She had been the apple of his eye, but he had sadly died of a heart attack a few years ago. Somehow Wendy had made Sally feel his death had been her fault. She never quite said so, but the intention of her words was always there. Having lost her most ardent admirer in her father, Wendy was going to make sure that everyone around her made up for her loss.

Wendy bossed everyone around unmercifully for her wedding. It had to be absolutely perfect. She was so sure it would be the most important wedding of the year that she invited one of those glossy gossip national magazines to photograph the whole thing. She was absolutely incandescent with rage when they thanked her but said she wasn't famous enough for their readers. It took her a week to get over the insult, but, in the end, she somehow managed to tell herself that it was their loss not hers.

Wendy, not her mother who was paying for the wedding, chose the most expensive local hotel she could find. She flirted unmercifully with the hotel manager, to get exactly what she wanted. She rang him almost every day with another request. His patience was almost exhausted, but he obliged her, as it was good business. She booked the best suite for herself so that she and her new husband would be able to spend the night there in luxury before flying off the next day for their expensive honeymoon. She assumed that everyone would be so delighted to attend her wedding that they would all want to stay until the early hours of the morning.

Sally had had MS for about three years by then, her main annoying symptom being extreme fatigue. Just about everything exhausted her. She asked, and to her surprise was granted, a small room at the hotel where she could rest if she became too tired to go on. And so the great important day arrived. Sally worked her socks off for her sister. She accepted that it was the most important day of her life and felt it was the least she could do. In any case, nothing was too good for her sister.

Not surprisingly the wedding went off without a hitch. It was absolutely perfect. Sally did her bit and attended to her sister all the time, becoming more and more tired as the day wore on. Until she could go on no longer. Her husband Damien literally had to carry her up to the room set aside for her. You should have seen the look on Wendy's face when Sally left her. One of her uncles caught the look and was astonished at what he saw. He later told Sally that, if looks could have killed, Sally would have died there and then. As it was, she was too exhausted to care.

That was the last straw for Wendy. She never forgave Sally for not dancing attention to her all day and all evening. How could she leave me on my most important day? Or something like that must have gone through her mind.

"I can't believe what I am hearing," said Dr. James. "This story seems unbelievable to me. I have heard of some strange family feuds in my time, but this one takes the biscuit."

Both Sally and Wendy had two children each, but Wendy insisted that she needed her mother's help more than Sally, so effectively forbad their mother from doing anything for Sally, such as occasionally pick the kids up from school or baby-sit, which she would have loved to have done. Their mother went along with it for the sake of peace, saying, "You know what your sister's like."

And so the one-sided feud had continued. Unfortunately, as their children were the same age, they all went to the same school. Despite Wendy telling her kids not to have anything to do with Sally's, they took no notice and were actually quite friendly to one another. But it didn't make life pleasant for Sally or her husband Damien. In fact they often had a bit of an argument as to who would pick the kids up from school in the afternoon. There was no problem in the mornings as Damien went to work fairly early so was able to drop them off before Wendy dropped hers off. The school had a special arrangement for kids whose parents wanted to drop them off early.

The problem was that, if they saw Wendy with her kids, the look of disgust was so strong from her that neither of them wanted to pick the kids up. They hated the experience. It was this stress that seemed to be making Sally deteriorate, or at least not continue to improve.

"And this has been going on for how long?" Asked Dr. James.

"Well, Wendy got married nine years ago. So I suppose that long, although the school runs have only been for the past few years. Damien and I are thinking of moving house so that the kids have to change school. But we don't want to. The kids say they are really happy there and we love our house."

"I can't believe you haven't told me about this before," said Dr. James.

"Why? Could it be important?"

"Most certainly it could. Don't you remember how much better you felt for those vitamins and minerals I gave you intravenously. The large doses of vitamin B12 helped your fatigue to virtually disappear and it was possibly the magnesium that helped your legs to work so much better. Stress strips your body of many nutrients, magnesium possibly being the most important in your case. So we need to do something about your current nutritional status. However, I want to think about the situation with your sister, so please come back with Damien after evening surgery one day next week. Ask the receptionist to give you the last appointment. Please be prepared to wait if I am running late. In fact ring the surgery, if you can get through, to see if I am on time or not. I hate appointment systems. I so seldom manage to keep to the time allotted. I've told the other doctors, but they insist on sticking to the system.

A week later they both came back to the surgery. As expected, Dr. James was running half-an-hour late, but none of his patients minded as they felt he gave them what time they needed. If they needed a lot more time, he would arrange for them to come in on his day off if they could manage it, when he could take as long with them as they needed.

Once they had settled in and Sally had told Dr. James how she was, he asked them both a couple of simple questions. "Why do you let Wendy bully you? Why do you let her attitude affect you? After all, it's her problem, not yours."

Damien and Sally were not prepared for such questions. They took them by surprise. "On second thoughts," responded Sally, "Perhaps I should have been prepared for something unusual from you, Dr. James. What are you getting at?"

"Well, just think about it for a second. Wendy is the one who has the attitude. She is still annoyed at you for what she sees as a sleight to her on her wedding day, even though her attitude is totally ridiculous. Every time she looks at you in her nasty way, you wither under her stare. She wins every time. You lose every time. She has you exactly where she wants you, under her control. Neither of you wants to pick the kids up so as not to come under her spell. It's so bad and affects you both so badly you are even thinking of moving house."

"What can we do?" Asked Sally.

"Stop cowering," said Dr. James. "Change your attitude to Wendy. Don't let her affect you badly at all. Take the opposite approach."

"I'm not sure what you're saying, Dr. James," said Damien. "Could you please be a bit more explicit?"

"Do your kids go back to school next Monday?" Asked Dr. James.

"No. Next Tuesday."

"Ok!" Said Dr. James. "This is what I want you both to do."

The following Tuesday, Damien took the kids to school as usual. No problem. In the afternoon, both he and Sally together went to pick up the kids in the afternoon as usual, but, instead of parking their car wherever there was a space as far from the other cars as possible, they deliberately arrived early so as to be able to park as close to the school entrance as possible. There they sat waiting for the kids to be set free. Other cars started to arrive and mums and the occasional dad got out to chat with each other, waiting for their little ones.

Arriving a bit late, Wendy drove up ostentatiously in her large four-by-four and parked illegally on yellow lines. She was far too important to park anywhere else. And then she saw Damien and Sally and put on her most glowering glare. Damien and Sally, on the other hand, got out of their car, gave her the biggest smile they could and gave her a cheery wave hello, as though they were glad to see her. No more skulking down by the dashboard trying to pretend they were looking for something. They put on a grand show of happiness, trying to indicate how pleased they were to see her. They were showing her she had lost her power over them and that they were no longer affected by her.

She didn't like that at all. "I gather Wendy is now thinking of moving house," Sally told Dr. James a few weeks later as she walked so much better down the isle in the local supermarket where she had bumped into him.

Chapter 30

"The third story Dr. James told us about MS patients was quite similar to the one about Sally, but this one was about a big strong Greek man who had lived in England for many years. Where Dr. James did his eighteen months long locum there were many Greek families and they all tended to live near each other. However, one or two of them had wanted to live in bigger houses so had had to move into neighbouring districts. That was why Georgiou Spiritos lived in Dr. James's practice catchment area. He and his wife Sylvie had lived in that city for all their married life, their parents having moved to England after the Second World War, their fathers having been major players in the Greek Resistance movement."

Georgiou had built up a very large and successful meat importing and exporting business. Sylvie had produced two handsome sons and two beautiful daughters, all of who were destined to follow the classical Greek family traditions. The sons were the apples of their father's eye and could do no wrong. They were cheeky when they were young boys and got away with murder as far as their father was concerned. His attitude was that their behaviour was exactly like his when he was young and it hadn't done him any harm, had it? The girls were being groomed to become wives and mothers and to learn how to feed their husbands and children. It was all very simple and straightforward. Fortunately they were all perfectly happy with their lot in life.

Georgiou was forty-two when he first started developing symptoms suggesting multiple sclerosis, so he naturally went to their Greek doctor who was confused to begin with. He had attended many Post-Graduate sessions on Neurology but had never seen a case of MS personally. For reasons that were not clear to him, MS seemed not to be a condition suffered by Greek people, whose homeland was of course Greece, a Mediterranean country.

Because of his great success in business, Georgiou and Sylvie decided to move to a larger house, which was why he came under Dr. James's care. The fact that Greek people did not seem to develop MS was discussed in great detail. Dr. James wanted to know what was different about a traditional Greek way of life and the life Georgiou was now living. In the end it turned out that the biggest change had been from goats' milk and goats' milk products to cows' milk and cows' milk products. Especially cheese, which Georgiou absolutely adored. The other observation that they eventually made was that Georgiou had decided to stop sugar because he had been putting on weight, so all his soft drinks were 'diet' forms, all containing aspartame. Dr. James told him he had heard there was an epidemic of MS in American youngsters addicted to their favourite diet drink.

"Then there is the weather," said Georgiou. "It rains so often in England. I miss the sun, but seem better when we go back to Greece for a holiday to stay with my cousins."

"That could be because you are short of vitamin D. If the sun does come out, you are probably sitting in your office. If you do manage to get out into the sun, you are wearing clothes. There is a Canadian PhD MS researcher who believes MS will one day be defined as a vitamin D deficiency disease. I believe it may also involve magnesium, as vitamin D helps magnesium metabolism. Everyone thinks only of vitamin D and calcium. They seem to forget how important magnesium is. To be fair they probably didn't know anything about magnesium in the first place anyhow. I would think your job has its stresses, and stress strips the body of magnesium."

Georgiou improved considerably for Dr. James's' advice and was delighted with the whole approach, but then he got stuck at a certain level of improvement. He felt, however, that Dr. James had done all he could, so didn't bother him any more.

One day Sylvie came to the surgery for a small problem, so Dr. James asked her why her husband had not bothered to keep coming to see him, especially as they bumped into each other every so often in the city centre, with Georgiou walking almost normally one day, then limping badly another day. Each time Dr. James had invited Georgiou to see him in surgery, but he had always made some excuse and never came.

"It's the stress," said Sylvie.

"From his business?" Asked Dr. James.

"No. From his father and mine."

"Please get him here somehow," suggested Dr. James. "I'm sure I could help."

"Do you think you could?" Asked Sylvie.

"I would think so," responded Dr. James.

"Then I'll drag him here if I have to. I'll get his mother to insist. That usually works. He takes a lot of notice of her. Greek men think they are in charge of everything, but it is we women who achieve wonders."

So eventually Georgiou visited Dr. James once again, this time on a Monday.

"You're not walking so well this morning, Georgiou. You were better when I saw you in town on Saturday. What happened over the weekend?"

"Ach! It's my father and her father," grumbled Georgiou. "They keep spoiling the weekends, and they know it annoys me. I can't seem to stop it affecting me."

"What's all this about?" Asked Dr. James.

"Like all Greek fathers, mine has pushed me to do better and better all my life. He does it to my two brothers, but seems to push me more because I am the eldest. To the old-fashioned Greek men, the eldest is always the one who gets pushed the most. To be fair they did a wonderful job in the Greek Resistance during the Second World War, doing far more important things than I could ever do. So I let them get away with it, because somehow I feel they did their bit and perhaps it is this pushy attitude that made them what they were. But it drives me mad."

"Your response to all this could easily be why your symptoms change so much and why you are not yet symptom-free. We need to find a way of helping you, so tell me more about all this. Give me some examples."

"Well it doesn't matter how well my business is going my father keeps telling me I should be doing better. When he looks at my business accounts he criticises them and says my profits should be better, yet I don't think he can read a balance sheet to save his life. But I can put up with that. He means it for the best reasons, and it keeps me on my toes. Personally I think I have done a very good job.

"Unfortunately Sylvie's father is exactly the same. She is the apple of his eye, as he never had any male children. Unfortunately they were only able to have the one girl. When we got married, her father gave me a very long talking to, about my responsibilities to her, how I must look after her, provide for her, nourish her and give her Greek grand-children for him to play with, teach Greek things to and generally be proud of. I have done all of these things, but he, like my father, keeps on at me, in particular on Sunday afternoons.

"It's infuriating. The one day I have off work in the week, they invite themselves to tea. They don't even bring their wives. It's almost as if they want to have me to themselves, to make sure my nose is kept to the grindstone. I feel sure they know it annoys me, but that by doing so they will keep me at it. In any case, why would I not? I like my work, but I look forward to that one day away from the office to be with my family, but they won't leave me alone. They just turn up."

"Hm!" Mused Dr. James. "When did you last invite them to tea on a Sunday?"

"Invite them to tea!?" Exploded Georgiou. "You must be joking! Why on earth would I want to invite them to tea on Sundays?"

"They turn up uninvited, knowing full well that it annoys you, according to you. They are bullying you in a way. They have you where they want you. You are under their thumb. They are in charge. So get out from under their influence, but by subtle means. I want you to invite them both to tea next Sunday and to ask them to bring their wives. Take control of the situation. Get back in charge. Get this annoying effect out of the way. Keep inviting them, but always with their wives. It seems that leaving their wives at home is important to them. Perhaps their wives don't even know where they are each Sunday. Perhaps they pretend they are at the golf club. Do they play golf?"

"Yes they do. They're both quite good, as a matter of fact."

Sylvie very quickly understood what Dr. James was on about. She assured Dr. James that Georgiou would do as he had suggested. She particularly liked the idea that they bring their wives with them. She had a sneaking suspicion that was an astute suggestion.

Georgiou rang Dr. James that Sunday evening. "I did as you said and invited them both to tea and to bring our mothers with them. Surprise, surprise! Neither of them could come as they had an important golf match to play. I had a heavenly day and my MS is so much better today, thanks to you."

Chapter 31

"Dr. James seemed incredibly wise to me and most people," said Maud. "Apart from his unusual way of looking at medical problems, he seemed to have a good grasp of human nature. He was always trying to get people to think for themselves, to make decisions for themselves. He also knew that the way he wanted to practise medicine was not what most doctors did. He was aware that there were differences of opinion and that the way he worked was not the common way. He knew that many of his patients would receive advice to have a particular treatment that he wouldn't want them to have, yet they would ask his advice about it.

"He knew all of the local hospital Specialists because he attended Post-Graduate meetings all the time. Many of them admired what he did but felt it was too late to change their approach. Others could hardly look him in the eye. One or two of them asked him to see their wives or other family members on the quiet. Although he would see them he was not happy with their double standards. One of the Professors dismissed the value of acupuncture and osteopathy to his students, yet was happy for his wife to attend such people.

"It was things like whether to have chemotherapy or radiotherapy that so many patients asked his advice about. They seldom asked him whether to take drugs recommended by the Specialist for high blood pressure or asthma, for example, although he would make sure they worked and didn't cause any adverse effects, if they wanted to continue on them.

"He told us at his lectures that we all had to make decisions for ourselves, whether we liked to or not. He reminded us that we had made many decisions all our lives, for ourselves and our children, where to live, what house to buy or not to buy, who to marry or not to marry. He said we had all helped our kids decide what subjects to study at school, what clothes to wear, and sometimes even advise whether someone was suitable to go out with. 'Life,' he said 'is full of decisions. So why should it be any different when having to make a decision about health? It is no more important than many of the decision we have been making all our lives. I can't understand why so many people let their doctors make decisions for them. They have been making decisions all their lives, but suddenly, because it's about their health, they let someone else do it for them. Fair enough, listen to the advice, but please be involved with the choices.'

"Dr. James said all we had to do was to ask appropriate questions of the person recommending a particular treatment. As he said, 'If you are thinking of buying a house, you ask whether there is any rising damp, is a new road being planned to absorb the garden, is the roof in good condition, is the house subject to flooding? You make your decision whether to buy or not to buy the house based on the information you receive.'

"Because whether or not to have a course of chemotherapy was the most common question he was asked, he discussed that topic very carefully in one of his talks in the church. He was very clear on what his job was, namely to help people to make the right decision for themselves. He was adamant that he would not advise them to have or not to have chemotherapy. They had to make that decision for themselves, but they had to know what questions to ask their Specialist Oncologist, so he listed them for us."

First of all, Dr. James had to set the scene. Sitting in the front row in the church reserved for people he was going to talk about were four women, three of them with their husbands. One was Janet Theobald and the others were Trudy Gibson, Marion White and Vicky Downland. All four had, or had had, breast cancer.

Janet was fifty-six years old, while Trudy was only thirty-eight. Marion was forty-eight and Vicky was fifty-three. Janet had had a total mastectomy four years ago and many of the lymph glands in her right armpit had been removed at the same time. She had had many weeks of chemotherapy and radiotherapy, but all to no avail. Her cancer was still spreading. She was sick all the time and to all intents and purposes wanted to die as she felt so ill. The specialist had recommended another course of chemotherapy, with a stronger drug.

Dr. James asked Janet to take off her coat to show the enormous size of the arm that had had the glands removed followed by radiotherapy. He asked the nurse to put a tape measure round them. It was obvious for everyone to see. Her right arm was more than twice the size of her left arm and it was a horrible purplish colour, oozing clear liquid in several places.

Janet then took off her wig. She was totally bald underneath it. There was an audible sound of horror from everyone in the church. Dr. James told his audience that that was one of the side effects of many forms of chemotherapy. Others were that the drugs attacked rapidly dividing cells such as the bone marrow and the cells lining the intestines, so people often felt sick and caught infections all too easily because their immune system was damaged.

Dr. James then described Trudy Gibson's situation. She had had a mammogram four weeks ago followed by a lumpectomy. The surgeon had said he advised that he take some of her lymph glands out to see whether the cancer had spread to them. She had said that, if that was the case, then surely the cancer had already spread, so what was the purpose of taking them out in the first instance. The surgeon had said so that they could stage her cancer to decide whether to recommend chemotherapy or not. Her reply was an adamant refusal to let him touch her lymph glands, as she wouldn't be prepared to have chemotherapy or radiotherapy under any circumstances. Her mother had had breast cancer and the best treatment offered to her had not saved her life, and she had died five years ago. Trudy had no intention of letting that happen to her.

The surgeon simply said that modern drugs were more effective than the ones her mother may have been given, but he accepted her decision, as he could not guarantee that chemotherapy would be essential. He simply said it was given largely as a 'just in case' situation.

Trudy had asked Dr. James to help her make sure that any cancer cells that had escaped were dealt with by her own immune system, and that was what they were doing.

Forty-eight years old Marion White had had a mastectomy ten years ago followed by chemotherapy. As far as anyone could tell she was in remission from her cancer and felt very well. As far as she was concerned, the whole thing had been dealt with most professionally by all her doctors and she was a glowing tribute to the standard approach of mastectomy followed by chemotherapy, which had not made her feel particularly unwell, just a bit tired, but which she had got over quickly enough when the treatment was completed. Dr. James said it was important for people to meet someone whose standard approach had been a success.

The fourth woman was Vicky Downland. She was fifty-three years old. She had had a lumpectomy three years ago, the surgeon boldly pronouncing at her bedside that he had 'got it all'. There was no need for chemotherapy and she would be fine. Vicky had got on with life assuming all was well.

Unfortunately she had had a cough that just wouldn't go away, so she had had a chest X-ray that strongly suggested her cancer was back, in her lungs. The specialist wanted to pass a tube down into her lungs to take a biopsy to confirm the diagnosis, after which he was sure he would be recommending a course of chemotherapy. Vicky had yet to make up her mind what to do. She had asked Dr. James for advice, as he was her General Practitioner.

Dr. James thanked all four women for being so brave as to bare their souls and medical history to so many people, but, as they had heard other people's stories from Dr. James in the past, they felt being involved would not only help them with any decisions they had to make but should be of value to other people.

"The point I am trying to make," said Dr. James from the pulpit "is that each person's situation is very different from everyone else's. There is no typical answer. What to do has to be tailored to the individual, and each individual has to decide what to do depending on their own circumstances and attitude to life. Over the years patients have asked my advice about all sorts of things, though usually about whether to do something or not.

"So, right from the beginning I need to repeat that I cannot *make* any decisions for you, but I hope my advice will help you to make the right decision for yourself. I'm sure you have made many decisions in your lifetime, but you may not have thought at the time that it was very important which way any of your decisions went.

"But, first, what sort of decision do you have to make? It is likely to be one of the following, such as 'should I have a biopsy of my lump or not?' 'Should I have the lump removed or not?' 'Should I have chemotherapy or not?' 'Should I have radiotherapy or not?' 'Should I have a particular drug or not?' 'And should I let a surgeon operate on me or not?'

"When a patient in front of me asks my advice on questions such as those or similar ones, my first question is to ask them what their current feeling is. So, I ask them whether, at this stage, they are inclined to have the treatment or not. On a scale of 0 to 100, with 0 being definitely *not* to proceed and 100 being definitely *to* proceed, and with 50 as the point of balance, I ask whether they are at present anywhere above or below the 50-point mark? I then say to them 'See if you can answer that question before you go any further, but don't worry if you remain resolutely at the 50-point mark.'

"If they are able to make a decision one side of the 50-point mark, I tell them to make a note of it now and write down their decision somewhere where they can refer to it whenever you want to. I tell them it is very important that they recognise the decision they have already made, because this is their *status quo*, their current position on the decision they need to make. From that time on they need to receive fairly strong information and justification to change that status quo. I tell them not to change their status quo without a good reason.

"Another way of looking at how to make a decision is 'If in doubt, don't'. If you are not sure whether to marry someone or not, don't. If you are thinking of moving house, why are you considering it? 'Oh! I just fancy a move!' or 'It's springtime and all my friends are moving'. Those are not good enough reasons, but 'I can't stand the house I am living in!' or 'I really love the look of that house and I would love to live in it' *are* good enough reasons to move, all other things being equal.

"So, with these thoughts in mind, let us now consider the first question 'should I have a biopsy or not?'

"One of your doctors, a Specialist I assume, has recommended that he stick a needle into the lump you have found and consulted him about. Possibly your General Practitioner has felt the lump and wants to refer you to a Specialist for the biopsy. Whichever is the case, you still have to decide whether to proceed or not. The purpose of the biopsy is to make a definite diagnosis, or to confirm or reject a suspicion of cancer. Doctors in mainstream medicine feel uncomfortable if they can't make a definite diagnosis by having a sample of the lump examined under a microscope.

"A further reason is that, once the diagnosis has been confidently made, it helps the doctor to decide what the most appropriate treatment is for that diagnosis. The doctor who examines the sample under a microscope will also stage the cancer, which is medical speak for how bad it is. He will also help the cancer Specialist with the prognosis, which, again, is medical speak for what your chances are in the long run. Remember, most doctors assume you will do whatever they suggest. To be fair to them, most patients do follow their advice, usually not asking any questions at all. After all "You know best, Doctor" is an easy way out of making a decision for yourself.

"I remember one cancer patient who consulted me not so long ago had to wait in the waiting room after she had seen a Consultant", said Dr. James. "After quite some time, she asked the nurse why she was having to wait so long, to which the reply was 'The doctor is deciding how best to treat you'. The nurse was visibly shocked when the patient said, 'Do you mind. I will decide what treatment I have'. What doctors and staff sometimes forget, or may not even be aware of in the first instance, is that The General Medical Council, in its booklet 'Duties of a Doctor' says, 'Doctors should encourage patients to be fully involved in decisions about their care'.

"But I have digressed a little, as I often do, so, back to the point in hand. At this stage, i.e. before the biopsy is taken, no one really knows what is going on, unless you have many lumps that have appeared and he is sure what it is, or the doctor merely wants to do the biopsy because it is what he always does. In the circumstances, there is no point in asking him what treatment he is likely to recommend, because he doesn't know himself yet. However, you could ask him what treatment options he is likely to recommend if the biopsy were to turn out as he suspects.

"In the main, the treatment options for cancer are an operation, radiotherapy, chemotherapy, some other drug regime, probably hormonal in some way, or a combination of them. If you have breast cancer, you may be advised to have a lumpectomy, a wedge resection or a mastectomy, with or without subsequent reconstruction, as well as possibly various parts of your lymph system in your armpit being removed. This may be followed by local radiotherapy and a course of chemotherapy, occasionally one of them without the other.

"Biopsy of a breast lump is not usually painful, but the simple procedure of sticking a needle in it, sometimes a fairly wide bore one to obtain a reasonably large specimen, and sometimes more than once, can occasionally inflame the whole area. Some of my patients have told me that they felt the biopsy made their cancer grow faster after it had been done. To be fair to the surgeon who took the biopsy, he probably assumed he was going to proceed fairly soon to some sort of operation anyway, so that it shouldn't matter.

"If the biopsy is what a doctor might consider a 'run-of-the-mill' procedure, then you need to ask yourself a simple question, and, at the same time, decide where your answer would be on the 0 to 100 scale. Would you proceed to have whatever treatment the Specialist recommends? Would you be prepared to have a local lumpectomy, a mastectomy with or without a degree of axillary clearance? Would you be prepared to have radiotherapy and/or chemotherapy?

"If you would be prepared to have some of these options but not others, it is important to tell your Specialist, because it may make a difference to whether he decides to do the biopsy or not. If, however, you would not be prepared to undergo *any* of the treatment that might be recommended, there is no point in having the biopsy in the first place. That is why it is so important for you to consider the points I have just made. The chances are that the surgeon would be somewhat put out by your questions, and is likely to ask why you have come if you are not likely to follow his advice. Presumably you could say something like 'I would like you to tell me from your experience of feeling thousands of breast lumps whether you think mine is a cancer or not'. Hopefully he would be willing to give an opinion.

"To digress again, I always try to explain as fully as possible to all my patients what is likely to happen at a later stage in certain conditions, for example, when a woman attends my surgery in the early stages of a pregnancy, especially if it is her first pregnancy, so she has not had any previous experience of what will happen over the next few months. Remember, scans that are used so frequently nowadays were not available when I was first in General Practice, but the principle I am on about is still the same.

"I would explain the frequency of visits, what we would do at each visit, and all the blood tests that it was wise to have done. I would explain that, at approximately sixteen weeks, she would be offered a blood test to see if there was the possibility that her baby had some sort of abnormality. If this were positive, it would be repeated to make sure a mistake had not been made in the laboratory. If it were still positive a more specific test would be done. If there were no doubt that the baby did have a problem, then she would be offered an abortion.

"I feel it can sometimes be very difficult for people to make a decision when they are suddenly confronted with it, like some of you might be now. So to have to consider, as early as possible, what one might do were a particular problem to arise at a later stage, is worth thinking about. In those days, I felt that mentioning a remote possibility to a woman in the early stages of pregnancy, when her hormones had not really got going, gave her a chance to consider her attitude at a time when it didn't matter, and would probably never occur anyway.

"You might think this was not a good idea, but I never found anyone who felt I was wrong to bring up the subject that early on. I feel the attitude I held then was right and still is. Doctors sometimes have a habit of thinking they must make 'the right decision' for the patient, so may not to give all the options. As far as I am concerned, my patients are just as intelligent as I am, so, if I explain things to them properly, I am teaching them everything I can for them to decide what to do for themselves.

"Having explained this to the woman (and I always insisted her husband be present or at least a close family member or friend at the time), I would then ask if she had any idea what attitude she would take. Inevitably some would say they had no idea. Others were wise to say they would have to think about it, which was exactly why I had mentioned it so early. Then there were a few who said that, no matter what the result, they wouldn't have an abortion under any circumstances. I would then suggest that, in that case, *there was no point in having the blood test done in the first place.*

"Do you see what I am getting at? If you are not prepared to have the treatment that would be recommended as a result of a test, why have the test done in the first place? This situation entirely applies to you if you have decided *not* to have the treatment that your Specialist is likely to recommend. However, it changes if you *might.*

"The next question on that list that you may need to decide upon is "Should I have the lump removed?" The same applies to "Should I have an operation at all?" The answer to this one depends upon a number of factors, but remember, you have been recommended to have an operation by a *Surgeon.*

"Some years ago a friend asked my advice about his mother. She had been found to have an obvious breast lump, which was clearly a cancer, when she was being washed in the shower. However, she was totally unaware of it or its significance, because she also had fairly bad Alzheimer's Disease, although we didn't call it that in those days. Her son naturally took her to her General Practitioner who referred her on to the local breast cancer centre, where she was advised to have a mastectomy. When my friend asked me whether she *needed* to have the operation, I suggested that perhaps it wasn't necessary in the circumstances of her other health problems, especially as the whole procedure of going into hospital, having a general anaesthetic and all those bandages would likely confuse her even more.

"So my friend went back to the hospital Consultant and asked him if the operation was really necessary and also asked him if he would recommend the operation if his own mother were the patient in question. He duly replied that there was no need for the operation to be done. When my friend asked him why he had made the recommendation in the first place, he said, "Because I'm a Surgeon and my job is to operate." My friend's mother died of old age a few years later, none the worse for not having the mastectomy.

"I have no doubt that today's Surgeons are caring people. They know that patients are better informed than ever before. They now accept that patients are likely to ask a lot of questions, and are not always going to accept immediately any advice they are given. Gone are the days of Sir Lancelot Spratt of the 'Doctor In The House' film, when a patient was cowed, or bullied, into accepting his advice. Woe betide anyone who had the temerity to even ask him a question. To him the patient was something to operate on, but to be fair, he was also an excellent surgeon.

"What I am really saying is that you need to examine your personal position. You also need to ask your Specialists a number of questions. Perhaps the first one should be 'With all the experience you have had over the years, could you please try to tell me what, in your opinion, is likely to happen to me if I do not agree to an operation?' In addition you could also ask, 'What is my prognosis if I do have it?' And, 'Are there any alternatives?'

"At this stage we need to know the state of your cancer, how minimal or how bad it is. We need to know if anyone has indicated that you only have a short time to live, or have they told you that everything should turn out well, and that you should have many more years of active life? If that is the case, does it depend upon your following what has been recommended?

"In an attempt to help you answer this last question, I would like to move on to consider the next three questions, basically whether you should have chemotherapy, radiotherapy or some other drug treatment.

"If you have cancer, all of these treatments are likely to be fairly toxic, although some people seem to cope with them remarkably well. As I have already explained, chemotherapy usually makes people feel unwell to a degree, and, for now, you need to assume it will make you feel bad. Yes, you will be given other drugs to minimise the adverse effects, but they don't always work, and may even make things worse. The side effects of the drugs given to you to minimise the chemotherapy's side effects may themselves have other undesirable effects. How you will feel I cannot possibly tell you, as we are all different and no one has yet been able to identify who will feel bad and who will not.

"Nevertheless, you must ask your Specialists what they think might happen to you. Of course they will hope their treatments will work for you, otherwise they wouldn't recommend it. They also know that part of the long-term effects of radiation in particular, and possibly chemotherapy, is that they cause cancer itself. There is nothing new about this, but they are dealing with the 'here and now'. It is well known that, if a young woman has radiotherapy to her chest wall for Hodgkin's Disease, there is a significantly increased risk of her developing breast cancer in possibly twenty years time. No one ever seems to think of giving her anti-oxidants, for example, to try to prevent her developing it.

"If you suspect that your Specialists don't feel you have much of a chance, even if they treat you, you need to ask two simple questions. 'What is my prognosis if I don't have any treatment?' And, 'Will your treatment give me a *useful* extension to my life', in which case you have to decide what you and they mean by the word 'useful'? Perhaps you could also ask, 'How do you think I will feel during what is left of my life, if I do have your treatment?' You could also challenge them by asking, 'would you have the treatment you are recommending if you were in my shoes?' If the Specialist replies, 'Possibly not', you can guess what he is thinking. Remember, he feels he must try to help you if he can.

"So what sort of answers to these questions might you receive? Let me first paint a possible picture that may or may not apply to you, but is similar to two of our ladies in the front row. You had breast cancer five years ago, which was treated with a mastectomy followed by a few weeks of local radiotherapy, then a six-month course of chemotherapy. Everyone was happy with the outcome and you were seen regularly for follow-up when you were examined, blood may have been taken for a few tests sometimes, and you were given the all clear. Your routine visits to the clinic were recently extended to one year.

"A few weeks ago you developed a cough, which lingered on longer than usual. However, friends had had much the same, as there was a nasty bug going around at the time. So you didn't think anything of it. In due course you decided to consult your GP about it when you felt a pain in one of your ribs. Having listened to your chest and not heard anything wrong, he suggested a chest X-ray 'to be on the safe side'. When he received the report he arranged an urgent appointment for you back at the hospital. More X-rays, blood tests and extensive scans were done, for you to be told, "I'm sorry, but the cancer has come back and it has spread into your lungs and many of your bones".

"You now have what is described as 'terminal cancer'. You have been given three months to live. 'We could try a course of chemotherapy, if you like,' says the Specialist. Incidentally, Janet knows this is what her situation is, and she has encouraged me to say so.

"Now your questions take on a different angle. You have basically been told that there isn't much that can be done for you, but that they are prepared to try something if you would like them to. You have one or two simple questions. First, "How many weeks or months longer is your recommended treatment likely to give me?" If the answer is something like "Possibly three months", you have to decide whether those three months are important to you. Perhaps you have something personal to sort out, possibly your will or something else important, that needs a little time. After all, you may well have been advised to go home and 'put your things in order'.

"You could ask that question in a slightly different way and say, 'How much more *useful* life is your treatment likely to give me?' At the same time you also need to ask, 'How am I likely to feel with your treatment?' 'Is it likely to make me feel ill?' 'Is it likely that the treatment you are recommending will make the remaining time I do have left hardly worth having, assuming that I am likely to have to spend some of that time in hospital?

"All of the answers you need to weigh up for yourself. *You* have to decide whether the time you are likely to have left would be best spent with your family. *You* have to decide whether the extension to your life that the recommended treatment, with its possible unpleasant effects, is worth having. To some people, any extension of their life is worth having. To others, what is on offer may not be.

"What I have described so far is likely to cover many people who have a decision to make. You don't need to be in as extreme a situation as I have just described. If, nevertheless, you have a problem of any sort, whether it is serious or not, the questions I have outlined are still appropriate. It's just that the answers will be different. There is one other question that you could ask, whatever your condition, and that is what Oxford Don Michael Gearin-Tosh asked of his Specialist when he was diagnosed with Multiple Myeloma, a condition that is usually fatal within a year or two from diagnosis. 'Can you cure me?' When he was told there was no cure for his condition, he basically said, 'Then I don't want your treatment. I will find a cure for myself.' He wrote a book entitled 'Living Proof. A Medical Mutiny'[♥], when he was still alive eight years later! It makes fascinating reading.

"Whatever your condition, however bad your situation is, unless it is an out-and-out emergency, take as long as you need to come to the right decision for yourself. In my experience, the longer you take to make a decision, the more doubts you are likely to throw up about whether to proceed or not. That then puts you somewhere

---

[♥] To obtain a copy of this book, see Appendix 2, note 7.

below the 50-point mark. If, however, you are clearly above the 50-point mark and want to get on with things, do so and stop worrying about it, but be positive and sure that the treatment approach you have chosen *will* be successful.

"Talk it through with those you trust, those closest to you, after you have all the information you can obtain. If necessary, you could ask for a second opinion. After all, the answers to your questions will be given according to the experience of the doctor you ask them of, apart from which some doctors don't like to be asked awkward questions and may try to evade them. Another doctor may have a different opinion, or he may give you much the same answers. To be fair, no doctor can be sure, so he can only give you what he believes is likely to be the right answer, based on his own statistics, observations and experience. He also knows that some patients survive longer than others, but he doesn't know why that is, or who will be fortunate to survive longer than he anticipated.

"Make sure you have had an answer to all the questions you need to ask. Don't ask too many people to help you in your decision-making. Keep it to a small circle of people you think you can rely on to help you decide. But, remember, some of the advice may be conflicting, so may confuse you even more. Consider why someone gave you a particular piece of advice. Have they had a similar experience before with one of their own close relatives? Did that person do well, or was it a total disaster?

"In many respects, if someone has had a previous experience of this sort, they may not be particularly suitable to ask, even if they are sympathetic. Their reply is likely to be influenced by their experience. They are not likely to see it from *your* point of view, only theirs. On the other hand, such experience could open your eyes in a particularly relevant way. Would it be sensible to ask Judy for her opinion, since all the treatment failed her mother? How about asking Marion, whose full treatment was a success?

"Beware of people who say, 'If I were you, I would do so-and-so'. They are not in your shoes, and you are not in theirs. In my opinion, the best people are those who let you do most of the talking, prompting you every so often, allowing *you* to come to your own conclusions".

"That talk was really one of the longest of them all," said Maud. "Dr. James had started off by telling us he was going to talk about a very important subject, possibly one that might affect any one of us at any time in our lives. He also said that tonight's demonstration might well upset a number of people, but he would totally understand if people looked away at certain times. He said he would illustrate other aspects of decision making next time, which he duly did.

"He thanked the four ladies for being so willing to let their problems be aired so thoroughly. He felt they had been very brave.

"That story had a sad and a happy ending. The way Dr. James and the Reverend Henry Middleton looked after us all seemed to draw the community together. Three of the volunteers had a husband and family to look after them. Janet Theobald, the one who was very severely affected, did not. As a result of Dr. James's talk that evening a group of local people got together, unbeknown to all of us, and decided that Janet was one of us and needed our help. Their spokesman came to Dr. James and Rev. Middleton and said they wanted to help. Apparently one of them knew Janet's background and how sad it was. Without saying exactly what it was, she said Janet was a proud and rather secretive person, but who had no family left that she knew of. She felt Janet's real problem was that she didn't have anyone to love her. They wanted to do something.

"Dr. James and Henry Middleton went to see Janet a few days later and asked her if they could help her in any way. She told them that Dr. James's talk had totally opened her eyes about her situation and had helped her to decide not to have any more chemotherapy. She said she was sure the Specialist was trying to tell her that it was a waste of time and that it wouldn't do her any good. Dr. James offered to let the Specialist know of her decision.

"Janet also said she had now accepted that her life was coming to an end, and that all she wanted was to be allowed to pass away at home with dignity. She had lived in Stead Norton for fifteen years and had been happy there, even though she had not found it very easy to make friends. She just wasn't that sort of person.

"Henry Middleton said there was a group of people in the village who wanted to help. That brought a smile to her tired face. Her ordeal at Dr. James's talk had worn her out, but she felt she was now at peace with the world and was happy to pass away. 'There is a book that has always been my favourite. I would love to read it one more time, but I haven't the energy. Would it be possible for some of those kind people to read it to me please?'

"'I think that is exactly the sort of thing they would love to do,' said Henry Middleton. 'We will also organise a rota of people to sit with you some of the time and prepare food and feed you. Have you any idea what you would like to eat?'

"Janet said she had very little appetite, so they didn't press her on the subject, but the group soon found a way of helping. A few days later, Dr. James came to visit her. The District Nurses had been in and done a wonderful job getting her properly organised. Janet had retired to bed where she was comfortable. Her heavy right arm was carefully bandaged every day and placed on a soft pillow. 'I'd like to be the first person to read to you, if I may', said Dr. James.

"A week later it was clear to Dr. James that Janet didn't have long to live. 'I am ready to die' she told him. 'Everyone has been so kind to me. I didn't know there was so much love in Stead Norton. My solicitor visited me a couple of days ago. I have changed my will and asked him to be an executor of a special request I have made. I have asked the Reverend Henry Middleton to be another executor, but I would like you, Dr. James, to be the main executor with the final decision on all matters. I signed the will this morning.

'I probably have only a few days left on this earth. It will come as a surprise to many people that I am quite a wealthy woman. I don't live in luxury even though my house is comfortable. I have never wanted for anything special. But I have had a particular interest and apparently an unusual ability. Somehow I have been able to understand company Annual Reports and read between the lines. I seemed able to recognise when they were telling the truth and when they were telling lies. That helped me to invest wisely.

'I have left over two million pounds for a trust fund to help young students study medicine, but I want them to practise the sort of medicine you have practised here, caring medicine, not just drug and surgical medicine. My friend Joyce recorded all your talks in the church. I felt I couldn't sit there long enough to enjoy them and I didn't have any idea what they would be about. I found them absolutely fascinating. I have listened to them so many times. I only wished I had followed some of your advice so long ago, but I didn't. I suppose I am like the majority of people.

'I appreciate you can't force doctors to practise how you practise, but there must be sons and daughters of some of the people you have helped who would love to learn to work that way. I will happily leave it to your judgement, knowing perfectly well you may make the odd mistake.'

"Dr. James said he would be honoured to do as she wished. He already knew of a boy and a girl in separate families who wanted to study medicine because he had been so helpful to their parents. Neither family could afford the costs. Dr. James said they would be absolutely thrilled. He went round the next day with two seventeen-years olds who hugged Janet gently and promised they would use her money wisely and frugally.

'Now I can die in peace,' she said, and, with a little smile on her face, she gently slipped away.

Chapter 32

"Janet Theobald was buried a few days later," said Maud. "In some ways it was really quite sad, but the whole episode woke us all up. We suddenly realised there were people in our area who needed help, even simple things like taking someone to hospital for an appointment. So the 'Friends of Stead Norton' was set up. Some people wanted to call it after Janet Theobald, but they agreed not to do so when Dr. James told them of her generosity towards medical students and said that her endowment was to be called the Janet Theobald Medical Trust.

All agreed, however, that they needed a Cancer Self Help Group, free for anyone to attend from anywhere, not just the local area. The District Nurses thought it was such a wonderful idea, people supporting each other, and agreed to help run it. Somehow it was felt that cancer had a special need, although Dr. James regularly tried to take the fear out of the 'Big C' as it was sometimes called.

The Cancer Self Help Group met every Monday evening in the Town Hall. Dr. James attended every other Monday, joining in the relaxation and visualisation exercises, then going round discussing how people were and offering appropriate advice. Just about everyone who attended the Group meetings wanted to do something for themselves, even if they were also having standard hospital treatment, so he had a willing audience.

Gradually over the years it seemed that patients who attended survived not only longer but also appeared to get over their cancer better than was expected. It was just like the patients with the leg ulcers that eventually healed. They quite simply seemed to do better. After Janet Theobald died, no one could remember anyone else dying of cancer, although someone probably did.

Dr. James gave mini talks to the Cancer Group every so often, and when the next one was planned, that meeting had to be held in the church because the small Town Hall room couldn't take so many people who wanted to attend that evening.

One of those sessions happened two days after Dr. James had given a talk to a group of nearly one thousand people in a large hall in London on the Saturday. Other Doctors and Practitioners had also given a talk, so he basically intended to tell them all about what he had learned, in the hope it would help some of them. One of the points he had made in his London talk was that his impression was that so many people did well who attended the Self Help Group. However, he acknowledged that it was only an impression and he didn't really know the facts. So he decided to find out.

The Group had a signing-in system so that the nurses could be aware of who was there, how often they turned up and what their cancer was. If someone who attended regularly stopped coming, one of the nurses would visit them at home in case they were in difficulties. The list was therefore of value, so on this particular occasion they knew how many people had cancer and how many were merely keeping the patients company. On this evening there were forty-eight cancer patients out of a total of nearly one hundred and fifty people in the church.

Dr. James explained that he had told the meeting in London that it was his impression that the Group had a better outcome than occurred in the general population, repeating that it was only his impression, but that he wanted to find out. He asked everyone who had cancer to raise their hands and the nurses counted forty-eight as the register had indicated. He then asked them to indicate how they thought they were doing.

"Hands up those of you who feel your cancer is under control and you don't have any worries about it." Twenty-five people put their hands up. "Hands up those of you who believe you will soon have complete control of your cancer and expect to get rid of it soon and be given the all clear." Ten people put their hands up. "Hands up those of you who believe you have completely overcome your cancer, i.e. are now former cancer patients". Another ten people put their hands up. "Hands up those of you whose cancer is not under control and who are receiving or need more treatment." Three people put their hands up.

"Any idea why you three are in this category and everyone else is not?" Asked Dr. James from the pulpit.

"It's my first visit to this Group," said one lady. "I've never been before."

"The same with me," said a second.

"I'm the same," said the third.

"What interesting statistics!" said Dr. James. "It doesn't prove a thing, but the only people here whose cancer is not under control are three people who have never been here before. Everyone else is moving forward. If you three ladies join us regularly I wonder how long it will be before you would be able to put your hands up when asked one of the good news questions?"

Those three ladies went away with their heads held high. After Dr. James's talk, so many people came up to them and told them how they could beat their cancer if they wanted to. It was all down to Janet Theobald whose life and death had changed so many people's lives.

Chapter 33

"**I** jumped forward a bit," said Maud, "when I started talking about the Cancer Self Help Group yesterday. There are so many stories of Dr. James to tell you. I was so lucky, if you want to call it that. I not only had Dr. James talk in the church, but everyone seemed to want to tell me their own stories. It was as though I was the local storyteller, like I'm told Red Indians had in their tribes, so I could pass them on. I've never thought of it like that before. I amazes me how easily I can remember so many episodes. My body may be starting to wear out but my mind still seems to be ok."

"Most of the stories you have told me about Dr. James," said Patrick, "are really quite long and complicated, although one or two are not too long. Can you remember any more short ones? Short stories can be just as interesting. I have a number of books of short stories. In some ways I enjoy them more than full-length stories."

"The one that immediately comes to mind," said Maud "is about Roger Henderson. He was a top executive somewhere in London. Quite a lot of people like him live around here. Commuting to London is not a problem for them as they do a lot of work and reading in the train. Like so many of them, they have a doctor in their company as their company employs so many people, in his case, about two-and-a-half thousand, I think, so more than all those registered with Dr. James."

Roger Henderson's problem was a chronic lower backache. He had apparently consulted no end of people all over the world, as he travelled a lot, having business connections in many countries of the world. He had seen the best Orthopaedic Specialists in America and London, consulted and been treated by many osteopaths and chiropractors. All to no avail. Occasionally something helped a little, but not for long.

It was his wife who suggested he ask Dr. James for help, having sat at the back of the church when he gave one of his talks. One of her friends had suggested they go together. "What on earth can a country bumpkin of a doctor possibly do for me? I've seen the best doctors in the world. I've had every test and scan known to man, and I have tried all their various drugs. Come on, Love. What can he possibly do for me?"

"No idea," said his wife. "If I did know, I would tell you what to do myself. But I don't. Give him a try. Can't do you any harm, can it? Bet you a fiver he helps you. I don't usually bet, but I'll wager a small amount on this one."

Eventually Roger did consult Dr. James. It was shortly before Christmas. He was most apologetic for consulting him as he was not registered with him, but Dr. James simply said, "What can I do to help? What's the problem?"

"It's my back. It aches much of the time and can be very bad at times. I've seen so many people all over the world, and had so many X-rays and scans but nothing shows up. The only thing that does seem to be found, usually by osteopaths or chiropractors, is tenderness in the muscles of my lower back, but not always. Massage and heat seem to help, but usually for only a day or so, but even then it is still there a bit, so the massage doesn't cure it completely. But then it is back again as bad as usual. I even tried back massage every day for a week once, which helped a certain amount as long as I had the massage, but it was back again as soon as I stopped. My back hurts a bit all the time, and sometimes really quite badly. It's also affected my golf swing, not that I'm much good. It's just that golf smoothes the course of business along sometimes. Any ideas, Doctor?"

"Yes," said Dr. James, "I think I can guess what the problem is."

"You are joking," responded Roger. "How can you possibly know?" Dr. James wrote something down on a piece of paper and sealed it in an envelope.

"Do you want to sign across the back and keep this in a safe place, or will you be happy for me to put it in a drawer and see if I am right?"

"You keep it. No, on second thoughts, I'll ask my wife to look after it. It was she who suggested I consult you. She will be intrigued that you diagnosed me so quickly, and on so little information."

"Ah! That's where you are so wrong. You have given me a lot of information, possibly more than you realise. But I would just like to examine you myself, if you don't mind, but there are one or two more questions I would like to ask you." After answering the questions, Roger undressed sufficiently for Dr. James to examine him.

"As I expected, I stick to my diagnosis. I could tell you what I suspect here and now, if you like, or I could take a blood sample, which I would like to do anyhow, and give you an injection of something to see if it helps. If you like a bit of a mystery, I won't tell you what it is. That would be a bit of fun. What I want to inject you with is not a drug, but it may induce in you an interesting sense of warmth for a few seconds. You will also have a strange sensation in your throat. Don't worry. It won't do you any harm. I've done the same to many other people and given myself the same injection just to test its effects."

"My wife said I would enjoy meeting you, Dr. James. All the Specialists I have met, especially the ones in America and London, have had what one can only call an 'official approach'. They were courteous at all times, and approached me with an attitude that suggested they were top men in their field, with a confidence that they would be able to sort me out. To be fair to them, I never told them how many other people I had seen about my back. I felt that would make me too much of a challenge for them. You? You're somehow different. Yes. That's the word. You're different. You're relaxed with yourself. Ok! Let's do it your way. Give me that injection and let's see what it does."

Dr. James prepared things to take the blood sample and give Roger the injection. "I hope you don't mind if I close my eyes when you stick the needle in, Doctor. Let me know when you are going to start," he said.

"The needle's already in," said Dr. James.

"Gosh! I didn't feel a thing."

"I've taken the blood sample. Here comes the injection. It will only take about ten seconds."

"Oh my goodness!" Said Roger. "I see what you mean. That was a most interesting sensation. Didn't last long though."

"I'll send your blood sample in today's post. The lab will e-mail the result tomorrow afternoon. If you would care to come to tomorrow evening's surgery if you can make it, I can show you the result. Please bring your wife with you. I would like to meet her. She sounds a very sensible lady.

"Good evening, Mrs Henderson. How nice to meet you," said Dr. James when she and her husband entered the surgery the next evening. "How's your back, Mr Henderson?"

"Gone!" He said. "I can't believe it. It has completely gone for the first time in ages. It's incredible. Will it last?"

"I'll talk about that in a minute, but first let me show you your blood test result. Here it is." Dr James passed it to them both. He let them look at it for a while.

"I have a magnesium deficiency? What's that?" asked Roger.

"I'll explain in a minute. Did you bring that sealed envelope with you Mrs Henderson? Good. Please open it. What does it say?

"A magnesium deficiency!"

"That's amazing, Dr. James. You were so confident so early on. I'm truly astonished.

"You have not only a deficiency of magnesium, but one of the lowest the lab has ever seen. The lab director rang me this afternoon to tell me so. In some ways it's surprising the injection I gave you yesterday did the trick. You are so low. You'll certainly need more magnesium, and we'll have to talk about that in due course."

"But what made you think of a magnesium deficiency, and why am I so low in it? After all, if I remember right, you made the diagnosis after I had only been here a few minutes, and with no tests at that stage to back up your ideas."

"Perhaps the simplest way of answering your question is to say that you told me you had seen so many people and had had just about every test known to medicine. You have clearly seen a lot of real experts of one sort or another and I accepted their expertise. In particular, it was clear to me that you did not have a structural problem. That had been ruled out many times. No. It was the tenderness in the muscles of your lower back that you described that made me suspicious. Also it had to be something no one else had thought of.

"Can I look at the reports on my various blood tests, please, Maria," Roger said to his wife. "I've just had an idea. Yes," he said, when he had looked for something. "I thought I remembered having a test for magnesium, though I had no idea what it was. Here it is," he said, showing it to Dr. James. "It seems to be ok."

"First, it's right at the very bottom of the lab's reference range," replied Dr. James, "but it is also serum magnesium, a virtually useless test as far as I am concerned. Only about one percent of magnesium is in the blood serum. Magnesium is an intracellular mineral, which is why my test was done on your red blood cells. If your serum magnesium is low, you really are in trouble, but it rarely is, but it is still tested as a routine.

"Then there was what I found when I examined you. I noticed how cold your hands were, as it was not particularly cold in here at the time, and, although you told me you open your bowels usually once a day, I took that as meaning more often than not you don't. I could clearly feel you were constipated. Opening your bowels once a day is not good enough. It should be a minimum of twice a day, and three times is quite normal. Basically one meal in and one meal out, if you get my meaning, so long as you eat enough fibre overall."

"So what does that all add up to?"

"Calcium – which I'm sure you have heard of – is important for the contraction of muscles. Magnesium is important for their relaxation. So cold hands indicates spasm of arteries, which don't relax properly."

"That's most interesting," interrupted Roger. "My hands did feel warm for the rest of the day. I mentioned that to you didn't I, Maria? What else?

"Constipation means your bowels don't relax properly. Backache says your back muscles can't relax properly. It's all very simple if you know anything about nutritional medicine."

"So why am I deficient in magnesium? What's the cause?"

"There are basically two simple explanations, although there may be others. The first is diet, not enough green leafy vegetables and too much calcium from dairy products, the two together. The second is stress. Stress strips magnesium from your body, as well as other nutrients such as B vitamins. I would imagine your business is very stressful."

"You can say that again."

"Unfortunately the more stress you suffer from, the more you squander magnesium, which in turn means you handle the stress less well. It's a classical vicious circle."

"And I'm right in the middle of it. How do I reverse things?"

"I would recommend you temporarily stop all dairy products, especially cheese with its very high calcium content, and eat more green leafy vegetables. That should solve the dietary side of things. Then we need to supplement you with magnesium. Unfortunately, I am of the opinion that magnesium absorption from one's diet is under the influence of an enzyme that is magnesium sensitive, which effectively means that, if you are magnesium deficient, you can't absorb magnesium from your diet properly, but you can if your magnesium levels are improved by other means.

"The best way of improving your magnesium levels is to give you a few more doses intravenously. We could give it intramuscularly, but they can be quite painful, although not if I add some local anaesthetic to the mixture. After that, you can try supplements by mouth, but a lotion to rub onto soft skin is far more effective."

"When should I have the next injection, then," Roger asked.

"Let's see how long this one lasts and give you another when the backache starts to come back. That OK by you? One last thing. I need to teach you relaxation exercises, ones you can do as soon as a stressful event occurs. Unless you need to respond immediately, sitting back and taking time to relax can be worthwhile considering."

Roger had his next magnesium injection three days later, and five days after that, after which the magnesium lotion♥ Dr. James gave him seemed to hold things well enough. He asked for an injection every so often if he had been through a particularly stressful time.

That Christmas, Roger gave his wife Maria an enormous Christmas card, with a five pound note in it and the words, "Your winnings, My Love. Happy Christmas. Thank you so very much." It was a crisp new note. Maria had it framed and put on their mantelpiece.

♥ To obtain a supply of transdermal magnesium lotion, see the Appendix 2, note 8.

Chapter 34

"You said Dr. James saw some medical colleagues or their wives. Were there any interesting stories about any of them that you can tell us?" Patrick asked Maud.

"I think he saw a few, but I don't remember much about them. Because they were about fellow doctors or their wives or families, he probably kept most of the stories to himself, so as not to embarrass them. I told you the amazing story about Judy and her second baby that virtually died in the womb, as had happened with her first baby. Her husband Gregory was a GP whose practice was not far away. He was one of the few that were so delighted with the result that they were both happy for Dr. James to talk about them at one of his church meetings.

"There was one other I can remember. In a way it was quite similar to Judy and Gregory's story."

Dr. Evan Jones and his doctor wife Blodwen practised about ten miles from Stead Norton. They were both very Welsh. They had lovely musical singsong types of voices. They were both very popular and happy where they were. They had been married for about ten years but Blodwen never became pregnant. Everyone thought it was such a shame, but then Blodwen was a good doctor and loved her work, so people thought that maybe they did not want a family of their own. Then one day it became all too obvious that Blodwen was pregnant, and everyone was pleased for them both. Theirs seemed to be one of those happy areas when most of the young women seemed to be pregnant every so often.

Blodwen gave birth to an apparently healthy baby in the local hospital. Everything went well and the happy couple brought their baby boy home. Blodwen had stopped working at the practice about a month before she was due to deliver, with the intention of going back to work as soon as reasonable. With their combined salaries, they were able to afford a nanny.

Within days it was obvious that all was not well. Their baby started to cry and then seemed to cry all the time. It would partially stop if it was picked up, but it would still cry but not so loudly. As soon as it was put down it would start all over again. It seemed to be inconsolable. It cried all through the night. No one could pacify it. Neither Evan nor Blodwen got a wink of sleep, so they agreed to take turns and stay up with the baby on alternate nights. There was no way they could last like that, so arranged for the baby to be taken into hospital for some tests.

The senior Paediatrician took charge of the baby. They considered every possible angle, but, despite everything they did, they couldn't find anything wrong, yet the baby continued to cry all the time. It was a very disturbing influence on the other babies in the ward, and seemed to set them all off and make them all cry. The place was bedlam. The Specialist said he could find nothing wrong with the baby so discharged him home, saying he was just one of those babies that cried a lot and he should grow out of it eventually, but he had no idea how long it would take.

So Blodwen and Evan took their baby home and arranged for a nurse to sit up with the baby all night in another part of the house so they could get a decent night's sleep. But that didn't work for long. Besides, they could hear the baby crying, so didn't get much sleep themselves. The longest any nurse stayed was about a week. They couldn't find anyone who was willing to stick with a howling baby for any longer.

Blodwen and Evan were at their wits end, and they were afraid their baby was dying. He wasn't putting on weight, as he should have done, so they arranged for the baby to be admitted into hospital again, if for no reason but to give them a few nights' rest. Once again tests were done but they couldn't find anything wrong with the baby.

Blodwen and Evan went back to hospital to take their baby home. They were walking disconsolately towards the baby unit when they bumped into their friend Dr. Gregory who was visiting one of his patient's new babies.

"My God!" Exclaimed Gregory. "You two look awful. You look as though you have both been on duty all night for a week. Surely it can't be as hectic as that in your practice?"

"It's not our practice," said Evan. "It's our baby. We have admitted him twice for investigations, but they can't find anything wrong with him. He just won't stop crying – all day and all night. He is driving us all mad. I can understand why some desperate mums murder their baby if they have to go through what we are going through."

"Come on. Let's go and see him," said Dr. Gregory. And so they entered the baby unit. As soon as they opened the door, Blodwen said, "The poor mite. That's him. I can tell his cry anywhere. It's so loud. Whenever he's here he sets off all the other babies. It's as though they are crying in sympathy. They have asked us once again to take him home, as they still cannot find anything wrong with him. But there must be some explanation. It's not natural for a baby to cry so much and never stop."

"I agree," said Dr. Gregory, after they had all taken a look at the miserable baby. "I have an idea. Hang on a second. I won't be long." And with that he walked out of the baby unit.

A few minutes later he came back in and said, "Ok! Gather up your baby and all his things and come with me. We are going to see someone. I'll lead. Follow me in your car." And with that they drove to Dr. James' surgery, where he had just finished his morning surgery and was waiting for them.

"Do you know Dr. David James?" Dr. Gregory said to Evan and Blodwen.

"Only vaguely," said Evan. "I think we have talked at some of the Post-Graduate Meetings. How nice of you to see us. Gregory didn't tell us where we were going when we left the hospital just now, or why he has brought us here, so I'm a bit confused."

"Don't be." said Gregory. "All I ask is that you keep a totally open mind and tell David everything you can and let him ask you some questions. I warn you. This may take an hour or more. I've let my surgery know where I am. Do you need to do the same?"

"No! We're ok for now."

So Evan and Blodwen told Dr. James the simple facts that their baby just wouldn't stop crying, also that it was not putting on weight and in fact was still losing. They admitted they were afraid they were going to lose the baby. They told him of all the tests that had been done in hospital, but nothing had appeared wrong.

"They have checked everything possible," said Blodwen. "There is no abnormality. The baby is as normal as any other baby, in their opinion. They simply say he is one of those babies that keep crying, but that he will eventually grow out of it. But why is he still losing weight? We are feeding him regularly according to all the books."

All the time the baby was crying, with Dr. James watching closely, so they had to speak loudly to be heard. "Would you undress him for me, please. Let's look at him properly." Dr. James took his time and carefully examined the baby. "How can anyone say there is nothing wrong? Of course he's not right. He's crying when he shouldn't be. What do you notice? Can you see what I can see?"

"He's cried so much, I suppose we are not looking that closely any more," said Blodwen. "We just want him to stop crying, but he won't."

"How can he?" Said Dr. James. "He's in pain. Look at his tummy. He's bringing his legs up. It's his tummy that's hurting. When he cries his tummy becomes all hard. His cry is a cry of pain. The poor little mite is really hurting. That's not the cry of a baby that simply wants to be cuddled or fed."

"But in the hospital they said they couldn't find anything wrong with him anywhere. Everything is totally normal, they said."

"Structurally, perhaps, but not functionally. It's obvious something is not right. I may need to ask you some questions about your pregnancy of him in due course, but first we must help him out of his misery, poor little thing. What do you feed him on?"

Blodwen showed Dr. James the baby milk they had with them. "This is what they have recommended in the hospital. They say it is the best formula around. All their babies have it."

"Have you given him anything else such as orange juice? Did you breast feed him at all?"

"No we haven't given him anything else. I tried to breast feed him for about a week, but it was hopeless. I had so little milk. I'm afraid I gave up rather too easily. I'm a bit embarrassed about admitting it."

"When did he start to cry?"

"It must have been shortly after he was born. He was fine to begin with. We were so happy when we took him home."

"Could he have started to cry after about a week?" Asked Dr. James.

"Something like that," said Blodwen. "I'm not sure what you are getting at?"

"Is there possibly a coincidence that he started to cry when you stopped trying to breast feed him and gave him formula milk instead?"

"I think it was a few days later."

"Perfect timing!" Said Dr. James.

"I'm as sure as I can be that the formula milk doesn't agree with him. Just look at his tummy. It's all tight. That's where he is hurting. So it is logical to me that something you are putting into his intestines is causing the pain. As that formula is the only food you have given him, I'm sure that is the cause. But let's see if we can prove the point and get him out of his misery."

Dr. James made up some formula milk, asking Blodwen to check how much powder to how much water she would normally use. He then made a dilution of that powdered milk, adding four teaspoonsful of fresh water to one teaspoonful of milk. Opening the baby's mouth he put one drop carefully under its tongue, using a pipette he had fetched from a cupboard. He then made a second dilution from the first dilution he had already made, putting a drop of it under the baby's tongue using a fresh pipette about ten minutes later. Within two minutes the baby seemed to be crying less forcefully than before.

Dr. James made a third dilution from the second dilution he had made earlier, and put one drop carefully under the baby's tongue about ten minutes after he had dropped the second dilution there. The effect was dramatic. Within a few minutes the baby stopped crying for the first time in ages, or so it seemed to Blodwen and Evan. He stopped pulling his knees up towards his chest, and he visibly relaxed. His face became calm and he looked normal.

Blodwen picked him up and smiled at him. Despite his being only a few weeks old, she was sure he smiled back at her. Perhaps the pleasure of being out of pain and simply changing his face to one of normality instead of being in agony was sufficient to give the impression he was smiling.

"That is truly a miracle," said Blodwen. "Look at him. He's so beautiful. The poor mite. What have we done to you? I'm so sorry for all the pain we have caused you." And with that she wrapped him up in a blanket to keep him warm and folded him in her arms. Gently rocking him, within minutes he was sound asleep, clearly totally exhausted from all his sleeplessness, which had gone on for so long for such a tiny baby.

"As I said," said Dr. James, "I accepted that there was nothing structurally wrong with him, so there had to be something not functioning properly. I've seen this so many times, but his is the worst case I have ever come across. Many babies react badly to the formula milk they are fed with, either crying or vomiting or a bit of both. However, they tend to do it sporadically, not all the time like your baby did, so the connection is not made. The dilution treatment I have just given him totally proves to me that the formula milk was causing him all that pain. What we have to do now is find a milk that suits him. Let's hope that won't be too difficult. He is in great need of food that suits him. He is clearly underweight and undernourished."

Blodwen and Evan's baby settled down well enough and they soon found a formula milk that suited him. He started to gain weight and the Health Visitor remarked on how quickly he caught up to where he should have been. Blodwen, in the meantime, decided not to go back to work as early as she had planned. “I know I should have persevered with breast feeding him. Breast milk is the right food for babies. I owe it to him to look after him myself. He has become the most precious thing in my life. I really thought we were going to lose him. He was clearly dying before my eyes.”

“The way Dr. James helped many people seemed to be so remarkable that it changed the lives of many of them,” said Maud to Patrick and Lynda. “But to Dr. James the explanations were nearly always simple and straightforward. He said it was sometimes just a matter of looking at the obvious or occasionally looking for the unusual. For Evan and Blodwen the experience was life changing. Blodwen was so upset by the whole event, especially her own guilt at not having persevered with breast-feeding, that she decided not to go back into General Practice for the time being. She studied the whole subject in great detail, including the impact of formula feeding on babies in general. She went on as many special courses as she could find. She became an expert on the subject and offered help to anyone in the area, especially those who were undecided about whether to breast-feed or not. Her own experience and enthusiasm helped many women to become enthusiastic breast-feeders themselves.

“A couple of years later, Dr. James was invited to give a talk to the local group of General Practitioners. He was introduced by Dr. Jones as ‘The Doctor who saved my baby’s life’.

‘And mine!’ Added Dr. Gregory.

“Every time I think of that baby, it brings tears to my eyes,” said Maud. “It makes me wonder how many babies there are all over the world who have the same problem that no one seems able to solve.”

“It just goes to show how important breast-feeding is,” said Lynda. “That wouldn’t have happened if Blodwen had breast-fed the mite.”

“Actually, it might have,” said Maud. “Dr. James told us about Evan and Blodwen’s baby, with their permission of course. In any case, they were sitting in the front row of the church as the evening's special guests. He completed the evening by telling us another story."

Maria Anthony and her husband Simon gave birth to a baby girl, Jessica, in the local hospital. Maria had read all the books she could get her hands on while she was pregnant, about pregnancy in general and about breast-feeding. She was adamant that she would feed her baby herself, as everything she read told her that that was the best way to start her baby's life.

Unfortunately Maria found that, not only did she have difficulty producing breast milk, but also that her baby didn't seem to do very well on it, or put on the weight she was supposed to do. Jessica didn't seem to find her mother's milk suited her, and, although it was obvious she was hungry and would start sucking willingly, she would suddenly stop and start to cry, and, how ever much Maria persevered, her baby wouldn't continue feeding.

So Maria expressed her milk and kept it to give to her baby later on, but the same thing happened, the baby would show enthusiasm to feed, only to stop and cry soon after she had started. Maria couldn't understand what was wrong. There was nothing in all the books she had read to explain what was happening. It just didn't make sense. Her baby was not doing well and not putting on weight, although she was only a few days old, and she seemed to wail too much, not a full-blown cry, just a sort of moan that said something was not right. The midwife did her best, but agreed that something was wrong. She suggested Maria take Jessica to see Dr. James.

Dr. James listened carefully to everything Maria said. "Have you given your baby anything apart from your breast milk, such as orange juice or anything like that or any vitamin drops?"

"No. I've only tried to give her my breast milk and of course some boiled water occasionally. She takes that well enough. She is clearly not happy, as she keeps on moaning, sort of crying but not quite, like she is now."

"So would I be right in saying that your milk somehow doesn't suit your baby, because it would appear she wants to feed from you, yet as soon as she starts she says something like 'hey I'm hungry, but I don't like this stuff. Yuck!'"

"I doubt if she can think yet, but yes that's about right. But I thought mother's milk is the perfect food for babies, so why won't my baby take mine?"

"I can only assume there is something wrong with your milk, something in your diet that is coming through that is making her reject it. Did you also say that you are having difficulty producing milk in the first instance?"

"Well it's not flowing as well as all the books say it should. I have occasionally tried to express it and I'm surprised how little I can produce."

"I think that confirms in my mind that you need to change your diet. The question is, what might you be eating now that is not only inhibiting your milk production but is also making your baby reject it? It can be quite tricky to work that out. In the meantime lets try an experiment and see if it will help your baby stop crying, and possibly prove my point."

Dr. James asked Maria if she could express some milk, which she did with a little difficulty. Dr. James made a note of it. He then made dilutions of that milk as he had done with the formula milk for Blodwen's baby, putting a drop of each dilution under the baby's tongue every ten minutes or so. The effect was interesting as the baby stopped moaning when the third dilution was given to her.

"As far as I am concerned, that proves that something in your milk doesn't suit your baby, but you don't look convinced."

"Hm! Ok she has settled down, but I can't see how that proves your point. It could be a coincidence."

"I agree, so shall we try something else? It might make your baby cry, but it won't do any harm." And with that Dr. James put a drop of her neat breast milk under the baby's tongue. The baby grimaced then started to cry in a few minutes. Maria picked her up and tried to comfort her but she wouldn't stop.

"This is what she can be like at times. She eventually settles but this is likely to go on for at least half-an-hour."

Dr. James put a drop of the same dilution that seemed to settle the baby before, and she stopped crying within a minute.

"The way I see things, the right dilution helped her to stop to begin with, your neat milk made her cry as she has cried before, then the same original dilution soothed her so she stopped crying. It's not proof, but it satisfies me that we have demonstrated that your milk doesn't agree with her. Do you feel a bit more convinced now?"

"Well. What you did certainly seemed to make a difference to her. Perhaps you're right. It's just that I have read so many books on breast-feeding and not once have I come across anything like this. I would have thought at least one of the authors would have known about this."

"I agree, but you might find it interesting to talk to Dr. Blodwen Jones. She had a similar experience, so I'll give you her telephone number. She is fascinated by all stories about breast-feeding, and is keen to learn from women's experiences. But in the meantime we need to sort out your diet so that you not only start to produce more milk more easily, but also produce milk that your baby enjoys. Are you willing to change your diet?"

"Could I speak to Dr. Jones first, please?"

"Let's see if she's at home," said Dr. James, picking up the telephone and ringing a number. As luck would have it, she was in.

"Good morning, Blodwen. David James here. I have a young lady here with me, Maria Anthony, who would like a word with you about her breast-feeding. Have you the time for a quick chat or would you like her to come over?

"Dr. Jones said she would be delighted to see you straight away if you are free to go over now. I'll give you her address. She's not far away. Do you have a car? You do? Good. I'll wait here for a couple of hours, so that you can come back for us to work out what diet for you to follow, if you decide to do that. I have plenty of things to do in the meantime."

About an hour later a totally changed Maria came back into Dr. James' surgery.

"Dr. Jones is an amazing woman. She is so enthusiastic about breast-feeding. I told her what had happened with my baby and what you had done with those dilutions, and then she told me what you had done for her baby. She was absolutely astonished by what I told her, and, like me, she said she had never heard of such a thing, nor was it in any books or described by any of the so-called breast-feeding experts. She was really excited by my experiences. She said she is on a national breast-feeding council and was looking forward to telling all her colleagues about it. She said she is due to give a lecture in a month's time, and would love to include something about your ideas. So she asked me to come back immediately and ask you what to change in my diet. She suggested I also put avoided foods back in to see if it upsets my baby or not. She said you would know what she meant. Do you?"

"Yes I do, but I will need to explain it to you so you understand what might happen. Anyway, shall we start?"

Dr. James then took as detailed a dietary history as was possible.

"Your diet is really quite good, except for your penchant for cola drinks. Otherwise I can't fault it in terms that most dieticians would recommend. However, I have a different attitude and don't agree with everything that others consider to be correct. I gather you have increased your milk intake since your baby was born, on the understandable reasoning that milk is good for you. As it happens, many other doctors and I think cow's milk is only for calves and not for humans. I also accept that many other doctors don't agree with me. Anyway, I will give you an article I wrote about it so you can decide for yourself.

"In the meantime, I would like you to start by giving up all dairy products and all forms of caffeine, so coffee and tea and decaffeinated varieties, cola drinks and chocolate immediately. I can't identify anything else at this stage that I would like you to avoid, but there is always the possibility that there is something else. We'll just have to see how things go."

"How long will it take for this to work if your advice is correct?" asked Maria.

"Very quickly if you stop now," replied Dr. James.

"Actually I was in such a hurry this morning and so keen to come to see you that I didn't have any breakfast this morning at all. So in effect I haven't eaten since supper last night. Funnily enough I thought things were a bit better this morning. When you asked me to express some of my milk, I was able to get more out than I was expecting. I even thought she took to the breast a bit more willingly than usual, so may be you are right. Actually I won't miss milk. I only increased it because my mother told me to, and, if I am being honest, I think it has made me more mucousy. I keep clearing my throat, something I don't usually do. I've heard milk can do that to people, so I wonder what else it might do?"

"That was all Maria needed to do," said Maud. "She was thrilled that her baby took to her breast with gusto. As with Jayne Worthing, she so enjoyed the experience that she became a breast-feeding enthusiast. Apparently she was willing to demonstrate that having a coffee upset her baby. First she expressed some milk to be given to her baby later on, and then she had a coffee, while her husband filmed how the baby didn't like her breast milk at all, but accepted the expressed milk. She did this three times, as well as giving the baby milk she had expressed after having a coffee. Jessica didn't like it at all, but guzzled down expressed milk that didn't have any coffee in it at all. Having filmed it each time really convinced Blodwen's audience. Cow's milk didn't do the same, but Maria herself felt a lot better for giving up dairy products. More to the point her baby started to grow normally."

Chapter 35

"I would have thought Dr. James's reputation would have spread far and wide," said Patrick. "Didn't people try to consult him from outside his practice area?"

"Dr. James said he loved the system of the National Health Service, where people didn't have to pay for treatment. He couldn't understand how they managed in America, where medical care is so expensive, and not available to everyone. His only complaint was that the NHS didn't seem to want to practise the way he did.

"He was also absolutely appalled at the horrendous waste. He had a friend who ran a small Pharmacy in the next town, who told him that, if someone reacted to a drug they had been given a prescription for, or if they decided not to take the drug after all and gave it back to the Pharmacist, all those drugs had to be returned to a central place where they were destroyed. Apparently his one county alone destroyed hundreds of thousands of pounds worth of drugs every month. He couldn't imagine the cost and the waste across the whole country in one year.

"Dr. James did once receive a phone call from a woman in Israel, whose daughter had multiple sclerosis. She begged him to see her, so he did, and the young lady flew over with her mother and father. They were fortunately fairly wealthy".

Heather Herzog had had MS for about five years. She was thirty years old when she consulted Dr. James. She walked slowly and awkwardly with two sticks, dragging her left foot along the ground, as she couldn't lift it properly. Her right leg wasn't much better. She had rejected using a Zimmer frame, or worse still taking to a wheel chair. She had been only very slowly deteriorating over the past two years, and thought she might soon stop getting any worse. She hoped Dr. James might be able to help reverse her condition. He asked her how she had heard of him but she was rather evasive, so he didn't push it.

Heather's father had hired a large comfortable car and fortunately was able to drive right up to the surgery entrance, where he dropped Heather off. She was a very stubborn, independent young lady and wouldn't be hurried, but it took her rather a long time to reach his consulting room. Dr. James came out to meet them and carefully watched her way of walking. Eventually she sat down in front of him.

As with all such complicated patients he went through her history very carefully. He had sent her a questionnaire to think about and complete before she came. He said he wanted to know all about her. He didn't want to miss anything of importance, as it would not be easy to ask her questions once she had returned to Israel.

When he examined her, he did not find her jaw out of line as he hoped he might, although he recognised she had almost as much difficulty with her right leg as her left. What he did find, however, was that she suffered considerably from pins and needles down both legs and partially in her arms, had been under a lot of stress and clearly was nutritionally deficient because of poor eating habits.

When asked why she ate so badly, she simply said she hadn't realised how important it might be, but said she would improve from now on. Her parents were shocked at what Dr. James identified, but, as she had her own flat, they weren't aware how badly she ate.

"I noticed how white your skin is," said Dr. James, some time after he had examined her. I thought Israel is a sunny country."

"Where I live, it is for much of the year," said Heather, "but I keep out of it as much as possible. I don't want to get skin cancer. I saw a TV programme about it. It frightened me. In any case my eyes are very sensitive in the sun. I have to wear very strong dark glasses."

"How long ago did you stop going in the sun?" Asked Dr. James.

"Oh! I think it must have been six or seven years ago. Why do you ask?"

"And your MS started about five years ago?"

"Yes, about then, although I can't be absolutely sure," said Heather.

"When did you move into your own flat?" Asked Dr. James.

"I bought it for her as a twenty-third birthday present, when she finished at University. She went there two years late as she couldn't make up her mind what to study," said her father, "So almost exactly seven years ago. What are you getting at?" He asked.

"If you have an accident, acute appendicitis or a heart attack, or something like that, it is obvious what the matter is with you and doctors can treat it. If you eat a poor diet, are exposed to a toxic chemical, or are under stress for a long time, or something of the sort, symptoms don't usually develop suddenly. They tend to develop slowly so you don't connect the possible cause with the symptoms. There's too long a gap. It took many decades before we realised that smoking caused lung cancer among other things.

"Heather moved into her flat to be on her own seven years ago. Her atrocious diet probably began then. She also saw the TV programme about skin cancer some time around then so stopped going in the sun. Her eyes became more sensitive to the sun as time went on, but she can't remember when that became a problem. Her optician might be able to clarify that point.

"The point I am trying to get at is that Heather's nutritional deficiencies possibly began about seven years ago when she moved into her flat to be on her own. Such nutritional inadequacies would take months or years to cause an obvious effect, although why it might cause MS is difficult to say. And exactly which nutritional deficiencies actually occur are also hard to predict. As she became a vegan, and a very poor one at that, a vitamin B12 deficiency was very likely, hence her pins and needles. Then she kept out of the sun, so a vitamin D deficiency was very likely. There is a PhD researcher in Canada who believes MS will one day be redefined as a vitamin D deficiency disease.

"Ok. Stay out of the sun if you want to, but please take vitamin D3, possibly 10,000 International Units to begin with, eventually reducing to half that dose. Most people are not aware of the importance of vitamin D to magnesium metabolism, assuming it is only important for calcium absorption.

"To cap it all you were under a lot of stress for about two years until two years ago, because of your infuriating boy friend, who wouldn't leave when it was obvious the relationship had come to an end. Stress causes a magnesium deficiency among other nutrients, so that plus your probable vitamin D lack and all the other things I have mentioned, it is not surprising something went wrong. Why you developed MS rather then asthma, arthritis or something else is something I can't answer. To me it doesn't matter. If we can find the causes of any condition and deal with them, the person should get better. That's why I am happy to see a patient with any condition. I feel my job is to keep asking the question 'why?' Incidentally, eye sensitivity to bright light is an indication of a magnesium deficiency."
"It's like a detective story. You have put all the pieces of the jigsaw together. How fascinating," said her father."

"Yes. I have considered myself a medical detective for a long time now," said Dr. James.

"One hears so much these days about genes and genetic influences. Could they be involved?" Heather's mother asked. "We haven't been able to find anyone in the family who has MS."

"Yes you are right. It seems to be very much the scientific area of interest to so many researchers at present, and genetic modification is what a lot of teams are working on. But it worries me. I am concerned about all the problems they may cause in their attempts to change our genetic code, but there is nothing I can do to stop them trying. No doubt we will be hearing of the latest miracle of genetic engineering in the press soon. The trouble is they only pick out what they think will sell their papers and don't seem interested in what the real story is. Also they seldom follow up such stories, so you never hear what happened in the end or how successful the whole thing was.

"I have a very simple approach to genetics. Our genetic code makes us what we our, the colour of our hair, whether we are tall or short, whether we like opera or not. You know, the every day things of life. I also believe our genetic code decides whether we will develop

MS, migraines, asthma, cancer or any kind of medical condition. You could say it is a form of 'predisposition'. It is our risk factor.

"As far as I am concerned, our genes don't cause our conditions, but they do make them likely to occur. Let me explain that a bit better. I saw a man many years ago who suffered from migraines. His mother, brother and an uncle had all suffered from migraines, so he clearly had a genetic predisposition to migraines. It clearly ran in his family. I started off by recommending he stop eating cheese and chocolate and drinking red wine, the most common causes of migraines. His headaches stopped and he stayed off those three items for about four months in the first instance.

"I then suggested that he consider trying a small amount of each of them to see if they were all causes of his migraines, but to do so when a headache wouldn't be too much of a nuisance to him if one occurred. I also told him that, if he did develop a very severe migraine, I would be willing to visit him at home and give him an injection of something to help him over the worst of the reaction. As a result he found that cheese and red wine were apparently ok, but the chocolate trial gave him the worst migraine he had ever had. He was literally crawling up the wall with pain and had vomited several times by the time his wife rang me. I went out and gave him an injection of a combination of a strong painkiller and an anti-sickness drug. He fell asleep in about ten minutes.

"That man has stayed off chocolate ever since and has not had another migraine. He has decided to stay off chocolate for the rest of his life, something some people simply cannot imagine. Such people have never suffered the way he did when he did the chocolate challenge after not having any for a few months.

"The point I am trying to make with that story is that he clearly has a genetic predisposition to migraines, but is symptom-free if he stays off chocolate. By doing so, he switches off his genetic make-up. When he ate chocolate he switched his genes back on again. Were he to have some chocolate even now he would probably soon demonstrate he still has his genetic predisposition."

"Are you suggesting," interrupted Heather, "that perhaps we can liken his migraines to my MS, and that all we have to do is find out what my equivalent to his chocolate is?"

"Absolutely! Spot on! You've got it in one," said Dr. James. "The only problem is that it is not easy or straightforward identifying the causes, especially as there is likely to be more than one cause. That's why a very detailed history is so important and also keeping an open mind for all sorts of possibilities. In the end, it is my job to come up with ideas, but you are the one who has to be prepared to try them out. It is only then that we discover whether I was right or not."

"That's so simple, so logical. It makes so much sense. Now I see why you needed to go through my history in such detail. You were looking for my chocolate," said Heather. "Why can't other doctors work like you do?"

Dr. James gave her a lot of advice about her diet asking her not to eat certain foods and to try to consume more of others. However he felt that there was no point in changing her diet until she was back home and in control, although if she could begin eating better while in England, it would start her healing process. Her parents said they would look after her.

Having written down his advice, Dr. James then gave her an intravenous infusion of vitamins and minerals, including large doses of vitamin B12 for her pins and needles and quite a lot of magnesium for the stiffness in her legs and to help the stress she had been under. Heather and her parents then drove round the country, sightseeing as much as time would allow. He asked them if they could find a doctor in Israel who might be willing to repeat the infusion, as she would probably benefit from more.

Four days later, an excited Heather rang Dr. James from Israel to say that she had walked almost normally from the plane to their waiting car. She had felt things were starting to improve as she got to London Airport, but, as a special mobile cart had been arranged for her, she decided to use it and didn't have time to think about it.

"How are your pins and needles?" Asked Dr. James.

"Oh my golly!" She cried. "They have completely gone. That's amazing! I've not thought about them at all."

"The nutrients I gave you in the infusion seem to have corrected the deficiencies your poor diet may have caused, the large dose of vitamin B12 helping to clear the pins and needles, and the magnesium and the other B vitamins probably helping the rest of your problems. But don't become complacent. It will take some time before all your symptoms clear totally. You are lucky you have never had any mercury amalgam fillings in your teeth. They can be quite a problem. You may well be starting to benefit from the vitamin D capsules I gave you and your improved diet. It's up to you, but consider whether you are prepared to go into the sun at all. I know most people say don't be in the sun around midday, but there is a theory that five minutes, and I mean only five minutes, in the sun at midday is very beneficial. There is no chance of your burning, especially if you do only one minute the first few days and gradually work up to five minutes. As I said to you when you were here, you have very pale skin, so take it gently. Don't put any sunscreen on at all, but whether you do this or not, I leave entirely up to you."

Heather kept in touch with Dr. James over the next three months, telling him that things had continued to improve overall and that she had felt so much more healthy, even without another infusion of nutrients. But then she started to develop pins and needles in one of her legs and both legs became a bit stiff.

"You probably need another nutrient infusion," said Dr. James. "Have you been able to find anyone in Israel to do them for you?"

"To be fair we haven't looked for anyone yet. We were so impressed at my becoming so much better with the infusion, we wondered how long it would last, so three months is not bad. My mum said she would bring me back to England. When can you fit me in again?"

"Wednesdays are my easiest days to give you an infusion, so I will leave it up to you to make the arrangements. Today is Wednesday, so next week or the week after if you like. Incidentally, it might be sensible to give you two infusions separated by a few days if you can manage it. The ideal space is probably seven days, but if you can't stay that long it doesn't matter. I will fit you in over the weekend if necessary. I can always do some paper work. There's so much to do anyway."

"My dad has discovered we have a cousin in London, who has said he will put us up any time. They were thrilled to find they had a relation his side of the family. He apparently knew about us, but didn't know where we were or how to contact us. So a week will be no problem. We already have seats reserved for two weeks time on Tuesday, as mum cannot come over next week. So we can confirm them and arrange our return flights. With the new-found freedom your infusion will give me I will be able to get around so much more easily and do more sight-seeing. The UK is such a beautiful place and there is so much to see."

Heather came over with her mother as arranged and had the two infusions, one week apart. The first one of the two had the same remarkable effect, the second one making her virtually symptom free. Their London cousin was astonished. He saw it for himself. When he heard about Heather and her MS, he searched the net and only found demoralising information. There was no cure, it all said, and just about everyone gradually got worse and ended up in a wheelchair, although some seemed to stop deteriorating at a certain level.

He had a friend who was a Consultant Neurologist who came round for supper one evening. He told him what he had seen, but he couldn't believe it when the doctor effectively dismissed it all, first saying he didn't believe it and, in any case, where were the double blind clinical studies, then said, 'Well! It won't last.'

The effect of those two infusions lasted six months, and the next two lasted seven months. In the meantime, because Heather was eating a far better diet and taking the supplements Dr. James had recommended, her whole health improved even more and she felt really well. She had continued to eat a far better diet, and had attended classes in Israel for people who wished to be vegan. She hadn't fully realised just how important it can be to know what you are doing if you wish to restrict your diet in such a way. It was for that reason that Dr. James strongly recommended some capsules of desiccated fruits, vegetables and berries♥.

Seven months after the third set of infusions, Heather rang Dr. James in a bit of a state. "What's the matter?" Asked Dr. James. "I can hear in your voice that something is not right."

"It all seems to have gone wrong," said Heather. "I am so bad. It all began about a week ago. I can hardly move my legs, although the pins and needles have not come back."

Heather told Dr. James everything she could, but he wasn't able to put his finger on what the problem was. "An infusion or two should help you, but there is something you have not told me and some question I have not asked you."

"My mum and I have booked our flights, so we'll see you next Wednesday. I hope you can fit me in?"

"No problem," said Dr. James. "See you then. In the meantime, keeping thinking of an explanation."

Heather duly came and she and Dr. James had a long discussion about what could have caused her to deteriorate. They were not able to put their fingers on anything, so Heather had her first infusion of that visit. Although it did help a bit, it didn't have the hoped-for effect. She was really disappointed. Before she left, Dr. James decided to examine her, not expecting to find anything to explain why she had deteriorated. "You have a sore-looking area on your tummy. It's quite inflamed. Have you been scratching yourself or something? What this all about?" Asked Dr. James.

"That's where I inject myself three times a week. Perhaps I ought to stick the needle in somewhere else," replied Heather.

"What are you injecting yourself with?" Asked Dr. James.

"Some drug my Professor put me on. I've got a container in my bag. Can you get it out, please, Mum?"

♥ See Appendix 2, note 2 for further information.

"Why are you on it?" Asked Dr. James. "What reason were you given to go on it?"

"My Professor said it would help reduce the frequency of my attacks."

"But you weren't having any attacks!" Said Dr. James.

"Well I did start to deteriorate and needed to come back for more infusions. Weren't those attacks? I told my Professor that I had improved a lot for the infusions, but needed to have them again every so often. He told me that was all nonsense, saying that vitamins and minerals could never do that, so he put me on this drug."

"I suppose you could say they were attacks of a sort, but I would say they were the result of your running out of the beneficial effect of the nutrient infusions. It's a matter of interpretation. Your Professor obviously doesn't believe in vitamins and minerals, yet you have seen the beneficial effect they had on you. I work on the assumption that, if you do something and something happens, it is likely that they are connected. Yes there is always the possibility that they are not connected, but start by assuming they are. As far as I am concerned, you had some infusions and you improved amazingly, and more than once. It looks as though you have deteriorated since starting this drug. Is there a timing coincidence? When did you start injecting yourself?"

"About three weeks ago. I didn't like the effect they had on me. They made me feel I was coming down with a cold, but it would clear before the next injection was due. Each one seemed to make me feel more ill."

"Well, it's up to you," said Dr. James. "If I were you I would stop injecting and see what happens. If that doesn't help you can always go back onto them. Only time will tell. Have you booked to stay for a week?"

"Actually we have open tickets. We felt sure you would be able to help me but we weren't sure how long it would take."

"When did you last give yourself an injection?" Asked Dr. James.

"Actually I am due one today but I forgot to do it in the rush to get here today. Having been so much better I have not needed to plan ahead so much, but since I have deteriorated, everything takes so much longer, especially going to the toilet."

"So are you willing to do without the next injection and see what happens?"

"You haven't been wrong so far, so yes, of course."

Heather improved very quickly. By the time she came for her second infusion, she was walking much better. The next one improved her even more.

"I can't believe that drug made me so much worse, but I am so much better for stopping it."

"I'm sure it has helped some people, but, in fact you are the second MS patient I have seen who was made worse by that drug. I saw another MS patient from outside my catchment area last year in June, who was fifty per cent better by October. She then told me she was not going to come back to see me until some time in the spring, and she told me why, so I wrote it all down in her notes. I accepted her reason, because that was what she wanted to do, and left it to her to contact me when she wanted to.

"Some time in the March she rang me and simply said she was going to have a steroid infusion. I didn't have her notes in front of me and could hardly remember her, but asked her why she needed the steroids. She told me she had deteriorated. When I asked her why she had deteriorated she said that her Specialist had said that was what sometimes happens and there doesn't need to be a reason. He said that's what MS does to some people. I'm not really sure why she bothered to ring me, but she did. I offered to see her again and she said she would make an appointment soon.

"In the end she had three courses of steroids with reasonable benefit to begin with, but the last one virtually did nothing. Her Specialist said he couldn't give her any more and to wait and see what happened. That's why she came back to see me. By then I had looked up her notes because I was intrigued with her."

"What happened when she came?" Asked Heather.

"Well she was clearly worse than when I had last seen her, though not quite as bad as when she first came to see me. I asked her to tell me what had happened since her last visit, and she told me she had had the three courses of steroids. I asked her 'Why did you need them?' To which she replied 'Because I deteriorated.' 'Why did you deteriorate?' When she said she didn't know, I asked her when she had started to deteriorate and she said some time possibly early in November. When I asked her what she did around then she said she couldn't remember doing anything special. When I said 'last October you told me you were not going to come back to see me until some time in the spring or summer because you were going to do something. Did you do it?' 'Did I do what?' 'Did you go onto that drug your Specialist had recommended to you?' 'Oh that! Yes of course I did, as he said it would help me.' 'Did it help you?' 'Well no, but it couldn't possibly be why I got worse' she said. 'Did the steroids help you?' 'To begin with yes.'

"'Let me get this straight,' I then said to her. 'You improved when you had a course of steroids, so you accept that the steroids were responsible for that improvement, yet when you became worse after you started on that drug you don't accept that it may have been the cause. You can't accept one and reject the other. That just doesn't make sense. If you do something and something happens, you should surely assume there might be a direct connection.'

"I had a really hard time convincing her that there might be a connection. Somehow she had accepted everything her Specialist had said to her, without thinking for herself. I wrote a letter to her General Practitioner about my thoughts and he apparently saw the logic of my argument and encouraged her to stop the drug, saying that she could always restart it if it turned out I was wrong, which I had already also suggested."

"Did she stop the drug? Was it the same as mine?" Asked Heather.

"Yes she did," said Dr. James, "and yes it was the same drug. It only took her about two weeks to notice the difference. Her Specialist said she had been put into a trial of some sort of the drug to see what its long-term effects in MS were. Her experience apparently opened his eyes to what might happen to some MS patients and he started to look to see if others were similarly affected. I understand he found one or two others with similar adverse effects, about half his total seeming to benefit, while the rest it did nothing for, neither good nor bad."

Chapter 36

"We've talked about so many of Dr. James' patients, but I haven't asked you two how you are. Are you both well?" Maud asked Patrick and Lynda.

"I think you could say we are both in the best of health," said Lynda. "Yes we do sometimes get a bit tired, but that's usually after we have been doing a lot and getting to bed rather late. I do like my eight hours sleep, and can feel a bit out of sorts the next day if I can't be in bed that long. I don't think there's anything unusual about that. Most of my friends say the same. Perhaps we should come back as dormice in the next life!"

"What about your PMT?" Suggested Patrick.

"What's PMT?" Asked Maud.

"Pre-menstrual tension. It's what a lot of women suffer from about a week before their period starts."

"Oh that!" Said Maud. "We never had any problems of that sort when we were young. It seems to be a new disease, if you can call it a disease. Perhaps we didn't have time for it. I was pregnant seven times and breast-fed all of the kids for well over a year, and then it was some time before our periods started again. In fact I remember getting pregnant after two of them before my monthlies started up again. Also you young ladies seem to start your periods so much younger nowadays than we did. I don't think mine started until I was sixteen. Some local girls are starting around ten. Certainly they seem to have the bodies of young women so much earlier than we did in our day. I remember Dr. James commenting on that at one of his talks.

"He told us our world is awash with hormones. So many young women taking the contraceptive pill and so many older women on hormone replacement therapy. He once asked me if he was imagining things. Did women in the past suffer from post-menopausal problems like they seem to nowadays, or is that a new situation, he wanted to know? Then there were all those hormones being injected into the animals we eat, as well as so many chemicals in our environment that have oestrogen-like effects.

"I told him we didn't talk openly about women's problems in those days, but we did talk to each other over the garden wall more than they do nowadays, so perhaps we did give each other a lot of useful therapy.

"Dr. James said he was sent away to school from the age of seven, poor mite, moving on to his senior school when he was thirteen. He told me that he had always sung quite well in church at home during the holidays, so it was natural for him to join the school choir, as a treble. I think that's the boys' version of a soprano. He and many other boys stayed as a treble for over two years, his voice eventually starting to break when he was about fifteen, so he couldn't sing treble. A year or so later he rejoined the choir as a bass.

"Many years later, he was invited as one of many former school choristers and musicians to attend a special celebration musical event for the retiring head of music. The school choir sang special songs. By then the sixth form at the school had taken in girls, many of who were now in the school choir as sopranos and altos. There was not a single boy as a treble or alto, but some young ones were now bases or tenors. He asked his former teacher where all the young boy trebles and altos were, only to be told that their voices had virtually all broken by the time they started at the school at the age of thirteen. Such hormonal changes had only taken about twenty or thirty years to occur. It shocked him.

"Dr. James was convinced that too much oestrogen in all its forms is somehow getting into everything we eat, drink and come across in so many ways. He was unhappy about it, but was aware there was little he could do about it. On the other hand he felt that our bodies could tolerate a lot of the harm we did to ourselves, but that, if we somehow overdid it, that was when we would start to break down, by which he meant that was when we started to produce symptoms or become ill. He thought PMT, or whatever you want to call it, was just one of those situations.

"He described what he called the Total Load Syndrome, a term that had first been coined by one of his American mentors, Dr. Theron Randolph, I think it was. Put quite simply he meant that, if we did too may wrong things in life, it would build up a problem within our bodies and gradually catch up with us, so that we would suffer in some way. For example we might not be able to sleep because we were worried or drank too much coffee. We might become deficient in certain essential nutrients because we ate a poor diet. We might smoke cigarettes. We might drink too much alcohol. We might eat certain foods that we weren't aware were possibly harmful to us. In fact, any one of the things his stories have pointed out to individual people. Then suddenly when our total load was just about full, but not quite, we might pick up a simple infection that would lay us low and make us far more ill than it should have done. From then on things would seem to go wrong more often or we would develop some sort of disease like asthma, Irritable Bowel Syndrome, arthritis or even cancer, depending on our genetic predisposition.

"Dr. James said that, in his experience, it was not uncommon for a typical infection such as glandular fever to have a far more extreme effect on young people who had abused their bodies as students by drinking far too much alcohol, eating poorly and staying up and partying far too late into the night. Occasionally it badly affected someone who had not done those things, but who had worn themselves out studying and worrying about exams, but who was also training extremely hard as an athlete, for example. He found that advising them about good eating habits and giving them injections of vitamins helped them get over their infection far more quickly, if he caught them in time. This particularly happened when young people were affected so badly and so quickly that they had to leave University and come home to recover at home with their parents. They would then come under his care.

"He said the University doctors were always amazed at how quickly young patients under his care had recovered and were back at their studies. Some of them even rang him, but he doesn't think any of them took any notice of what he did. He said he never did any formal studies on things like this, but felt sure a good observer was capable of noticing what happened to people if a doctor was willing to look and keep an open mind.

"Dr. James tried to explain something quite complicated," said Maud. "I'll try to get it right but my memory isn't what it used to be so I may get in a muddle.

"He tried to explain how our bodies are remarkably adaptable structures. He said this idea was first suggested some time in the middle of the twentieth century by someone called Professor Hans Selye. I remember his name because it reminded me of Peter Sellers. This doctor said we can insult our bodies time and time again, yet they nearly always forgive us. But their forgiveness is not for ever. If we abuse them severely, they show their disgust, by producing a symptom, but if we don't repeat that abuse too soon, our bodies have the ability to recover. However, if the abuse is not too strong, but is repeated regularly, our bodies are somehow able to adapt to the insult.

"Dr. Selye apparently described three stages. Stage one he called the stage of reaction, stage two the stage of adaptation, with stage three the stage of breakdown. I'm not sure those were his exact words, but something like them.

"Dr. James used smoking and drinking alcohol as his two examples. He said that when kids smoked their first cigarette behind the bicycle shed at school for the first time, it nearly always made them cough, sometimes violently, or even feel or be sick. It would make the experienced ones laugh. That was stage one. But, instead of being turned off smoking by how awful it made them feel, because they were under peer pressure, or trying to look cool or simply wanting to be in the good books of an older boy, they would persevere and try again and again.

"Eventually smoking a cigarette would no longer make them feel unwell, although it might take quite some time for them to be able to smoke without coughing. So long as smoking made them cough, they were in stage one. Once smoking no longer made them cough, they had reached stage two, the stage of adaptation, when their bodies had somehow learned to tolerate the insult. This stage of adaptation could last for many years, depending upon many things, such as how many cigarettes they smoked, and whether they abused their bodies in other ways, such as eating poorly or drinking a lot of alcohol.

"Dr. James was always interested in why anyone still smoked cigarettes in this day and age, with there being so much information about the harm it does. People often said to him they liked to smoke. They associated it with the end of a meal and drinking a cup of coffee, for example. Others said they didn't smoke much and knew of people who had smoked all their lives and had lived to be a hundred years old before they died, so surely that suggested that perhaps it didn't do all that harm if they didn't smoke too many.

"Then there were the people who said they could give up any time they wanted to. When challenged to do so they would make all sorts of excuses that they didn't particularly want to, so why bother?

"The people he really respected were those who said they would love to give up, but felt so awful whenever they tried. These were the people he helped to stop by giving them some simple explanation and telling them what to do. But I'll tell you about that another time," said Maud to Patrick and Lynda. "I want to finish off what I was saying. So where was I?"

"You were still in stage two," reminded Lynda.

"Oh yes! Thank you. I think I was getting towards the end of stage two, which could go on for many years, depending on a number of things. Perhaps the first sign that stage three had begun would be when the person found they could not start the day without having to smoke a cigarette. Fancy having to have to light up a cigarette while still in bed! That's surely telling you something. Many heavy smokers apparently say they need a cigarette to help them cough up all that phlegm in their lungs, not realising it is the smoking that has caused all that phlegm in the first place, or perhaps not being willing to admit it to themselves.

"Sometimes for no obvious reason, or possibly if someone became ill with 'flu or something similar, the body would effectively say 'I can't keep this up any longer. I've tried to manage for this long, and I've just about kept going, but this infection is the last straw. I've had it! I can't go on any longer!'

"The person would start to cough every time a cigarette was smoked. The cough would slowly get worse, but because of the 'flu, he - it usually is a man - wouldn't take any notice of it. Eventually other things would go wrong, so he would visit the doctor who would advise a chest X-ray, lung cancer eventually being diagnosed. Stage three, the stage of breakdown, is now well and truly established.

"Dr. James said you could see the same pattern developing with alcohol. By and large, however, the initial drinking of alcohol doesn't usually make a person as ill as the first cigarette, he said. But he knew many a friend and many a patient who were made quite ill whenever they drank alcohol, but they were simply not willing to give up, as it was so much a part of their social life. He felt sure it was a major reason why some people could not lose weight. He said a lot of women in particular admitted alcohol was their worst offender for putting on weight. They would give up all alcohol for a while to be able to lose sufficient weight to be able to get into a favourite dress for a special occasion or wear a bikini on holiday, and then undo all the good by going back to their old drinking habits and put on weight again. He said that was called yo-yo dieting. He said he was fascinated by human nature.

"So stage one was not so clear, but stage two was extremely common, many people possibly staying in stage two for the rest of their lives. Stage three would develop when the person could not start the day without a drink of alcohol, and cirrhosis or cancer of the liver would clearly indicate that stage three was well and truly established.

"Interestingly enough he said that these three stages were the stages most often described for addictions, which everyone knows occur when people use hard drugs like heroine, morphine or crack cocaine. But he said they also applied to other addictive substances such as sugar and coffee in some people. He said it was amazing how some people would wail if he suggested they give up coffee, tea, sometimes cheese or perhaps supposedly healthy foods such as tomatoes.

"I hope I got that explanation right. It fascinated me. It explained so many things to me," said Maud.

"You started all this when I mentioned Lynda's Pre-menstrual problems. Did Dr. James ever talk about that?"

"Yes, and that's another story, but I'm a bit tired. I think I will go to bed, if you don't mind," said Maud. "See how I feel in the morning.

Chapter 37

"Remind me to tell you what Dr. James told us about women's pre-menstrual problems," said Maud, some time in the morning after a good night's sleep, when they were having a mid-morning cup of tea and a slice of her usual cake. "But before I start a new story, I want to finish the point Dr. James tried to make about how things can cause problems when they come together, whereas they may not when they are on their own. This is part of what he called the total load syndrome. I have never had the slightest difficulty remembering some of these complicated names. All his talks were recorded and we all bought a copy, the money raised going to a local charity. They raised quite a lot. We listened to them so many times, they almost became part of our language."

Dr. James described a very wealthy man who was a tax lawyer, charging companies an absolute fortune to defend them against the Inland Revenue. He was a member of a group of lawyers who worked in London who called themselves 'The London Barristers Hay fever Moaning Club', or LBHFMC for short. They all suffered from varying degrees of hay fever, but this particular man in question, Douglas Winthrop, suffered from a terribly runny nose, constant sneezing, painful sore runny eyes, shortness of breath, and a wheezy chest. He also felt generally lousy. He in particular said he couldn't concentrate on anything serious when he was like that. His season was fairly early on, caused mainly by grass pollen.

Douglas was so bad when at the height of his problems that he refused to take a brief at that time of year. He said it just wasn't on to appear to cry in front of the judge, however sympathetic he might have been. But he would still travel up to London and cough and splutter all over his colleagues, who would apply the appropriate sympathy, hoping he would be sympathetic to them when they were in trouble.

This went on for years. As he worked in London and had a small flat there where he could stay overnight if sessions with clients went on to the early hours of the morning. He consulted many Allergy

Specialists in Harley Street, being referred by his private London General Practitioner. Many treatments were made. They variously tried to desensitise him to the pollens their tests suggested were the cause of his problems. A number of drugs were prescribed, even a short, sharp course of steroids at the start of his hay fever season. None of them made the slightest difference to him, some of course giving him nasty side effects.

Douglas had lived in a beautiful large house on the outskirts of Stead Norton for many years. He didn't need to travel up to London every day as he had a huge library of legal books at home and often stayed there to study and prepare a case on behalf of a client. It was his wife who suggested that he consult Dr. James. She had attended every one of his talks in the church and was fascinated not only by all the stories he told, but also the way he had solved many people's problems when no one else had been able to. She felt her husband would be a perfect test case for Dr. James's most unusual abilities.

To begin with her husband was sceptical. "For goodness sake!" Said Douglas. "I have seen the top Allergy Specialists in London. What on earth makes you think a simple country bumpkin GP can possibly be of any help to me?"

"Well, I will bribe you to go. If he is not able to help you, I will buy that beautiful old Rolls Royce Silver Cloud that you have been lusting after for so long. God only knows what you will do with it and where you will put it, but I grant you it is a lovely vehicle." Douglas's wife Hilda was even wealthier than he was. She was the only daughter of a wealthy member of the House of Lords, equivalent to The Supreme Court in America, who had died a few years ago and left her all his money, as his wife had died before him. As with members of the medical profession, it was not unusual for the daughters of lawyers to marry other members of the legal profession.

So Douglas went to see Dr. James. He found it an intriguing experience to wait his turn to see Dr. James. In London he always had a fixed time for all his appointments, as he was paying for them. He had already paid a small fortune to no avail. He actually admitted later to his wife he had enjoyed talking to the other people waiting to see Dr. James. They all said he was a really brilliant doctor and that they were so lucky to have him as their GP.

Douglas introduced himself to Dr. James. He told him that he probably wasn't on his panel as his usual GP was in London. When he explained where he lived locally, Dr. James said he wondered who lived there, as it looked such a beautiful house and garden. Dr. James said there was no problem as he could put him down as a temporary resident.

Douglas explained his problems. To his surprise, Dr. James asked him quite a lot of other questions, questions that had nothing to do with his hay fever, so far as he could tell.

"Apart from hay fever, are you well? " Asked Dr. James.

"I have high blood pressure, probably caused by the stress of my work, for which I take tablets recommended by my London doctor. I also have a bit of arthritis, but not too bad. Other drugs control that well enough."

"So how many different drugs are you on?"

"I take two for my blood pressure, a calcium channel blocker and a diuretic. I have my own blood pressure kit and take it two or three times a day. When I take it, it is always lower than when my doctor takes it. He calls it the white coat syndrome, although doctors don't seem to wear white coats any longer, not even in hospital. Even when I take it, it is not as good as my doctor would like and he is threatening to put me on a stronger one or add a third drug.

"I also take an anti-inflammatory for my arthritis. I've also just been prescribed one for my cholesterol, although I didn't think it was high. Apparently the latest approach is to bring it down even lower than was once considered ok. I'm thinking of not taking it and I haven't been to the chemist yet. I've heard they can have some nasty side effects that I don't fancy. I have a shrewd suspicion it is the latest idea to drum up more profits for the Drug Companies."

"The whole cholesterol question is shrouded in confusion. I know of a number of doctors who adamantly insist it is important to bring everyone's cholesterol level down as low as possible. They half-jokingly suggest statin drugs should be added to our water. They conveniently forget the side effects they can cause, including the very high level of suicides, accidental deaths and strange unexplainable incidents that happened to those whose cholesterol levels were brought down very low in the original studies. I was talking about cholesterol levels in the hospital corridor some time ago when one of the senior, nearly retiring physicians walked by and obviously heard what we were talking about. As he passed he said 'Never have your cholesterol levels measured, man. It will cause you more stress than anything I know'."

"Fascinating!"

"Anything you buy from the chemist?"

"Oh yes. I tend to suffer from acid, so take an antacid I buy locally, which is ordered specially for me. It is an unusual one. Rather expensive. I tried various sorts until I finally settled on the one I now use. Most others didn't help much. I have tried to leave them off, but if I do so, I suffer quite badly. I seem to need them.

"I have had a whole lot of tests. There's no doubt my main allergy is to grass pollen, but I also have a smattering of symptoms during the rest of the year, probably caused by house dust. It's not the house dust mite, but something in dust, which they haven't been able to identify. I'm not too bothered by that. It's the hay fever that ruins my summer. The grass pollen season can sometimes go on for weeks.

"I have a suspicion I am picking up other allergies, as my season seems to be growing longer each year. I have considered living abroad somewhere where I can escape from it all, but no one can come up with a sensible suggestion. I don't really fancy winter in New Zealand or Australia. They are a bit too far away for me. In any case, I wouldn't know what to do all that time, and my wife is not willing to come with me. She likes English summers too much, especially if the weather is nice, which is of course when I am likely to suffer."

"Have you ever considered the possibility that you may have a food intolerance? An intolerance is somehow different to an allergy. A food allergy gives you immediate symptoms like a rash with strawberries and breathing problems with peanuts. An intolerance is less obvious and tends not only to build up slowly but also may produce quite a wide range of symptoms that are difficult to equate with a food you have just eaten, because, in any case, you may eat that food regularly. Unfortunately there is no easy way of identifying the culprits. Very careful observation and making a comprehensive diary can sometimes be useful, but you have to make notes not only every day, but also as soon as you eat anything. The problem is that most people forget and then try to remember what they had at that last meal.

"I could try to guess, but from the information you have given me so far, I suspect you may be reacting to something unusual, so I could well miss what's causing your problems."

"Is there a test I could have done on my blood?"

"Actually there is. It's quite a good test, but you have to be aware no test of this sort is perfect. It can give false positive and false negative results. In my experience it is about seventy-five per cent accurate, by which I mean it comes up with useful information in about seventy-five per cent of people who are willing to pay for it. I'm afraid it's not available on the NHS♥."

"Ok! Let's do it. My hay fever season might start in a couple of week's time, so I want to get on with things. How long will the results take?"

"Less than a week. I'll ring you as soon as I have them."

Within the week, Douglas was back with Dr. James. "So! What did the test come up with?"

"Well, it's actually rather interesting. I have never seen such an usual result. It could be one of those false results. On the other hand, if it is right, it could explain quite a lot. It has certainly come up positive with three foods I could never have guessed. Well, possibly one of them. There are a few foods to which you have what I suppose one would classify as a possible reaction, but it has been my

♥ For information about this test and how to obtain one, see Appendix 2, note 9.

experience that, if you avoid the main ones, the lesser ones stop causing problems.

"So the three ones this test suggests you have a definite reaction to all begin with the letter S, soya, sesame and salmon. Do you eat much of these three?

"Do I eat much of them? You bet I do. Being a Jew, though not a very strict one I might add, I do follow a number of rules, so I eat a lot of sesame and soya products. I went to Scotland for a golfing holiday a few years ago and came across the most perfect salmon you could ever imagine. As I am now fairly well off, I have some of that salmon flown down to me here every week. It costs a fortune, but it's worth every penny. So! In answer to your question, yes I do have salmon, lots of it!"

"Would you be prepared to stop eating those three for a while and see what happens? There are certainly plenty of other foods left."

"Hm! I don't know what my wife will make of this idea. We have rather a lot of supplies in the house, but still. Other people can eat them for now. How intriguing!"

"It can take a while for things to improve when you change your diet. Let's see you again in about a month, if that would be convenient for you. I'm sorry I don't have an appointments system here. I never wanted one. My father didn't have one and the doctor here before me didn't have one. They were probably never thought of before that. Some time after I came here, I asked people if they would like an appointments system, but no one said yes. Not a single person. I suppose it's because I have two surgeries virtually every day, so a patient can see me as soon as they want to. They might have to wait a while if there's a bit of a queue, but life is so much slower out here in the country. They just sit out there and chat to each other. I gather quite a few friendships have developed as a result.

"Sorry! I have digressed a bit."

"No problem. I thoroughly enjoyed doing just that. People here are fascinating. I saw an approach to life that one could never see in London, where everyone's in a hurry."

"Yes. I agree. Anyway we could chat about it all day. So see if it affects your acidity, for instance. Use that as a test. In about a week, see if you can do without your antacid, for example. So don't take it automatically, but have some with you. Take some if you need it, but use that as an indicator of an effect of changing your diet. Of course you will still be taking your blood pressure regularly, so I suggest you continue to do that and record it diligently. I assume you do that?"

"Yes. Here's my record."

After scanning it quickly, Dr. James said, "Yes. It is a bit above a so-called ideal level for your age, but it's not too bad. I can understand your London doctor being a bit worried, but if it doesn't change with the changes to your diet, I may suggest you take some magnesium, which you could be low in because of your stress. I may add one or two other things, but let's first see what happens.

Four weeks later an astonished Douglas went to see Dr. James.

"I went up to London yesterday to do some research. I have a particularly tricky case at present that has gone on much longer than I expected. Normally I wouldn't have been prepared to do so much at this time of the year, and in fact probably wouldn't have been able to concentrate properly, but somehow I got really involved and forgot all about my troubles, and, strangely enough, even forgot what time of the year it is. I went to lunch where I usually go, and bumped into some of my hay fever club members. To be honest I had completely forgotten about them and my hay fever. Most of them were snuffling and sneezing and had sore red eyes, but, when they saw me, they were astonished. They all said 'what happened to your hay fever?' It was only then that I realised I didn't have any. I can tell you it came as a bit of a shock to me. How can that be?"

"Actually it's quite simple. I assume you have stayed off sesame, soya and salmon all this time."

"Yes I have."

"How's your blood pressure, and your acidity?"

"My acidity stopped after about a week, as you said it might. I took some of my tablets with me wherever I went as usual, but haven't chewed one since then. As for my blood pressure, I showed my recordings to my London GP last week and he was most surprised. He even advised me to drop one of my tablets. Incidentally I have dropped the anti-inflammatory tablet for my joints and I have decided not to take the statin for my cholesterol. I must say my GP was fascinated by your letter. Thank you for sending me a copy. I appreciated it."

"The human body is an extraordinary structure. I continue to study its workings, because I am convinced we have so much more to learn about it. Far too many doctors take what they know for granted. They seem to be stuck in a time warp. They are not willing to look beyond what their teachers taught them so long ago. They blindly follow what the majority do.

"Not so long ago, nearly every patient was bled and purged to let out what they called in those days the evil humors. Doctors eventually realised that it did more harm than good. An Austrian doctor Semmelweiss was ostracised and went mad when he tried to get doctors to wash their hands. Doctors would dissect a filthy, rotting corpse to demonstrate anatomy to students, wipe their hands on a cloth, and then examine women in labour wards. They must have killed thousands each themselves. Yet when someone pointed out the error of their ways, they effectively got rid of him. The prevailing attitude at the time, which they all believed in, was that pus, which they called 'laudable pus', was a good thing and was helping the process of healing. The fact that it not only didn't heal but that people died in agony from it passed them by.

"No, I would explain it like this. Unknown to you, you had an intolerance to those three foods to a far greater extent than one might have believed. They were obviously doing your body a lot more harm than anyone realised, including you. So your body was in a state of alarm. It had, in fact, already told you that something didn't agree with you because you developed acidity, arthritis and raised blood pressure. I could say 'how much more of a warning do you need to start looking at your life style?' But you didn't and no one suggested that you should. Your problems were just one of those things. It happens to lots of people. Doctors are inclined to say, 'Here. Take these tablets. They should do the trick'.

"Then along comes your reaction to grass pollen and one or two other things, and you blow a gasket. Your body says 'I have given you a number of warnings, but you are taking no notice of me. Here comes another one. This one will really make you suffer'.

"By good fortune you chose to consult someone who has a totally open mind and is willing to look around the situation. I accepted the fact that you had consulted some top allergy Specialists. Whenever such advice doesn't work, I always consider the wrong diagnosis has been made or that we have to look somewhere else for an answer to the problem."

"You were very clever. When we first met, you almost ignored my hay fever problems and seemed to be more interested in my other symptoms, to such an extent I went along with you, virtually forgetting what I had visited you for. It was my wife who suggested I consult you. She has told me all about your lectures in the church. She has been utterly fascinated about the way you go about things. You could make an absolute fortune working in London."

"Money isn't everything. The NHS pays me a good enough salary. I'm perfectly happy here. I love my life in the country. I love the people here. Most of them are so content, not thrusting their way through life and over everyone else trying to get somewhere in a hurry. I'm no crusader. I will teach any doctor who wants to learn from me, but I am ahead of my time. There are other doctors like me and we all say the same. May be our style of medicine will become more acceptable in the future. Who knows?

"In a funny way, I was hoping you wouldn't be able to help me. Don't get me wrong. I really am grateful, but my wife said she would buy me a lovely old Rolls Royce Silver Cloud that I have been lusting after, if you failed. I should have known better. She is a very wily and intelligent lady. You must meet her some time. I will now have to pay for the car myself."

Chapter 38

"You asked us to remind you about Dr. James' attitude to pre-menstrual problems. Is this a good time now?" Asked Patrick.

"Thank you for reminding me," said Maud. "He gave a fascinating talk on the subject."

At one of his evening talks in the church, after telling a quick joke to make sure everyone was awake, Dr. James started by saying, "This evening I want to talk about something I have always found to be important, something that is very common, something that many women suffer from, but something that is remarkably easy to resolve.

"I'm talking about PMS, by which I mean pre-menstrual syndrome instead of PMT, which stands for pre-menstrual tension. Although many women suffer from a variety of symptoms that I will describe shortly, they don't always have mood swings. Often when I have asked a woman if she suffers from PMS, she says she doesn't, because her moods are not affected. When I clarify what I am asking, she then will usually admit that she does have some symptoms, some of them quite severe, which do disturb her life at the time.

"There are probably about as many men in church this evening as women, and I am glad to have you all here, because some of you men may be affected when your wife feels unwell at the time. I remember a friend of mine trying to come up with a good way of publicising a test he had produced for pre-menstrual problems. In the end he came up with the telling phrase of 'Five Million Men Suffer From Pre-menstrual Syndrome in the UK Every Year'. Yes, men do often suffer when their wives feel unwell at this time of the month.

"So to set the scene, I want first to describe a normal monthly cycle, and, when I have finished, I wonder how many women here tonight will say to themselves 'I'm nothing like that! He doesn't know what he is talking about!' I'm sure there will be plenty of you.

"But first I would like to clarify something. Women produce three hormones, namely oestrogen, progesterone and testosterone. Yes, women do produce some testosterone, but of course not as much as men. Well I hope not! To a degree, the more testosterone a woman produces up to a certain level, the more interest she is likely to have in sex. If she produces too much she may suffer from acne or have polycystic ovaries. Progesterone is only one chemical, whereas there are at least three oestrogens, namely oestriol, oestradiol and oestrone. Oestradiol is the one most commonly referred to when doctors talk about oestrogen.

"So now I want to describe what is considered to be a 'classical' menstrual cycle, where one period starts twenty-eight days after the previous one. A cycle is usually described as starting on the day your period begins. On that day, and for the next seven days, your levels of circulating oestrogens and progesterone are low. Around day 7, a part of the brain called the hypothalamic/pituitary area starts to produce a hormone called follicle-stimulating hormone (FSH for short), which stimulates the ovaries to bring to complete maturity the most mature Graafian follicle, by producing more oestrogen.

"At day 14 another hormone, leuteinising hormone (or LH for short) is released also from the hypothalamic/pituitary area to make the Graafian follicle release its egg for fertilisation. This is called the time of 'ovulation'. The Graafian follicle stays active by starting to produce progesterone, the levels it produces increasing to the end of the cycle.

"From mid-cycle onwards, i.e. from ovulation, the levels of oestrogen vary from women to women. In some they continue to rise, in some they remain fairly steady, while in others they may fall. Whatever actually happens, there remains more circulating oestrogen in the second half of the cycle than in the first half. What is important at this time is the relationship between oestrogen and progesterone. In women who suffer from any symptoms of the pre-menstrual syndrome, there is a dominance of oestrogen *relative to* progesterone. The actual levels of the hormones are not particularly important, so long as there are enough, but, if there is too much oestrogen and not enough progesterone *relative to each other*, pre-menstrual symptoms will be suffered.

"The female of the species is designed to reproduce, and oestrogen's job is, of course, to make you into a reproductive creature. It develops the breasts, the ovaries and the womb (uterus) in the main, although it can also affect many other parts of the body. There are oestrogen receptors in nearly every cell of nearly every tissue of the body; so, under the influence of oestrogen, you become the female that you are.

"Because we are all different, some women have more oestrogen receptors (or possibly more receptive ones) in some parts of their bodies than in others. Hence pre-menstrual hormonal imbalances produce different symptoms in different women. Some suffer horrendous mental symptoms, such as mood swings, depression, anxiety, agitation, sleeplessness, and in fact just about any mental symptom that it is possible to suffer from. Others suffer from tender, swollen breasts, and periodic breast cysts, or may become constipated, while many are not aware of any particular pre-menstrual problems, yet they eventually develop polycystic ovaries or fibroids.

"All of these medical problems are indications of a dominance of oestrogen relative to progesterone, and it is now recognised by many doctors that too much oestrogen is not good for you. Unfortunately, it is not only the oestrogen that women produce themselves that is involved. So much of our world is polluted with hormones, mostly of an oestrogenic nature. Plastics, pesticides, petrochemicals all have oestrogenic activity. Such chemicals are called xeno-oestrogens or false oestrogens. Our world is awash with them.

"The point I am trying to make is that, with a history of pre-menstrual symptoms of any sort, or polycystic ovaries or fibroids, you are likely to be affected by oestrogen dominance in some way. As I have said, too much oestrogen is not good for you. If you have had pre-menstrual symptoms of any sort, and to a degree that they were at least a bit of a nuisance, rather than merely an awareness that your period was due, you have probably been exposed to a little too much oestrogen every single month, and for as many days as your symptoms lasted.

"The late Dr. John Lee wrote some wonderfully illuminating books on this and related subjects, the simplest one being entitled 'Natural Progesterone; The Role of a Remarkable Hormone♥'.

"The reason why I am mentioning his book is because doctors tend to talk all the time about oestrogen and ignore the importance of progesterone. I believe progesterone is far more important than it is given credit for. While oestrogen is clearly good for you, too much may not be. On the other hand, progesterone seems to be all good.

"I have already mentioned the fact that, under normal circumstances, a woman starts to produce progesterone roughly at the time of ovulation, so about mid-cycle, although, to be fair, exactly when ovulation actually occurs can vary considerably. Most doctors assume it occurs around day fourteen of a twenty-eight day cycle, but I can assure you that is not necessarily the case. Many a woman has avoided having intercourse around that time to prevent her from becoming pregnant, only to find her plan didn't work!

"Some time towards the end of her cycle, a woman may produce between twenty to forty milligrams of progesterone per day, and the more she produces the less likely she is to suffer from pre-menstrual symptoms of any sort. Towards the end of a pregnancy she may produce two hundred milligrams of progesterone per day, and, if she is one of those lucky women who felt fabulously well throughout her pregnancy, she may well have produced as much as four hundred milligrams of progesterone per day. So what I am saying is that it is reasonable to say that progesterone is quite good for you. Its main function is to prepare the womb for pregnancy and, if a pregnancy occurs, to keep the afterbirth functioning well throughout. So, don't forget progesterone."

Fiona Wilson was dragged to Dr. James's surgery in tears one day, by her mother.

"This can't go on much longer," said her mother. "Just look at her. She's in a terrible state. It's the same every month. She looks all

---

♥ To obtain a copy of this book, see Appendix 2, note 10.

bloated. She can't stop crying and when I try to comfort and cuddle her, she pushes me away saying her breasts hurt. The poor lass. She doesn't know what to do with herself. You've got to do something for her, Doc."

"Can you talk to me about it?" Dr. James asked Fiona.

When she had managed to stop crying, she said, "Mum's right! It's the same every month. I feel awful for about two weeks building up to my period, only to suffer from terrible tummy pains for about a week when it starts. I only have about one reasonable week a month. My poor husband Donald. He's at his wit's end. I wouldn't blame him if he asked me for a divorce."

"Don't be silly," said Fiona's mother. "He loves you to bits. He just doesn't know what to do for the best. He's asked me so often how to handle the situation. Should he try to cuddle you or should he leave you alone to your misery? He wants to help, but he just doesn't know what to do."

"Fiona?"

"I have a very fixed menstrual cycle. It's exactly twenty-eight days. I know when I ovulate, always on day fourteen, which I dread, because I know what's coming. I then start to feel miserable, I start to put on weight, my breasts start to hurt, and I snap at Donald. I just can't help it. He knows I don't mean it, but I still do it. It's not as though he does anything wrong. It's just me. Things just get worse and worse as the days go by. I don't want to do anything or go anywhere. I'm useless. By the time my period starts I may have put on eight or ten pounds in weight. It's ridiculous. Although it gathers all over to a degree, most of it seems to be in my boobs. They become enormous. I have to wear a much bigger bra. They are so painful, and become worse if I don't wear a bra. When my period starts, they go down and for the next two weeks I have reasonable sized breasts. But before my period you would think I was a completely different woman. Unfortunately I then have a lot of tummy pain for about the next week. The week before I ovulate is comparative bliss, even though it's not all that good."

"What stage are you at today?" Asked Dr. James.

"My period will start in six day's time. I feel awful today, but it will get even worse over the next few days," wailed Fiona. "Please help me, Doctor. I can't bear the thought of this going on for the next twenty years. I might do something silly one day. There's no point to life like this. I might as well end it. No, I don't really mean that, but it's so awful. We moved here about three years ago, to be nearer my mother. Donald agreed as he thought it might help. Mum has been wonderful, so has Donald, but it hasn't made any difference. My last GP suggested I try the pill, but it didn't make any difference. All it did was to make my blood pressure go up and I developed some veins in my legs."

"I think what you said a few seconds ago tells me how bad you feel. Yes, I agree. It's not fair. Let's see if we can stop you getting any worse this month. It may not work immediately, but, with any luck, it might help a bit. It is clear to me that you are suffering from oestrogen dominance, so we need to antagonise all that oestrogen, and the best way to do it today is to give you a dose of homoeopathic progesterone at a strength of 200C. Here! Let's put a drop under your tongue now. Repeat the dose two more times today and do it three times tomorrow and every day until your period starts, then stop it. One drop is enough. Two is not an overdose, merely a waste. Don't have anything to eat or drink for ten minutes before or after a dose.

"The most important thing to remember now is that I'm going to help you. That's a promise, but it may not happen immediately.

"There's a lot I want to go through with you, but now is not the right time. I would like to see you again as soon as your good spell begins, and, if your husband could come as well, and your mother of course, so much the better. As you are so sure of your cycle, let's see if we can organise a day and time, around eleven o'clock, when I should have finished morning surgery and made all my phone calls. Oh! And be prepared to stay an hour or more. There is a lot for me to ask, and a lot for you to tell me. I'd like you to take this form away with you and fill it in in your own good time. Please bring it back with you. I would also like you to read these sheets. They will explain a lot to you."

About two weeks later, a completely different Fiona walked into Dr. James's consulting room, with her husband and mother.

"Good morning, Mr Wilson," said Dr. James, shaking him by the hand. "I'm glad you were able to come. Fiona has told me how understanding you have been. She really does seem to have a bad time. Your support is very important for her."

"It's so good of you to spend all this time with us. We really appreciate it. Fiona told me what she said to you when she was last here. I was really upset that she could even think of ending her life. I love her very dearly. It's just that I haven't a clue what to do when she is feeling so awful. To be fair, neither does she. She doesn't know what to do with herself."

"Did the homoeopathic drops make any difference?" Asked Dr. James.

"Well something did," replied Fiona. "I'm in my good phase at present, but it seems somehow better than usual. It may have been your promising to help me that did the trick. It gave me such hope. It even lifted my spirits for a while. All I can say is that things did not get any worse as they have always done, and even got a bit better, although I was left still feeling a bit swollen and sore, though nothing like what I was expecting. Do you think things will improve even further?"

"They most certainly will, especially if you start the homoeopathic drops as soon as you ovulate, which is when you start to produce progesterone. As you only started them halfway through your pre-menstrual phase, and you had already started to suffer from the effects of too much oestrogen, there was a possibility they would not do much last time. As I explained on those sheets I gave you, there should normally be a particular balance between oestrogen and progesterone during the second half of your cycle, but in your case, you either don't produce enough progesterone or somehow what progesterone you do produce doesn't do its job properly.

"Many women don't ovulate, so presumably don't produce any progesterone, so it's not surprising they suffer from pre-menstrual symptoms. But you do ovulate, so presumably you do produce progesterone. The question is why does your progesterone not do its job of balancing oestrogen? I can only assume your progesterone receptors are not working efficiently for some reason. May be the number of receptors on your cells has diminished in some way. May be they have lost their sensitivity. May be they have been poisoned or damaged or interfered with in some way. I don't know what the explanation is. However, I hope that the homoeopathic drops will somehow correct whatever is the cause, somehow improve the functioning of the progesterone you do produce. Only time will tell.

"In the meantime I want to go through your history very carefully and see if we can find any reasons why all this has gone on." And with that, Dr. James read the forms Fiona had given back to him.

"I see your periods started fairly early. You were only eleven. Did you suffer with any of these problems at that stage?"

"A bit, but not too badly. So many of my friends said they had the same problems we assumed it was what all women suffer from. We just took it for granted and we tried to laugh about it, but it didn't always work."

"So when did they start to become more than a bit of a nuisance?"

"Probably not until my late teens, or possibly when I was around twenty. I suppose they just got gradually worse without there being a sudden increase."

"What sort of a teenager was she?" Dr. James asked Fiona's mother.

"Absolutely wonderful. She was not like so many teenagers you hear of today, arguing with their parents all the time and wanting to go out all dolled up and stay out all night. No! She would get up early before going to school to cycle to a farm not far from where we lived and help out with the horses they had there, in exchange for a ride at the weekend. She loved it. She would come home after school and change quickly to go there after school, then come home and do her homework. She would spend most of the weekends with the horses. No. She was a model daughter."

"Thanks, Mum," said Fiona.

"But it's true," said her mother.

"What did you do at the farm?"

"I helped muck out the stables. Actually I really enjoyed doing that. There is something fascinating to see the mess horses make in their stable overnight and to clean them all out and have them looking all tidy for when they come back in at night."

"Did you help in any other way on the farm?" Asked Dr. James.

"Not that I can think of," replied Fiona.

"I'll leave that question for you to ponder for now. So let's look at your diet."

"Ah! Now there's a point of contention between us," said her mother. "Fiona was always a beautiful slim girl and she wanted to stay that way. I thought she read far too many of those idolising teenage magazines about pop stars and celebrities. They weren't available in my day, so I used to comment every so often, but didn't want to argue with Fiona and alienate her from me. I'm afraid she didn't eat at all well. It used to worry me. She drank far too much in the way of fizzy drinks, especially the diet forms, with all those nasty chemicals in them.

"What I didn't understand," continued her mother "was why she also ate a lot of sugar in one form or another, like chocolates and ice-cream, and yet stayed so slim. She must have been one of the lucky ones. As she didn't get fat, I suppose she assumed eating all those things weren't doing her any harm. I'm afraid her diet was rather poor, and I don't think it has improved much over the years."

"Have you had much in the way of antibiotics?"

"No. In fact I can't remember when I last had a course, but I must have done at some time I suppose."

"Have you ever had thrush?"

"No. I have been spared that problem. So many of my friends have though. Nobody seems to be able to help them get rid of it."

"Have you had much in the way of stress for any reason?"

"Not that I can think of. I feel I have been remarkably lucky in that respect. Again, so many of my friends seem to be stressed out with problems at work and boyfriends and such things, but I seem to have been spared that."

Dr. James asked her a number of other questions, but the answers were always in the negative. "Am I being awkward? I seem to be saying no to most of your questions so far. Am I making things difficult for you?" Asked Fiona.

"To be fair, most women who suffer from pre-menstrual symptoms say yes to many of the questions I have asked you, and it is not difficult for me to identify the probable causes and suggest a way of doing something. However, at the same time, it is not at all uncommon for me to find very little in the way of an explanation when I ask what I would call standard questions. That simply means I have not asked the right questions, or the patient has not answered my questions properly. Let me give you an example of what I mean.

"Some years ago a man consulted me because of his Parkinson's Disease. He only spent June, July, August and September in England, having a house in Spain where he lived for the rest of the year. He felt it was too hot for him in Spain during the summer months. Having lived in England until he retired, he was still entitled to be seen on the NHS when he was here. I treated him with a variety of approaches, and I'm pleased to say that his Parkinson's symptoms cleared completely after about two to three years.

"However, he had very strange skin on his face. He had seen at least two skin Specialists in the UK and two in Spain, and none of them could explain what it was all about or do anything about it. My approach to his Parkinson's Disease also didn't help either. I kept saying to him 'I have not asked you a particular question and you have not told me something important'.

"One day his wife came with him and said to me, 'Do you think the skin of my husband's face has anything to do with the fact that he was one of the British soldiers who stood on one of those South Sea Islands all those years ago and watched the first atom bomb being exploded?' He had been issued with special goggles, but the skin of the rest of his face had been exposed. His bad skin was probably caused by the long-term effects of a radiation burn. How could one possibly think of asking a question that would identify such a cause, and so long ago? You see what I mean? The man told me he was old and ugly and wasn't prepared to keep coming back to see me to deal with his face. So I merely told him to take certain anti-oxidants to try to minimise any more long-term effects.

"So! What are we missing with you? So far we have certainly identified a shocking diet, which is bound to have upset your hormones. Your body simply cannot be expected to function normally if you don't feed it properly. However, the severity of your symptoms suggests to me that there is something else, and that the two things combined together will explain why things are so bad. Let's go back to when things started to become a nuisance. I think you said possibly late teens. I have already written down here a question I want to ask you, but I want you to see what you can think of before I suggest something."

"In the summer holidays when I was sixteen, I went with a group from school to Spain. I can't think of anything special about that visit. We only spent a fortnight there. I had exams that year, but wasn't anything like as stressed about them as most of my friends. I had done my homework regularly so was well up with my studies."

"Fiona was amazing," her mother said. "She loved going to the farm so much, she said she could have spent her whole time there, so she set herself a proper timetable to make sure she did her homework properly. She did it all before going to the farm during the summer evenings when it was so light until nine or ten o'clock, going to the farm first during the winter months when the evenings got dark.

"No! We can't think of anything else," said her mother. "May we see what you wrote down, please?" Dr. James showed them.

"Farm chemicals. Of course! I helped them do sheep dipping three years running until they said there were new regulations about how to do them and who could do them. The first year must have been when I was sixteen. But why is that important?"

"Because many of those chemicals are oestrogenic, sometimes called xeno-oestrogens, i.e. have oestrogenic properties. You were already showing oestrogen dominant effects because of the symptoms you were suffering from in the pre-menstrual phase. It is my belief these chemicals also poison various receptors, so, assuming you produce good levels of progesterone after you have ovulated, I can only assume these chemicals somehow interfere with the normal functioning of your progesterone.

"Although I can suggest your poor diet may have been a precipitating factor, what I can't yet explain is why it caused the problems it did cause, rather than arthritis, asthma or perhaps irritable bowel syndrome, for example. Perhaps you have a genetic predisposition of some sort. Have any of the females in your family had any hormonal problems that you are aware of?"

"Mum?"

"The only women's thing I can think of is that my sister had a hysterectomy for fibroids three years ago, I apparently have a small fibroid and my mother had a hysterectomy, but we are not sure what for. When I asked her about it some time ago, she said in those days you didn't question the doctor. If he said you needed something doing you just let him get on with it, no questions asked. But surely that's not a hormonal problem is it?"

"It very much is, in my opinion," said Dr. James, "although many doctors don't seem to think of it as such. I've already said that there are many oestrogen receptors all over the place on women's cells. What we don't know is if some women have more oestrogen receptors on their breasts, their ovaries, their uterus, their intestines or perhaps even their brains. All I can say from my observations is that the range of symptoms women suffer from in the pre-menstrual phase is quite remarkable. All you have to do is acknowledge that something is going on at that time of the month, and, if the woman suffers from anything that she doesn't usually suffer from, then that effect is probably caused by too much oestrogen relative to progesterone.

"In your case, Fiona, your dominant oestrogen effect certainly seems to be influencing your breasts and your brain, and probably almost your whole body to a degree if I hear you right. The only one that fools people is the development of fibroids in the womb. Remember, oestrogen's job is to have a positive or stimulating effect upon receptive cells, so if oestrogen has a slight effect every month on your womb, and only on your womb, then you will most likely develop fibroids silently over the years.

"A woman may only be aware of a fibroid when she starts to put on weight in the lower half of her tummy without any obvious reason, or when she develops more painful periods if she is still having them. A post-menopausal woman can develop quite a big fibroid before she notices anything wrong, especially if she is a bit overweight anyway.

"So. There you are. We could have found it. You have what I would call three very strong influences causing your symptoms. First of all there is your genetic predisposition. That simply says that, if you do something wrong in your life, it may well come out as a specific hormonal problem. In your case it is horrendous pre-menstrual symptoms. Because your oestrogen receptors are particularly sensitive at present, possibly somehow made more sensitive by the farm chemicals, and you seem to have sensitive ones all over your body, or certainly in many areas, you have been unfortunate to suffer from a considerable range of symptoms.

"What started off allowing symptoms to develop was your poor diet. Nutritional deficiencies have a habit of declaring themselves in very strange ways, very often not the way one would expect. When I have given some patients with multiple symptoms some intravenous infusions of vitamins and minerals, the range of symptoms that may improve is quite astonishing.

"Things were bad enough with your genetic predisposition, your poor diet and the consequent nutritional deficiencies producing evidence of oestrogen dominance, when you then added the effect of oestrogenic farm chemicals. The reason they changed the rules was because so many farmers and their workers had developed a whole range of symptoms, which were eventually tracked to these chemicals. You were possibly not exposed for too long, as you were not a regular worker there. Is that the case?"

"Yes. I usually arrived after school when they were nearly finished, so perhaps only half-an-hour at a time, and not too many days each year. If it rained, as it often did, they didn't do sheep dipping, so I might not be involved quite often. It never occurred to any of us that I could be at risk.

"Well, I might be wrong, but I would like to take a blood sample to see what your blood levels of those chemicals are. If we can prove the point that way, that will be enough for me. If your blood levels don't show anything suspicious, I will suggest a sample of your fat be tested, if you are willing, as these chemicals are very fat soluble, but let's see what the blood test shows first."

"So what do we do now?" Asked Fiona. "Or more to the point what do I do?"

"As I say, I would like to take a blood sample, if I may. I might as well do some routine testing while I am about it. We can do that before you leave here today."

"While we are waiting for the result of the blood test, I would like you to improve your diet."

"I've already started by insisting she eat better," said her mother, but are there any specific pieces of advice to give her?"

"Yes. For now I will keep it simple. I would like you to stay off all dairy products, sugar, caffeine, which includes not only coffee but also tea, chocolate and cola drinks, white flour products wherever possible and junk food. I imagine you know what I mean by that.

You are lucky that you have never had thrush, otherwise I would have been far more strict with you to start with.

"Having said what I want you to avoid, let's list what you can eat. All fruit, vegetables, nuts, seeds, salad items, whole grains, eggs, fish and meat, all organic where you can manage, but don't worry if you can't. There's plenty for you to eat. The best way to avoid making mistakes is to obtain individual items and put them together like they used to in the past. Try not to eat anything in a packet or tin, or anything advertised. Eat as much as you can in an uncooked, raw form, steaming vegetables where possible. Please avoid microwave ovens as that form of cooking destroys a lot of the essential nutrients in the food. Soups are a wonderful standby. If you prepare a large amount, you can keep it in the fridge and take out a small amount when you want some and heat it in a saucepan."

"Actually the way you have described what I may eat sounds rather tasty, but I don't want to put on weight."

"Ok! I understand, so keep your obvious carbohydrate ingredients down to a minimum. That means not having too much in the way of grains, so probably bread and pasta, and potatoes. Don't worry about fat. Most people aren't aware that carbohydrates slow your metabolism down, whereas fat speeds it up. But where would fat come into the approach I have just suggested? I suppose any on meat, so you could eat more fish than meat, but oily fish are very healthy, and olive oil. Since I hope you will not be eating anything in a packet, there is no chance of your having any hidden fats. Avoid margarines. Many of them are only one step away from plastic.

"As an experiment, if you were to leave an open tub of margarine containing hydrogenated fat and oil in it in your garage, nothing will grow on it for ages, although it will eventually go rancid. If bugs don't like it, it is a good bet that it is not good for you.

"Try to get onto this form of better eating as soon as possible. The sooner you start before your next pre-menstrual phase begins, the more likely it is that you will have fewer symptoms this time. Don't forget to start the homoeopathic drops as soon as you ovulate. One last thing. I would like to give you an intravenous infusion of vitamins and minerals as soon as possible, today if practical, to improve your nutritional status as quickly as possible, and I can take that blood sample at the same time to avoid sticking in two needles. The only problem is that it takes at least one hour or possibly one-and-a-half hours. Can you spare that much time?"

"Yes I can. I want to get on with things. You have given me such hope."

Two-and-a-half weeks later, Fiona, with her husband, her mother and her father came to Dr. James's surgery. They insisted they were the last in that morning. Fiona entered first and did a three-sixty degree twizzle with her arms flung out to the side.

"Just look at me!" She said. "I should be fat, bloated and utterly miserable and my period is due in three days time. Well I may not be perfect, but the difference is truly amazing. If I don't get any better than this I will not complain. You're an absolute marvel, Dr. James. I could hug you. Thank you so very very much."

"The same goes for us," said the other three, coming in quietly after Fiona had finished her thankyous. "She really is a completely different person."

"Have the blood tests come back yet?" Asked Fiona.

"Yes they have. The routine ones were fine, but there was sufficient evidence of farm chemicals in your blood for me to feel that there is no need for a fat sample to be analysed. Now we have to clear them from your body. There are many ways to do that, so let's talk about the simple ones.

"First to remind you these chemicals are readily dissolved in fat so tend to be stored in your body fat, but there is also some circulating in your blood stream, so we need to help clear the blood. By doing so, we will slowly lower the levels of the chemicals in your blood, thereby lowering the levels in your fat stores. To be fair it will be a continuous system, so your blood will not become empty until there is no more to come from your body fat at all.

"The first approach I would like you to follow is to put a few drops of organic olive oil under your tongue and keep it there for a few minutes if you can. It might be sensible to do it near a basin so you can dribble into it if you need to or eventually spit into it. As the olive oil is fatty, the chemicals in your blood will be drawn into it. The area under your tongue is quite useful. Doctors advise people to place special tablets under their tongue if they suffer an attack of angina, you know, when they suffer a spasm-like pain in their heart.

"To begin with you may notice the olive oil turns a bit grey, but that won't last long. You can see why you must use organic olive oil. The whole purpose is to try to remove chemicals. You don't want to add any. Do this as many times during the day as is practical.

"Remember, what we are trying to do is eliminate the chemicals from your body, so we need to think of any simple system of elimination that you can easily use. So let's consider your skin. Perhaps the simplest approach is to soak in a hot bath in which you have put a big handful of Epsom Salts. Use it like a sauna. Keep the water as hot as you can comfortably manage, and stay in as long as is practical. Then get out and wrap yourself in two or three towels and sweat for a few minutes. That way you will eliminate some chemicals with the sweat. You can finish off with a shower to clean your skin.

"If you want to you could buy yourself a sauna and do it that way, but I have personally never liked the effect it has on me. However, there is a blanket-type of sauna that works well without needing to heat up♥.

"The third way of eliminating things is to use what I call our natural sewerage system, the bowel. If you think of it, the amount of useful ingredients we obtain from an apple, for example, is tiny. Apart from the water, which we can obtain from simply drinking the stuff, the great majority of an apple is waste or fibre. So I assume Mother Nature decided she needed to develop a system to eliminate the unwanted material, which is why I believe she invented the bowel. Having done so, she decided that it would have a system of its own, so we would need to keep feeding it by consuming regular amounts of fibre.

♥ For more information on these special forms of sauna, see the Appendix.2 note 11

"I once attended a very interesting lecture by a world famous surgeon, Dr. Dennis Burkitt, who showed us a slide which compared the size of local hospitals with the bulk of people's faeces. He said that the bigger the amount the people passed on average, and this was somewhere in Africa, the smaller the local hospitals, but when people passed only small amounts, bigger hospitals seemed to be needed. I find that an interesting observation. He didn't need to do fancy double-blind studies. He merely made an observation and came to a logical conclusion. It is possibly as a result of his observations that the medical profession now considers it healthy to consume a lot of food that contains plenty of fibre.

"I see from the form you completed for me that you used to become very constipated in your pre-menstrual phase, being somewhat better at other times, but still not good."

"Oh, golly yes! I usually didn't open my bowels for the whole of the two weeks before my period started. I would be in agony. But still not able to go. Then my period would start and I would have to sit on the toilet for ages. It was so hard I would make myself bleed. You're absolutely right. The range of symptoms I used to suffer from was quite extraordinary. I'm only just beginning to remember some of them as we talk. The very thought makes me shudder".

"Constipation has many causes. The obvious one is not drinking enough water, or drinking too many cups of tea and coffee. I'm afraid those drinks actually dehydrate you. Another that I have found in many people is an intolerance of milk products. I have no idea why it causes it. It just does. So many patients have told me their bowels started to function far better when they stopped dairy products. So that may have been an explanation in your case, but I think the main explanation is that the fluid you retained in your bowel wall, caused by your oestrogen dominance, effectively stopped the normal peristaltic motion that should make the contents inside them keep moving toward the end, so they didn't work properly. What are you like now?"

"It's astonishing. I am going to the toilet twice a day. That's totally unheard of for me."

"Many Naturopaths I have spoken to say that we should open our bowels at least three times a day, i.e. one meal in and one meal out, so long as our diet contains sufficient overall fibre. Remember what happens in a baby? You put food in one end and something almost immediately comes out the other end. As we grow older and feed ourselves poorly, we seem to lose our original bowel reflexes.

"So! Now your bowels are working so much better, you will have added a third elimination method. But it would probably be a good idea to improve the functioning of your main detoxification organ, your liver, so that what you put into your bowel is in the right form to be eliminated and not irritate your bowels in the process. I will give you some herbs that will cleanse your liver and generally stimulate it. It will be in the form of an herbal tea.

Four months later, an ecstatic Fiona attended Dr. James to say she was pregnant. "I know the exact day, date and time. After we had made love, I knew I was pregnant. Before you helped me, I was so ill so often I wasn't interested in sex. Poor Donald. Now he can't keep his hands off me. I love him so much. Whether our baby is a boy or a girl, one of its names will have to be Devon, as that is where I conceived. We went to a wonderful hotel there for a long luxurious weekend. Donald absolutely spoiled me rotten."

Chapter 39

"Gosh! That was complicated," said Patrick, "especially the bit where Dr. James explained all about women's hormones. Did you understand it all, Lynda?"

"Yes I did. Fortunately my basic training in anatomy and physiology is still fairly fresh, and I was always interested in that sort of thing. But I am amazed you were able to describe it so well, Maud. That was masterful."

"I'm not that clever," replied Maud. "If Dr. James had tested us on what he had said that evening, like an exam, I doubt if many of us would have passed at all. But, don't forget, I had a copy of all Dr. James' talks, and have listened to them many, many times. They fascinated us all so much. I gather some groups got together in the evenings occasionally and listened to them together, having a discussion about what they heard afterwards, probably accompanied by the odd drink or two, I wouldn't wonder," she added with a smile. "Anyway, that story has fair exhausted me, it took so long. I'll leave it for today, if you two don't mind. Why don't you go to the pictures, or something like that? I'll be all right on my own. I'm quite used to my own company."

"Are you sure?" Asked Lynda.

"Yes. I'll be fine. My touch of pneumonia must have gone by now, anyway. Off you two go. In any case, lovebirds like you two should be on your own occasionally."

The next morning, after a good night's sleep for them all, and after they had had breakfast and finished the washing up, Maud took them into the garden and they all sat under a big tree. It was a beautiful day, in complete contrast to what it had recently been like. Maud started the conversation.

"A few days ago I told you Dr. James wanted to specialise in Obstetrics and Gynaecology. He really loved that subject and was sorry the opportunity never came his way. I think he finally gave up hoping, when his plans to return to The Caribbean didn't turn out as he had hoped. Not being able to reach the status of Registrar there basically meant he was getting too old. There were too many younger doctors already halfway up the ladder toward Specialist status for him to have any chance. But he continued his love of the subject in General Practice. He amused us with the way he put it. In relation to his pleasure of delivering a baby, he described it as 'the fruits of other peoples' labours'. That's a pun on the word labour, just in case you didn't get it," said Maud to Patrick and Lynda.

"Dr. James slipped in amusing anecdotes all the time at his church talks. I remember him saying that he was the third of three children his mother had, spaced out about two years in between each, the fourth being born four-and-a-half years after he was, so a bit of a gap. As a four-and-a-half year old boy, he wasn't yet acquainted with the normal process of a woman giving birth to a baby. He was aware that his father, the local GP, was regularly called out at all times of the day and night to deliver a baby. But he was also aware that the postman delivered the mail and parcels every morning.

"So, when he was told a new baby was about to arrive, he would rush downstairs every morning to meet the postman, expecting a big box to be delivered, with breathing holes in its sides, and a baby all neatly wrapped up inside. He remembers being upset that somehow he missed the postman the morning the new baby arrived!

"Dr. James loved the way children think. He said they are so logical. To them everything is so simple, so logical. He remembered hearing a wonderful comment by a girl of about six. She was with her parents and one set of grandparents. She looked at them all and said 'it's all very well for you Mummy. You married Daddy, and you Grandma you married Grandpa. But me, I've got to marry a stranger!'

"Sorry, I have digressed again," said Maud. "I was telling you about how Dr. James loved to help women solve their problems. The story of how he saved Judy and Dr. Gregory's baby before it was born makes my heart go all aflutter whenever I think of it. Then there was the time he helped Dr. Evan and Blodwen's baby, when they were sure it was going to die. I don't know how many others he must have helped while he was here that he never told us about. There were probably hundreds of them, who knows? Then again, the way he helped solve Fiona Wilson's pre-menstrual problems. They were all about his unusual way of looking at things. He always wanted people to get back to being and feeling normal, and to do so there had to be an explanation as to why things had gone wrong.

"Dr. James said that he felt it was the duty of a General Practitioner to help at the most basic level. That meant, amongst other things, helping couples to start a family when they wanted to. So it always made him sad when a woman had a miscarriage. He told us all about Jackie Dunwoody at one of his church talks. There she was in the front row, gently swaying her precious baby in her arms, with her proud husband sitting next to her."

Jackie came under Dr. James's care when she visited her mother and father, who lived in Stead Norton. Jackie and her husband Bob had just bought one of the new houses on the outskirts of the village, but they hadn't moved in yet as contracts had not been exchanged. That was due to take place any day soon.

Dr. James was called to the house, where he found the place in an absolute turmoil. There were anxious faces all round. Jackie was upstairs in the spare bedroom, clearly suffering a miscarriage. Her mother had met him at the door, with tears in her eyes. "Poor love. She knows exactly what is happening to her. This is her third miscarriage. She is heartbroken. They so want a baby, and of course we would love to have our first grandchild. They are such a loving couple. It's not fair! Why should this happen to her? So many young girls get pregnant and have a baby when they don't particularly want one. Then when someone like Jackie desperately wants one, it all goes wrong. There's no justice in this world," she said, blowing her nose on a large handkerchief.

Dr. James climbed the stairs, followed by Jackie's mother. He spoke gently to Jackie. He didn't attempt to hide the truth from her as it was obvious she knew what was happening to her and that she would probably have to go into hospital to have her womb cleared out. She was weeping gently to herself. He then carefully examined her and what she had passed, and told her that she didn't have to go into hospital immediately as the miscarriage may have been complete. But he advised her that admission to hospital might be necessary in due course. It was up to her, but he asked if she could stay with her parents for now, and of course her mother said she could. He said he would like to ring and see if a midwife was available to come and tidy her up and make her feel comfortable. Fortunately one was able to come immediately.

While they waited for the midwife to arrive, Dr. James asked Jackie's mother to sit on the other side of the bed. He took hold of one of Jackie's hands and spoke gently to her.

"As you are about to come and live here, I am likely to become your doctor. You could join another practice a few miles away if they will take you, so I will leave that up to you. In the meantime I want to explain a few things to you. If you join my practice, I will spend a lot of time with you to find out why you have been so unlucky. Have you heard my talks?" He asked Jackie's mother.

"Just about all of them," she said. "They are truly uplifting."

"So you know my way of doing things. If Jackie wants my help, I will gladly give it to her. For now I simply want to help you get over your sadness with a few thoughts.

"The way I look at a miscarriage is that it wasn't the right time for the baby to enter this world. Its physical body may have tried but its spirit wasn't willing. Perhaps it was trying to tell you that there is something wrong with you that needs to be corrected before it is willing to try again. Because it will try again, so we must make life easier for it. That means somehow improving you and your whole baby making apparatus. At this stage I can't guess what we must do, but try not to despair.

"Think of your baby floating somewhere out there, waiting to come into this world to be with you. He or she hasn't died. That was merely the physical side of things having a go but not finding the environment right. Your baby is somewhere out there waiting for you. Picture a baby floating anywhere you like. Don't make it a boy or a girl, just a baby. Talk to it and tell it we are going to make things easier for it to come. Tell it to wait until you are ready. Tell it we will let it know when to try again."

There was a knock on the door. Jackie's mother let the midwife in. Dr. James said, "This is Francis Fulton. I will leave you in her capable hands. She knows what I think. We have helped a number of women who have had a miscarriage and they have all succeeded to have a normal live baby in the end. So start dreaming of your baby."

When Dr. James left, Jackie felt so much better. She loved his explanation for her problems. She was soon able to picture her baby floating in the sky on a fluffy white cloud. She felt it didn't matter whether he was right or not. The very idea he suggested she conjure up was sufficient to make her feel so much better, especially the idea that her baby wasn't dead, but merely waiting for the right moment to try again.

Jackie didn't need to go into hospital. Dr. James was right about that. Her miscarriage had been complete. She stayed with her parents until their new house was ready. She registered with Dr. James as she felt he had already been kind to her, and her mother told her of what he had done for so many other people, especially the ones with unusual problems. Dr. James invited her to visit him at his surgery when she was ready, asking her not to try to conceive until he had had an opportunity to talk to her. He told her he would like her to bring her husband and her mother with her if possible, and that her father would be welcome if he wanted to come. In the end he was away on business when the others met Dr. James a couple of weeks later after morning surgery. In the meantime, he had left his usual forms for Jackie to think about and try to complete before they met, and of course to bring them with her.

"Before we start trying to find out why you have had those three miscarriages, I want to explain one or two things to you. First, at this stage, I consider both the mother and the father to have an equal responsibility to achieve a perfect conception, so I will be going through your history as well, John, to see what we can find.

"Most people, and plenty of doctors, don't think about the fact that, in the initial stages, the sperm and the egg have very specific jobs to do, and it is very important that both be in prime condition when they meet. Once they have met, assuming they are both healthy, yes it is the mother's job to nurture the combination of the two and bring a healthy live child into the world. At this stage, all the father has to do is sit back and wait. His job is effectively over, although I hope he will look after his wife and be of as much help as she needs.

"It takes about three months for the origins of an egg to reach sufficient maturity to create a good baby, but four months to develop a good sperm. At that stage, I want the originators, that's you two John and Jackie, to be in excellent health. So what I am really saying is that ideally I don't want you, Jackie, to become pregnant until I feel you are both ready. That therefore means I would like you to use condoms for at least the next few months, possibly up to six months, depending on how long it takes to get you both in prime condition.

"All too often, however, couples are in a hurry to start a family, and they put me, and themselves, under a lot of pressure. Is my idea acceptable to you?" Asked Dr. James.

"That's fine by me," said Jackie. "I would like a rest for now anyway. Ok with you, John?"

"You know I will do anything to make sure we get it right. So where do we start?"

"Let's start with Jackie," said Dr. James. "Just give me a minute or two to look at these forms." And with that, he read them quickly, looking for items of relevance. When he was ready he said, "You've said yes to more than I expected. Are any of your problems really important, or are they just a bit of a nuisance?"

"I've had tummy upsets for quite a long time really. It's hard to remember when they started. I'm told its Irritable Bowel Syndrome, but I don't really know what that is."

"It's just what it says. You have a named diagnosis that basically describes your symptoms. I see you have had cystitis a few times. The end of the word ..itis comes from the Latin and means inflammation of, in this case your cyst or bladder. What I'm interested in is why or what's caused it. I see you acknowledge feeling tired. How tired? How does it affect you?

"Which question should I answer first? Let's take the fatigue. I rather assume it is because I work hard during the day at work, then have housework to do when I get home. I often fall asleep in front of the tele. Many is the time that John has had to wake me to say it is time to go to bed. Even after a good eight hours sleep, I don't wake up refreshed. On Sundays I sometimes lie in until midmorning, but it doesn't do much good. I can get up if I have to to go somewhere, so it's probably just me. A lot of my friends are the same."

"We'll come back to that later. What job do you do?"

"I work in the local photocopying shop; well I used to. I had to leave when we moved here, so I'm looking for a job. I'm not in a hurry. I might have a few weeks when I can please myself and get up when I want to and go shopping with mum or something like that."

"How long did you work there?"

"About six years I think."

"How old are you now?"

"I'm twenty-four."

"How old were you when you got married?"

"I was nineteen. A child bride many of my friends said, but I had known John since I was eight. We went to the same school for years. There was never any question about my not marrying him. It was the most natural thing in the world. We have virtually been inseparable ever since. Now all we want is to complete it by having a baby of our own."

"Don't worry. I'm sure we will soon put you right. How old were you when you had your first miscarriage?"

"Twenty-one. Twenty-two for my second, now twenty-four for my third. Does this all mean anything to you? Mum has tried to explain how your mind works. I can't see where it is leading."

"I deliberately asked those questions in a particular order so as not to give away what I was thinking of. It may be a long shot, but there is a time coincidence that you started working in the photocopying shop six years ago, presumably aged eighteen, and had your first miscarriage aged twenty-one, so two or three years later. Did you have good ventilation where you worked?"

"Now I come to think of it, they have only just put ventilation in. There were two of us working in a tiny room at the back of the shop. It had a chemical smell all the time, although we soon got used to it."

"I'm sure that wasn't a healthy environment," said Dr. James, "but who knows? It may have something to do with your problems. Usually I find a number of causes that, all together, seem to produce a problem, whereas on their own are not powerful enough to do much harm. To be fair to you, there are a lot of chemicals in our world that we are exposed to, and basically we are remarkably ignorant of what they do to our bodies. It seems they can be put onto the market with only minimal testing, possibly sometimes with none at all. Still there's nothing I can do about it except point out to patients the possibility they might be doing harm.

"Let's change the subject. For a woman of five foot four inches tall, I would say you are a little overweight at just over ten stones. Care to comment?"

"In my teens I was around eight-and-a-half stones. I was very active and played in school teams at netball and hockey. I was quite a good tennis player too. But since I left school I haven't really had time to do anything like that. If I'm being honest, I couldn't be bothered. I just didn't seem to want to do all that running around. It's a shame really because I quite enjoyed it at the time. Perhaps putting on a bit of weight also made me lose interest in any form of exercise."

"Any idea what your tummy problems are all about?"

"Not really. My last doctor tried one or two different tablets. The one I am on now seems to calm things down well enough, so long as I take them regularly.

"Have you had many courses of antibiotics for your cystitis?"

"Actually no. He didn't want to give them to me if he could avoid it, so I never had any. He said the most likely cause for it was a bug called E. coli. The E stands for some long medical name, and he told me it can be controlled by taking doses of sodium bicarbonate.

He was right. It works every time. He felt that doctors prescribe antibiotics far too easily and that they may be causing problems that we are not clear about."

"He sounds like a man after my heart. I absolutely agree with him. Sodium bicarbonate nearly always does the trick, but my next question is, why do you keep getting E. coli infections? Where do they come from? Presumably from your bowels. I have a suspicion we need to start there. Sort out your IBS."

Dr. James then proceeded to examine her carefully. He concentrated on her neck area some of the time. When he had finished he said he would like to take a blood sample for a number of routine tests, just to make sure everything was within an adequate range. Jackie got dressed. "So what do you think, Doctor?"

"Well I believe you have a few problems that shouldn't be too difficult to sort out, but they are somehow affecting your ability to hold onto a baby. We should be able to get that right soon enough. I think the first thing to do is to sort out your diet, get rid of your IBS and clean out any infections there that may be causing your episodes of cystitis. So I would like you please to stop all forms of dairy products, all caffeine, all alcohol, all junk food, any chemicals added to foods, all added sugar and all fizzy drinks.

"I would like you to eat a lot of vegetables, fruit, salad items, whole grains, fish especially oily fish, eggs and some meat. Try to buy organic wherever possible, but don't worry if you can't. Here is my explanation about dairy products. It should answer all your questions about it. I know everyone thinks milk is good for you but many doctors and scientists have a different opinion. You are perfectly at liberty to disagree if you want to, but I would like you to follow my advice for now and see what happens.

"You may have an unusual food intolerance, something that is not obvious, which is upsetting your bowels, but we've got to start somewhere. We can worry about that later. You may go through what are called withdrawal symptoms for the first few days, in which case you may feel more tired, have backache and possibly quite a nasty headache, although you don't appear to suffer from headaches as a rule."

"No. That's something I don't seem to suffer from, thank goodness," said Jackie, "but John does a little, every now and then."

"To make things easier, why don't you both follow the same diet for now. If you do, John, you mustn't let things slip when you are away from home, at work. So take food with you that you have prepared yourself, so you won't make any mistakes. Incidentally, if either of you does suffer from withdrawal symptoms, take a few doses of sodium bicarbonate, yes, our old friend. It will help to make your body become alkaline to antagonise the acidity that is produced at the time. That's why it helps your cystitis. The E. coli bug cannot survive in an alkaline urine.

"Things are not likely to have changed much in a week, but you never know. You would be surprised how quickly things do change with some people. I should have the results of your blood tests by then, so if you want to, come back in about a week or two's time. Oh, and before I forget, may I suggest you both have a good dose of old-fashioned Epsom Salts to give your bowels a good clear out as you start your new better eating habit.

"In the meantime, I will lend you an old-fashioned thermometer. I would like you, Jackie, to take your temperature for ten minutes in your armpit before getting out of bed in the morning. Not under your tongue as usual, but in your armpit. It is most important that you shake the thermometer down before you go to bed and not just before you use it in the morning, otherwise you will get a false reading. Leave it ready by your bedside for use in the morning. If necessary you may need to set your alarm for ten minutes earlier than usual, so that you have time to do it properly. On second thoughts, you can take it as soon as John gets up because you are a lady of leisure at present. Once it is ready, you can put the thermometer back on your bedside table and read it later on. It won't change. The reading will stay where it is until you shake it down again before going to bed. That's what the kink in the glass is for. Record your temperatures daily and make a note of where you are in your monthly cycle. Bring the results with you when you next come. I will tell you what all that is about when I next see you. If you have any problems or are worried about anything, please don't hesitate to ring me. I'm here to help."

"Now you, John. Your form only suggests you suffer from headaches occasionally, so you seem to be in good condition. Your job is as an office manager. Are you exposed to any chemicals in any way, perhaps at home in the garden, for instance?"

"No. Not at all that I can think of at present. By and large I would say I am quite fit. Just those headaches every so often."

"Ok!" Said Dr. James. "Do you think you could be on the same diet as Jackie? It should make things easier for you both. We can then see what happens to your headaches."

Jackie and John saw Dr. James more than two weeks later. "It wasn't practical to come sooner because John was very busy at work, and I went to stay with a friend for a while, who needed some help," said Jackie. "In any case, we were intrigued at what was happening to us. John had a fearful headache three days after we last saw you and my back ached something rotten. As we were both suffering in our own ways, we simply laughed and took some bicarbonate of soda, although laughing was more painful for John with his headache than it was for me with my backache. But both soon went and now we feel a lot better, John in particular.

"In the notes you gave us, you advised us to try to eat different things on different days and to try not to eat the same things every day. I was intrigued at your suggestion that I might have an unusual food reaction, so I watched what happened very carefully. There is no doubt in my mind that eggs somehow upset me, so I have cut them out completely. My bowels are so much better, almost normal."

"How are your energy levels?" Dr. James asked Jackie.

"Hm. That's the bit that hasn't changed much. I was hoping to come back in here bouncing with energy, but I'm afraid not."

"Have you brought your temperature charts?"

"Yes. Here they are. I was a bit surprised. I thought normal was 98.4° Fahrenheit, but I didn't get there once. The best I could manage was 95.8. We tested John and he was much better. What's the significance of that?"

"It is a good clinical indicator of how well your thyroid gland is functioning. Actually normal for your armpit is one degree lower, so 97.4 is normal. Even then you got nowhere near it, but John did. It suggests your thyroid gland needs a helping hand. Most of your blood tests were fine, but one of your thyroid tests was right at the bottom end of the reference range. Most doctors would tell you it is normal because it is within the local laboratory's reference range, but reference ranges are exactly that. They are advisory and should not be taken as sacrosanct.

"Reference ranges can vary between laboratories, and should be taken together with all other information. Because you are tired and a bit overweight, I thought you might have hypothyroidism, which would explain a lot. That is why I spent so much time examining your neck, but there is nothing wrong with it as far as I could see or feel.

"So you don't have clinical hypothyroidism, but, in my opinion, your metabolism needs help. All in all, I think you should benefit from some iodine to feed your thyroid gland. It will also help all your hormones. Most doctors think it is only the thyroid gland that uses iodine, but in fact many parts of your body need it. It is also good at killing off unwanted bugs, so swallowing it should help to clean you out. It is old-fashioned and safe. I keep using that word, but I like so many of the old substances. They have survived the test of time. I wouldn't be without iodine. I think it is one of the best chemicals to put on cuts and grazes.

"There is an old test to see if you are in need of iodine. Put a big drop on one of your wrists, put both wrists together so that you have a yellow dot on both wrists, let them dry and see how long it takes for the yellow dots to disappear. If they are still there in twenty-four hours, you don't need any, but if they disappear in a few hours, it suggests you are in need of iodine. This whole area of medicine has been thoroughly explained by Dr. Broda Barnes in an easy-to-read book, written especially for the public rather than the medical profession. ♥"

"So with any luck you have got your diet right. Your low thyroid functioning should improve with the iodine I will give you. I want you to take a mixture of vitamins and minerals, especially zinc. When I examined you, I noticed quite a number of white spots on your fingernails. Most people think that is a sign of a calcium deficiency. It's not. It means a deficiency of zinc, which, to be fair, most doctors have never heard of in relations to human beings.

"Zinc is important for a considerable number of bodily functions, including the efficient functioning of your immune system. Once you are pregnant there is some evidence that it helps to prevent certain foetal abnormalities, such as spina bifida, although folic acid has been clearly shown to be important for that. You could say your miscarriages may have been saving your baby from one of these deformities. But that's a long shot. There's no way I could say that every child with that problem might not have had it if their mother had had enough zinc during her pregnancy. These things are far too complicated and multifactorial.

"So the only thing we still need to do something about is getting rid of the photocopying chemicals. To be fair I don't know if they are relevant, but we might as well assume they are. I will give you an herbal tonic to stimulate your liver. You can make it and drink it like a tea. The instructions are on the bottle.

"Now that you are feeling so much better, John, I would like you to have your sperms examined in about a couple of months. We might as well check you in that way."

Jackie visited Dr. James every so often. The iodine drops he gave her seemed to help her levels of energy improve, and her extra weight gradually fall off, although Dr. James suggested it might be a combination of all the things she was doing. About four months after she had started his various recommendations, Jackie and John saw Dr.

♥ To obtain a copy of this book see Appendix 2, note 12.

James once again, a week after he had taken another blood sample to see what her thyroid levels were like.

"I'm much happier with these levels," he said. "They are now well into the middle of the laboratory range, so I can't possibly find fault with them. You have lost about a stone in weight, at a nice speed, although you may want to lose another half-a-stone to be perfect, also your morning armpit temperatures are now normal. On the other hand, have you noticed anything about them during this last month?"

"Yes. They are higher in the second half than in the first half. I feel that means something but I can't quite remember what."

"You now have an absolutely classical cycle. I don't see them very often. Your period starts twenty-eight days after the last one, and you ovulate on day fourteen, as indicated by the rise in temperature. As you, John, are also feeling so well, probably because you also changed your diet to a better one, I think you could now try for that baby as soon as you want to. If you want to time it perfectly, have intercourse when your temperature shows that rise, but surely it is better to make love when you feel like it and let nature take over.

"As the white spots on your finger nails have now gone, I would like you to continue on the iodine drops but change your supplement regime to capsules of desiccated fruits and vegetables♥. I will show you an interesting pilot study that has been done on them that supports the idea of a pregnant woman taking them throughout her pregnancy. Clearly the more you have in the form of fruits and vegetables the better. I think just about everyone agrees with that, and you will get all the folic acid you need. You could take a further 200mcg if you wanted to, just to be sure.

If you can afford it, I would suggest you also take them, John, but I'm afraid they are not available on the NHS. Incidentally your sperm count and the activity of your sperms is excellent, so that's that out of the way.

♥ See Appendix 1 for a copy of this study and Appendix 2, note 2 for further information.

Incidentally your sperm count and the activity of your sperms is excellent, so that's that out of the way."

A month later, an elated Jackie was back in Dr. James's surgery.

"We couldn't wait," she said. "I know it sounds silly, but I have dreamt many times of our baby hovering over us, apparently waiting to come to me. After we last saw you and you told us you thought we were ready, that night I dreamed that the baby had changed what it was doing. Until then it had simply been lying peacefully on its cloud, almost telling me it was quite happy where it was, suggesting it wasn't ready to come to me. But that night I dreamed it was no longer on its cloud, but was floating in the air diving towards me and back out again. Somehow I felt it was telling me that everything was right with us and that it could now come to me.

"Perhaps the most extraordinary thing was that I said to it 'ok. Come on then. Come to me." And do you know what it said? It said 'don't be silly. You've got to get pregnant first'. Poor John. I woke him up there and then, but it took another week before it happened. I know which night I got pregnant. So here I am. I have no fears at all that I will have a miscarriage this time, but I'm still going to be sensible. I'm sure those fruit and vegetable capsules made me feel even better within about two weeks. John thought he felt better after a week. Could they work that quickly?"

"I have heard of others seeming to benefit that quickly before, but I know of others in whom it has taken a year. Fortunately they could see the logic of them to just kept taking them. I know they cost a bit, but people who think these things through find they eat less food, so their monthly food bills are that much lower to compensate.

Dr. James repeated what he had already said to Jackie about the various stages she would go through. He described things as though he were going through it all with a first time pregnant mum, not someone who had already had three miscarriages. She took it all in her confident stride. The pregnancy went to plan, passing normally the stages when her miscarriages had previously occurred. She went into labour the day she was due. She delivered a seven pound baby boy, surprising every one at how quickly she progressed and how easy and comparatively straightforward the whole birth was. Dr. James had already given her some homoeopathic drops of arnica 30C, advising her to put a drop under her tongue every hour until she delivered and for the first day after she delivered, then slowly to tail off the frequency.

Jackie had her baby in hospital. She had wanted Dr. James to deliver the baby at home, but he said that, because of her history, hers was considered a special case, and the Specialist almost insisted, although she hoped she might be able to persuade Dr. James. He had no doubt that everything would be fine, but advised her gently to follow the Specialist's advice, who compromised by saying she could go home within hours of the birth if everything was alright. Jackie's labour had started at six in the morning, and she delivered four hours later. John attended the whole thing. Dr. James popped in to see them as soon as his morning surgery had finished.

"I hope you won't be too embarrassed," Jackie said, "but we would like to call him David after you, and Sam after my grandfather. Last night I had another strange dream. I haven't had one about the baby since he told me I had to get pregnant before he could come into me. A lot of weird things were going on as they usually do in dreams, some of which I haven't been able to connect with anything, but this time I saw him literally fly out of my tummy and land in my arms. As he landed, he said 'hello. I'm David.' So I knew he was going to be a boy. I had asked the hospital not to tell me whether the baby was a boy or a girl. Then he said 'do you like me?' The cheeky beggar. Then he fell asleep in my arms."

"They have already helped me with breastfeeding. I'm going to enjoy that. I intend to feed him myself for at least a year, hopefully for longer. I want to give him the best possible start in life. I shall talk to him all the time. That will teach him to be cheeky to me. So we will just have to see how things go."

"So another proud couple, sorry three of them, sat in the front row reserved for the evening's special people," said Maud. "No sorry.

Four of them, as Jackie was already pregnant again and well past the danger time. The vicar had a book prepared with a summary of each person's story. That's how I remember so many of them. I've got my copy here, and, of course, the recordings." ♥

♥For more information about preparing for pregnancy see Appendix 2, note 3

Chapter 40

"Was Dr. James alone in what he did, or were there any other doctors treating patients like he did?" Asked Patrick.

"He was apparently one of a small group of doctors in the UK," said Maud, "who started to practise they way he did, and they tried to meet twice a year to talk about their experiences. It started small and gradually expanded, but never involved large numbers of doctors, perhaps a hundred or so. Dr. James once told me their Medical Society was started by two senior Hospital Consultants who gave what they did a degree of credibility. Most of the doctors who became involved did so because they had benefited at the hands of a doctor like Dr. James, although he said he was one of the few who took it up purely out of scientific curiosity. He had been to America and Canada where a few doctors had started a Medical Society of their own, and he became a Fellow of that Society in due course, one of only three in the whole of the UK.

"Most of the doctors who became involved left the National Health Service rather sadly, basically because each first consultation needed so much time like 1½ hours. The NHS could never allow so much time, even though Dr. James did with the few patients he saw from outside his practice catchment area, like Heather Herzog. He said he could have easily gone into private practice, but liked the system of the NHS.

"As Dr. James was nearing retirement, one of his medical colleagues, Dr. Peter Dodson, who had started treating patients in a similar way roughly when Dr. James had, had a large private clinic in Scotland. Many doctors had sat in on his consultations and he kept hoping one of them would want to take over his practice, but no one seemed to be willing to take on such a responsibility. To do so would have been quite a risk."

One day a lady in her forties, Dr. Hilary McDonald, a PhD Psychologist working in the specialist heart department of one of the Scottish Teaching Hospital, consulted Dr. Dodson because of her rheumatoid arthritis. Her work was to help patients with any psychological problems they might have as a result of what they would have to go through if they had a heart transplant. As you can probably imagine, a heart transplant must surely create a lot of mental problems for some patients, let alone the suffering they are likely to have gone through before needing a transplant. Hilary McDonald had been all over the world and spent an absolute fortune trying to find someone who could help her. Fortunately she was very wealthy so the costs didn't matter, but, however much she spent, no one seemed able to provide her with any significant degree of relief. The arthritis was in her hands, feet, elbows, knees and jaw. Her large joints such as hips and spine seemed to be spared the worst pain, although they were affected a little.

Hilary went to see Dr. Dodson at the suggestion of a friend whose migraines he had helped. She had no idea whether he could help her or not, but was so desperate, she was willing to try anything. As usual he took a long history from her and examined her carefully, making copious notes about her condition. He asked her what approaches other doctors had tried. She said she had consulted three of the top Rheumatoid Specialists in America, which had cost her an absolute fortune. She had also seen at least two Specialists in the UK.

The first doctor had tried a variety of drugs, most of which had either not made much difference or had made her feel really quite ill so she had had to stop taking them. Some of the Specialists had tried a variety of drugs by injection, including gold injections, while others had tried to suppress her immune system. Nothing worked. She was becoming desperate. She couldn't sleep because of the pain so she was permanently tired and her joints were becoming badly deformed. As with many rheumatoid sufferers she was also anaemic.

It took Hilary a long time to get undressed and dressed again. She had brought a friend with her to help her, because getting anything over her head was almost an impossibility, and doing up buttons something she simply could not do. Life really had become very hard for her and she was thinking of stopping work. Travelling into a busy city on a daily basis from her home was such a problem.

When she was settled, Dr. Dodson said, "One more question. Has anyone suggested you change your diet?"

"No. Only drugs, by mouth, by injection and even up my backside. I thought someone was going to suggest I try snorting something up my nose at one point. I said so half jokingly to one of the doctors. He didn't find it at all funny. He was a bit autocratic. He didn't have a sense of humour. Anyway. Back to your question. Why do you ask?"

"My experience is that almost any condition, whether it be arthritis, asthma, irritable bowel syndrome or migraines, for example, is likely to improve if the person were to look at what they eat. From experience of many hundreds of arthritis sufferers, I have not found a single one who has not benefited to a degree from changing their diet, some only a little, some dramatically so. I have a list of foods that seem to cause inflammation in some people, but they are different foods in different people. You patients are not all the same, but certain foods crop up more often than others. I would like you to go on what we call 'an elimination diet', that means only eating a small list of foods that have been shown to be comparatively safe. You could start by fasting on water only for five days, but that is much harder and I don't think you need to go that far."

"Could my arthritis be caused simply by something I am eating that is somehow causing inflammation? Could it really be as simple as that?" Asked Hilary

"Yes. It's very possible. Did any of the doctors you saw ever try to think of why you have arthritis? I doubt it. They never seem to think of anything but suppressing the symptoms with drugs. That seems to be the way with modern medicine - suppress the symptoms. We discussed our approach at one of our meetings some time ago and I well remember Dr. James saying that he had had an argument with a doctor once who thought such an idea was ridiculous.

"Apparently the subject had come up at a dinner party he was at with his wife Elizabeth shortly before then and she had come up with an interesting explanation, which is difficult to refute. She had studied Biology at University as part of her overall training and had a good brain, apart from which she had been involved many times at parties helping to defend her husband's form of practice. She asked this doctor friend of theirs how he treated patients with arthritis, which received the expected reply of 'with anti-inflammatory drugs, of course.'

"'What does the patient do with those drugs,' Elizabeth asked. When the doctor friend appeared not to know what she was getting at, she said, 'to save me asking you any more questions, let me make my point. I assume the patient swallows the drugs, which enter the bloodstream and circulate round to the joints to put out the fire in them. If swallowing drugs can help calm the inflammation, why is it not perfectly reasonable to suggest that something swallowed in the form of a food caused the inflammation in the first place?' Their friend had no answer.

"Ok!" said Hilary. "Point taken. What's on your list of foods?"

"I want you eat only rice, lamb, peas and pears for the next two weeks and drink as much water as you like. You can mix them in any combination you like and you may well become rather bored eating only those foods. Please do not cheat and eat anything else. No gravy, no cups of tea, only filtered water to drink. You should lose some weight."

"That will be a bonus," said Hilary. "Any idea how much?"

"You could lose fourteen pounds in two to three weeks," said Dr. Dodson. "That should at least take some of the strain off your ankles, which should help over all."

Two weeks later, a thirteen pounds lighter Hilary strode into Dr. Dodson's consulting room with a broad smile on her face. Two weeks earlier it had taken her quite a long time to get there, in particular because his consulting room was upstairs.

"All that money I spent on all those doctors, and all I had to do was stop eating something. They've got a thing or two to learn. And all those nasty drugs they put me on. It makes me shudder just to think of them. I shall write to them all and tell them, but I don't suppose it will make any difference. They probably have closed minds. After all, they are top people in their profession. But you never know. I might get through to one of them."

Hilary then had the tiresome slow job of introducing foods back into her diet to see what the former culprits were. It took her many weeks and needed a lot of support from Dr. Dodson and his staff, but they were accustomed to this. The final outcome was a delighted Hilary, who told everyone in her department what had happened to her and how she had discovered the causes of her arthritis. Her best friend there was the Consultant-in-charge of the department, Dr. Josephine Maybury, who, much to Hilary's surprise, asked her a lot of questions and took a real interest in what she had done. She casually asked the name of the doctor, and eventually found out where he practised.

Josephine Maybury's mother had suffered from Irritable Bowel Syndrome for as long as she could remember. She had regular bouts of pain and nausea, though she was seldom sick. She alternated between constipation and diarrhoea, never knowing which it would be. She had many other bowels symptoms, in fact just about all it was possible to have. She had tried every drug anyone could think of, including any new one that came on to the market. One or two made a little difference to begin with, but none lasted for long. She became more and more dejected and depressed. She even mentioned suicide at one time, or, more to the point, said they would all be better off without her. Her husband was sympathetic but powerless to do anything useful. If her tummy was particularly bad all he could do was stroke it gently, which seemed to help a bit.

Josephine took her mother to see Dr. Dodson, who went through her history in his usual way. Then he told her that, as it was her intestines that were causing her so much trouble, he thought it was perfectly logical that something she was putting into them was upsetting them.

"Why on earth didn't I think of that?" Exclaimed Josephine's mother. "It's so obvious! Why didn't all my doctors suggest it?"

Josephine's mother went on to Dr. Dodson's elimination diet, and, as he expected, virtually all her symptoms cleared within about ten days. As she had been going through a phase of constipation, he advised her to have a suitable dose of old-fashioned Epsom Salts to get her started, which did the trick. She then had the tedious job of reintroducing foods to find the culprits.

"The point of this story," said Maud, "is that Dr. Josephine Maybury was so impressed by Dr. Dodson's treatment of her friend and mother that she went and sat in with him and learned as much as she could. When Dr. Dodson retired, Dr. Maybury left the National Health Service and took over his practice completely. Some of her doctor friends said she was mad to give up a promising medical career, as they thought she would become a Professor in due course, while others greatly admired her courage in changing stream at her time of life.

"Dr. James helped her to settle, and, as he had retired himself by then, he was free to spend many days giving her a helping hand. What particularly fascinated him was something Dr. Maybury once said to him. She told him that they had regular weekly departmental meetings when the Specialist Microbiologist would put up slides of biopsy samples of various tissues of the body. They would then discuss what they were going to do and how they were going to treat the patient. 'But the one question no one ever asked,' said Dr. Maybury, 'was 'why? What's the cause?' Now she asks every patient that question, and tries to help provide an answer."

Chapter 41

"Did Dr. James have any difficulty getting his message across to patients?" Asked Patrick.

"Oh Yes!" Said Maud. "Well to begin with anyway. When he first came here he settled himself into the practice carefully, but the way he sorted out Ada Townsend and old man Isaac Pemberton got round so quickly we soon realised we had someone special. Dr. James said he went into General Practice to start using the special skills he had learned by then, and he tried to apply them as much as possible when he did the eighteen month long locum in the big city centre. But he said he was never really happy there as people came and went too often.

"He wanted to look after people's long-term care, deliver their babies, see their children grow up and deliver their babies, much like the old-fashioned GP of a bygone year. As his father told him, in the old days, doctors joined a practice as a junior member, possibly became a partner after ten years, and eventually became the senior GP as the older ones retired or simply died of old age. His own father went through that process, staying in the same practice for fifty-five years, only retiring when he was eighty, and he wanted to practise the same way. That's why he came to our area to work in a single-handed practice. He said if he was the only doctor in the practice there was no one else to criticise him. He felt it was small and compact here, people being content to stay in the area and not keep moving around the place. A bit like me, perhaps, though not so much of a stick-in-the-mud.

"Dr. James told me once that he desperately wanted to start sorting people out the way he eventually did, but he felt he had to tread carefully to begin with. He didn't know people, nor did he know how they would react to something new, so he selected very carefully the patients who he hoped would be open to a different approach, usually people whose condition was bad enough to affect their lives or whose condition wasn't responding to the drugs a Specialist had put them on. Even then it surprised him how some patients were only interested in trying the latest drug.

"There was one young lady, Daphne Hinton, who initially seemed to question what he could do until he opened her eyes to her condition."

After he had been at Stead Norton for about a year, Dr. James received a letter from a local hospital Specialist about Daphne, who had been seen for her yearly follow-up appointment. The details in the letter and Daphne's diagnosis intrigued Dr. James, so he rang her up and suggest she pay him a visit as he might be able to help her. Her mother took the call and said she would happily bring Daphne in in a few days time.

Dr. James was in his surgery late one evening a few days later when Daphne's mother rang to say her daughter was coming in to see him in the morning, but to be aware that Daphne couldn't see how Dr. James could possibly help her when there seemed to be nothing more the Specialist could suggest. She reminded him that Daphne had an odd-sounding name to her condition.

When she entered his consulting room with her mother the next day, a rather serious Daphne immediately virtually repeated what her mother had said to Dr. James the evening before, that she couldn't see how Dr. James could possibly help her when her Specialist couldn't. "You see," said Daphne, "I have this unusual condition called Idiopathic Thrombocytopaenic Purpura."

"How long did it take you to learn that long name so that you could say it word perfect?" Asked Dr. James, hoping to relax her a bit, but to no avail. So he then said, "Until somewhere in the middle of the nineteen hundreds, doctors had to study both Greek and Latin. Then they dropped the need for Greek and finally Latin. When I studied medicine neither was a requirement, although I had studied both of them at school.

"Despite this loss of the need to be fairly good at Greek and Latin, many medical names, based on those two languages, have remained to this day. Perhaps the most commonly used medical words end in the letters '..itis', which basically means 'inflammation of'. Examples would be words like tonsillitis, appendicitis and cystitis, the first part of the whole world indicating the organ that is inflamed, so your tonsils, your appendix and your cyst or bladder. What I'm trying to say is that the names doctors give to many medical diagnoses are really a description of the symptoms you are telling him about, but in an old foreign language.

"So! Before you tell me anything about you, let me do the talking and tell you all about you."

"Can you do that?" Asked Daphne.

"Let's see then," said Dr. James. "If I were to examine you now, I would find bruises all over your body, or on certain parts of it, which are not painful to the touch like a normal bruise is after you knock yourself."

"How do you know that?" Asked Daphne.

"You have just told me. The last word of your diagnosis – Purpura – is Latin for bruising. The reason for the bruises can be found in the second long word – thrombocytopaenic – which basically means you have low levels of circulating thrombocytes, also known as platelets by doctors. Thrombocytes are responsible for clotting. If they overdo things you get a thrombosis. If you don't clot properly you bleed, a bit like Haemophilia, which you have probably heard of. That long word thrombocytopaenic is a mixture of Latin and Greek that simply means, as I've already said, low levels of circulating thrombocytes or platelets."

"Yes, my Specialist said that I don't have enough of something circulating in my blood. I didn't really understand what he said though."

"So that takes care of the words 'thrombocytopaenic' and 'purpura'.

"Have you any idea what the first word 'idiopathic' means?" Asked Dr. James. When Daphne said she didn't, he said, "Roughly translated from the Greek it means 'I don't know what the cause is'.

At last Daphne smiled.

Chapter 42

"**I** know you told us a couple of stories about cancer, but did Dr. James see many patients with cancer?" Asked Lynda. "I once worked on a ward with cancer patients. I couldn't stand it. I found it so depressing so I asked to be transferred to another ward. They all seemed to have lost hope. All their hair had fallen out because of the treatment they were being given and they all felt so sick. The ward seemed to smell of death to me, although it was probably the smell of chemotherapy. Everyone seemed so miserable. No one smiled. They had nothing to smile about. I hated it. I don't know what makes a doctor become an Oncologist. Most Oncologists I have ever met seem unable to look their patients in the eye. I did a short stint in the cancer Outpatient Department. Patients would ask questions, which the doctors would avoid answering if they could. It was horrible."

"Dr. James admitted that helping cancer patients could sometimes be really difficult. People called it 'The Big C'. It seemed to frighten them, and a diagnosis of cancer put the fear of God into them. I suppose it's because people think cancer is something gradually growing out of control in their body, a bit like some of those films about weird aliens growing inside the body and suddenly bursting out – well perhaps not quite so dramatic, but you know what I mean. For reasons he never understood, he said cancer patients put their complete trust in their Oncologist, leaving it entirely up to him to decide on the most appropriate form of treatment for them. 'After all, Doctor,' they would say. 'You are the expert.'

"Dr. James said he had a colleague who, when she was a junior doctor, was asked to give someone a dose of chemotherapy in an intravenous infusion in the normal way. The thought worried her and by mistake she dropped the glass vial of concentrated chemotherapy on the floor and it smashed. She ran off to find something to wipe it up with, taking a minute or two. When she came back, she found to her horror that the chemotherapy drug had literally dissolved a hole in the linoleum covering the floor. That put her off chemotherapy drugs for life and she refused ever to recommend them to patients from then on. If such drugs could dissolve a carpet so quickly, she wondered what on earth it would do to a person's body, even though it would be diluted before being given to the person.

"Dr. James had a similar attitude, preferring his patients not to have chemotherapy. He said if he ever developed cancer himself, he would rather die of the cancer than have chemotherapy. He said he had read a survey of Oncologists somewhere, which described that seventy-five per cent said they would not have chemotherapy if they were to develop cancer.

"However he insisted that it was not his job to tell patients not to have such treatment, nor did he ever encourage them to have it. He said that had to be a decision they made for themselves. I told you how he helped them decide when I described Margaret Webster and her pancreatic tumour. If he ever found someone who wanted to follow his approach, he said the first thing he tried to do was explain why they had developed cancer and take the fear out of the whole thing.

"To begin with, nearly all his cancer patients had whatever they were recommended to have by the hospital. You have to remember that doctors were considered Gods by most people and you didn't argue with them. You simply did as you were told. Dr. James once cheekily asked me if I knew the difference between God and a doctor. He said the answer was that God didn't think he was a doctor!

"However, as the years went by, he noticed more and more people with cancer questioning their Specialists. I remember very clearly Alison Goodyear telling me herself of her experience in the hospital. She was a feisty little thing, full of determination. She had been diagnosed with ovarian cancer and had just seen the Specialist, after which she waited rather a long time in the waiting room. When she asked one of the nurses why she was having to wait so long, she was told, 'The doctor is trying to decide how to treat you'. The nurse was visibly shocked when Alison replied, 'Do you mind! I will decide how I am going to be treated'.

"The other thing that might have caused the change in people's attitude was the internet. I haven't a clue what it's all about and wouldn't even know how to turn a computer on, let alone use one. But I gather it's something to do with information. Isn't it supposed to be like an information highway or something similar?" Asked Maud of Patrick and Lynda.

"You're not as stupid as you like to pretend, Gran," said Patrick. "But you're quite right. What would you do with a computer, anyway?"

"Cancer seems so much more common these days," said Maud. There's got to be a reason. You hear of so many people developing it.

"When people got it in the past, they just got on with the treatment, but so many of them died. I think young people today have seen what cancer or the treatment for it have done to their older relatives that they are beginning to question whether to have it themselves when they get cancer.

"Alison told me herself that she had looked up her condition on her computer and she said there were so many different ways of treating her condition she was rather confused. She asked Dr. James for his opinion, but he hesitated to tell her what to do until she said to him, 'would you recommend your wife to have chemotherapy were she to develop ovarian cancer?' He apparently said he hoped he would have kept a sufficient eye on her to make sure she didn't develop cancer, but, if she still had, no he wouldn't recommend it."

That did it for Alison. She made a decision there and then not to have chemotherapy. She asked Dr. James to tell her what to do. He said he would under no circumstances tell her what to do, but he would help her decide what to do. "So what are my choices?" Alison asked.

"What's your husband's attitude?" Asked Dr. James.

"I'm not sure," replied Alison, "but I know he will support me whatever I decide."

"Ok!" Said Dr. James. "Can you come back when I'm not so busy and we can have a chat, the three of us?

"Will it be ok to bring my mother and father?" Asked Alison.

"The more the merrier," said Dr. James. "I'll make sure we have enough chairs in here when you come."

A few days later, Alison, her husband, her mother and her father came and sat down in front of Dr. James.

"Before we start," began Dr. James, "I just want to let you know that I would like to record this discussion so you can have a copy and play it back as often as you like. Is that all right with you all?" They all said it was a good idea, so Dr. James turned the tape on.

"I'm so glad you persuaded Alison not to have chemotherapy," said her husband Dave. "The thought of her going through it absolutely scared me."

"Oh! I didn't persuade Alison not to have it. I would never tell anyone, let alone anyone as sure of herself as Alison, what to do. She made up her own mind entirely on her own. It was her decision and hers alone. That's right, isn't it, Alison?" Asked Dr. James.

"Absolutely!" Confirmed Alison. "I was already fairly sure that I didn't want it. My friend Debbie tried it. She had the same diagnosis as me, and she died a few weeks ago. I just wanted to hear if there were any alternatives I could try. Although I had probably made up my mind when I left here last week, I needed to know what Dave wanted me to do. When I got home he tentatively asked me what my plans were. When I said I was thinking of not having chemotherapy, he gave me the biggest hug he has given me for ages, not that he doesn't hug me often. I had no idea how strongly he felt about it. His attitude finally convinced me, as I then knew he would support my decision.

"Your opinion is very important to me," said Dr. James, "as I will be suggesting a number of ideas. I will endeavour to explain my reasoning so that you can see why I am suggesting it. If you decide not to follow a particular idea of mine you will hopefully have had a chance to think it through properly. If you don't understand anything, please don't be afraid to ask me to explain it again or in another way.

"The other thing I think it is important to tell you now, so you can stop me anytime if you wish, is that I will be telling you all sorts of things that may well stretch credibility to the limits. There are ages old theories as to why cancer develops in a person and I will try to mention all of the ones I can remember. Some of them may be relevant to you some may not. Some you will feel comfortable to embrace, others you may dismiss as too incredible for you to accept.

"Incidentally, you are all likely to be here for about two hours today. Can you all manage so long or do any of you have to be anywhere else?"

They all said no problem and also that they were so determined to support Alison that they would always come when she needed to, if they could. So Dr. James continued, "At every stage, if I suggest an idea, I will try to marry it up to your history, so show why the theory could be, not is, worth considering. So first I need a detailed history. Have you completed the form I gave you? It will form the basis of our discussions. Once I have all the information I will then tell you of my ideas."

Alison gave him the form, duly completed. Dr. James turned the recorder off while he spent a few minutes looking through it. Then asked her a number of questions. "I can already see what some of your problems might be from all the information here, so let me start with your history of lots of problems with throat and ear infections as a child, for which you had regular courses of antibiotics. You also had more for regular attacks of cystitis. So you have had more than your fair share of antibiotics, in fact my wife's and my share, as we have never had a course of them in our lifetime.

"What never had any antibiotics in your whole life? Not even when you were a child?" Queried Alison.

"No. Never, but then antibiotics weren't invented when I was young," replied Dr. James.

"That's amazing!" Said Alison. "But what does it mean?"

"Two things, really. The childhood infections strongly suggest a milk intolerance."

"Please don't tell me you are going to ask me to stop drinking milk," said Alison. "I love it. I drink at least two glasses every day, more if I can get it. Isn't it good for my bones, to prevent me from developing osteoporosis later on in life?"

"Many years ago," said Dr. James, "I was invited to be in the audience of a television programme discussing the work of Dr. Harry Morrow-Brown, the Derby Consultant Physician who started up the Midlands Asthma and Allergy Research Association. There were many general practitioners in the audience and every one of them agreed that, if a child failed to thrive in any way, especially if they developed a lot of tonsillar-type problems, the first thing to do was take it *off* animal milks and animal milk products, especially from the cow, as recommended by Dr. Morrow-Brown. Sometimes goats' or sheep's products were subsequently found to be acceptable, but often not. We all agreed that the child was likely to do well from then on, and we had all observed it on many occasions.

"As you have such a history, what I am really saying is that you have probably had a milk intolerance all your life. Can you imagine what that may have done to your body all these years, and what it may still be doing? If you had breast cancer, it would be particularly important to avoid milk and its products. I know that your cancer is in your ovary, but, in my experience, and the experience of other doctors who think like I do, it probably applies to just about everyone who develops cancer. After all, milk produces mucus, as many people will tell you, and mucus is probably a sign of inflammation. This has been thoroughly researched by Professor Jane Plant in her book 'Your Life In Your Hands'♥. She explains all about the myriad chemicals and hormones that are present in these products. While organic produce may be better in this respect, she and I do not recommend them, especially in the first instance.

"Professor Plant explains how she discovered that cow's milk products were causing her breast cancer and making it spread. She

♥ To obtain a copy of this excellent book, see Appendix 2 note 13.

now certainly recommends a dairy-free diet to anyone who has cancer, especially a hormonally driven one, as ovarian cancer must surely be.

"As for your understandable concern about osteoporosis, human beings are the only creatures on God's Earth that consume dairy products after weaning. Elephants don't, and look at their huge skeleton. I'll tell you more about that subject another time if you want me to, but I'd rather move on for now."

"Ok! Point taken," said Alison. "What was the second connection you were making?"

"Well it's about all those antibiotics you have had over the years, and I see you have had thrush. Have you had much?"

"Thrush has been the bane of my life. I have seen so many doctors about it over the years, but no one seems able to help me get rid of it. What's the significance here?"

"This is where the first rather far-fetched idea comes in. Most doctors are not the slightest interested in knowing why someone has developed cancer. They are only interested in dealing with the symptoms and condition presented to them. I, however, and doctors like me, want to know why cancer has developed so that we can try to deal with the causes, thereby hopefully relieving the body of a stress it would rather be without. Get rid of the cause, and the body can start to try to recover, to heal itself.

"I have felt for a long time that cancer is trying to protect us from something. Doctors accept that lung cancer is usually caused by smoking. What if we put it another way round and suggest that cancer is trying to protect the lungs from the effects of smoking? Yes it may seem a bit bizarre, and unfortunately the protective mechanism doesn't seem to switch itself off very easily.

"There are other things that doctors are aware can cause cancer. There's radiation, many chemicals, excess oestrogen, viruses. The usual approach is that these things cause normal cells to mutate into cancer cells, but I'm not so sure.

"Coming back to you, there is a theory that cancer is trying to protect us from a fungus♥, which in your case could be the thrush fungus called candida. As with courses of antibiotics, you have had more than your fair share of thrush."

"You can say that again," said Alison.

"I have a colleague on the south coast who is convinced that cancer, and in fact multiple sclerosis, is caused by a fungus and that all the person has to do to get better is go on a very strict anti-fungal regime and take certain supplements. The trouble is that his regime is too much for most people. So he may be right, but most patients can't tolerate his approach. Interestingly enough, if slides of a cancer tumour are looked at under a microscope using a dark field background rather than the usual bright lights, fungi and mycelial threads can often be seen.

"As another point, there seems to have been an alarming rise in the incidence of cancer. That rise may well have mirrored the rise in the use, and some people would say abuse, of antibiotics. Unfortunately when two things change in use or frequency, it is all too easy to say they are connected. They may be but it is just as likely to be a coincidence.

"Then there is the approach by a German doctor, Dr. Fryda, who says that cancer is caused by over-exhausting the adrenal glands through stress, which can have a bad suppressing effect upon the immune system, which you need to fight off cancer. You had all that stress when that young man kept stalking you a few years ago, and you had to go to court to get a restraining order against him. What must that have done to you?

"Then there is the possible connection with the Human Papilloma Virus. You had that abnormal smear a few years ago and a cone biopsy. That bug is a known cause of cancer of the cervix. What makes doctors think that it will confine its attention to the cervix? Why should it not also invade or spread further afield, to your uterus or ovaries?

♥This has recently been expanded in a book. For more details, see Appendix 2 note 14

"Finally you were on the contraceptive pill for ten years taking an unnatural pair of hormones for twenty-one days out of twenty-eight. There is some evidence that they can cause cancer. The statistics are not very strong, but, adding the whole lot together, it makes for quite an interesting story. There are one or two other things I could possibly add, but that should be good enough to be going on with."

The four members of his audience were silent for a while. No one knew where to start. Finally Alison herself was the first to speak. "I am speechless!" She said. "That was truly amazing! It all sounds so plausible. You put it together so clearly. It must have taken you years to learn all that. Where on earth do we start, or, more to the point, where do I start? Oh, and by the way. I went onto the Pill mainly because of awful pre-menstrual problems, which soon came back if I stopped it."

"That suggests a dominance of oestrogen relative to progesterone, so there's your hormonal factor. That'll do for now."

Dr. James said that he would like to start on what she ate. "I prefer not to call it 'your diet', but what you consume. Yes, I'm afraid I do want you to give up dairy products in their entirety, but also all forms of sugar, as sugar is the stuff that fungi feed on, as do cancer cells. Also all yeasty foods, so ordinary bread, mushrooms, gravy mixes and white flour products as they act like sugar, and potatoes cooked at a high temperature, so no jacket potatoes. When cooked like that more of the carbohydrate is converted into sugar than normal. And of course all forms of alcohol.

"Please also cut out all junk food. I'm sure you know what I mean. Stop tea, coffee, chocolate and cola and similar drinks. Caffeine doesn't actually cause cancer, but studies have suggested that it stops cells from dying by a normal process called 'apoptosis', which is basically a mechanism of pre-programmed cellular death.

"Drink as much filtered water as you like and I will be recommending some herbal teas. Limit your animal protein intake to organic chicken and turkey, eggs and fish, especially oily fish. Eat as much food as you can that can be eaten raw, all organic if possible, and try to make it seventy-five per cent from vegetables, salad items, nuts, seeds, whole grains and some fruit. Become a vegan if you want to. Because of your obvious fungal problems, it might be sensible to avoid fruit to begin with, in which case I will recommend you take some capsules of fruits, berries and vegetables that should be suitable in the circumstances♥. If you cook vegetables to make soups, steam them so they are not cooked at too high a temperature. I will give you some lists."

"I'm going to enjoy this," said Dave. "That all sounds so healthy. I will take charge of our eating habits from now on."

"I'm going to do the same," said Alison's mother. "We can all eat the same food and exchange ideas. It will be great fun."

"What a wonderful idea," said Dr. James. "You will not only be helping Alison but yourselves."

"You know. It's amazing!" Said Alison. "I'm already losing my fear of this thing called cancer."

"That's so important. People really are afraid of cancer, and they don't need to be. There are often many years before a cancer becomes a significant problem. Think of it this way. If you have a really bad heart attack, it may kill you. You don't have a second chance. With cancer think of it as a wake-up call. Think of it as a time to sort out your life, your living environment, your loves, your dislikes, everything about the way you live. So many people who have come through cancer have told me that developing cancer was the best thing that ever happened to them. Yes the original diagnosis shocked them, but, once they had got over the shock, they started sorting out their lives. They acknowledged that they had become complacent. They had developed an 'Oh it won't happen to me' attitude to life.

"It will take a while to get sorted out," said Dr. James. "Don't hurry. Don't turn your determination to follow this new approach into

---

♥ See Appendix 2, note 2 for further information.

a fetish. Don't let it become stressful. Take your time. Enjoy it. Start writing down a list of things that make you a lucky person, like your husband, your parents, your children, your friends, your home, a roof over your head, your comforts, running water, electricity. There are so many of them. Keep adding to the list as you think of something. Keep looking for the good and positive things. Positivity is so important.

"It's also a good idea to make a separate list of the bad things in your life, the things you don't like, the things that annoy you. Look at the good things list regularly and keep reminding yourself how lucky you are. Only occasionally look at the bad list, and then with only one purpose in life, that is to do something about it, so that you can cross it off the list as having been dealt with. Take control of your life.

"I want you to do relaxation and visualisation exercises, and I will give you a sheet that explains how to do them. I also want you to do some affirmations, which I need to explain. Affirmations involve you making a statement of what you want for yourself, which you claim you already have. You need to work out a series of words that you can repeat to yourself as often as you like, wherever you are. You can write the statement down and learn it by heart, if you want to, but it soon becomes second nature to you.

"What you say should all be positive. I hesitate to say you must not have any negatives in it, as that is using a negative phrase, but I need to use a few more negatives, just to get across the importance of the positive side of things.

"As you have cancer, part of what you say is 'I am free of cancer', not 'I do not have cancer'. If you had multiple sclerosis, you would say something like 'I am free of ms', not 'I do not have ms'. You also say things like 'I am free of pain'. As I say, everything is a positive statement, without any negatives in it at all.

"So you might invent for yourself something like this, "I am whole, healthy, happy, loved, loving, lucky, fortunate and worthy. I am free of cancer and free of pain. I can walk, run and go anywhere I want to. I can sing and dance, because I am so happy. I can do anything I want to, because I am in perfect health". There may be other words that you want to use for yourself, because of your personal circumstances. Even if some of what you say is not true at present, you say it as though it were true, in the hope that, by saying it, you will make it come true.

"Affirmations are very powerful, and many of my patients have said it was one of the most important lessons they learned from me. I have one myself, to which I keep adding something new whenever the need arises. But let me explain why I believe they are so powerful.

"There is now an enormous amount of evidence in the published medical and scientific literature of the influence on the body of a person's attitude to life. It is variously called psycho-neuro-pharmacology or psycho-neuro-immunology. That's a lot of '..ologies', but the point is that scientists are beginning to appreciate the extent that the chemicals we produce in bucket loads every day have on us all. They are also waking up to the fact that all these chemicals can have a dramatic effect upon the body, and that our attitudes can influence the chemicals we produce, creating more bad ones or more good ones according to how we think and act.

"Let me put that all a simpler way, by giving you some examples. You and I think it is intelligent to be able to talk to each other. But what is more intelligent than the fact that, if you cut yourself, millions of cells rush to the site of the cut to help heal it. To my way of thinking, that is intelligent, even if we don't think of it as intelligent in the normal way of thinking of things. So, all sorts of events such as that are going on in your body all the time every day, without you even thinking about them. You digest your food, you breathe, your heart pumps blood round your body all day long without you taking any notice of any of it.

"You may yourself have feelings that you can't fully explain. You talk of a 'gut feeling' about something. The sight of something or somebody or a place you visit 'rings a bell'. You have all sorts of emotions every day, and these are effected by chemicals that your body keeps producing. A sigh, crying, laughter, a sneeze, a shock all cause your body to produce a variety of neuro-chemicals, and are caused by a variety of neuro-chemicals, which your body has to metabolise, once it has used them for the appropriate purpose.

"So, why not try to make the chemicals that your body does produce predominately good chemicals? Why not try to avoid producing bad chemicals, the ones that do harm to your body? You may say, 'How can I keep releasing the good chemicals, and how can you show me that they are good?' Well, there is a very easy demonstration I give to all my patients to whom I teach affirmations.

"So let's try it on you. Will you all please look at Alison. Ok, Alison, please say 'I am happy'. Go on. Say now 'I am happy'. Alison duly said, "I am happy."

"Why did you smile when you said 'I am happy'? What made you smile?"

"I just couldn't help myself. Somehow saying 'I am happy' with you all looking at me seemed to make me smile without my even thinking about it. And everyone else also smiled. A smile is quite infectious."

"When I explain this, in nearly every case the person smiles as they say 'I am happy', said Dr. James. "Sometimes it is a rather poor smile, or a general relaxation of their facial muscles, but nearly always they smile, and often it is a very big, happy smile like yours. Perhaps I cheated a bit by asking everyone to look at you, but somehow it reinforced the effect. By saying 'I am happy', the thought process caused the production of happiness chemicals that, in turn, caused your facial muscles and skin to give the appearance of what we all know is a smile.

"Ok, so that is a quick response to a thought process, but it perfectly illustrates what I am trying to get at. If, by saying 'I am happy', your body releases chemicals that make you appear happy, why is it not perfectly reasonable to suggest that, if you say 'I am whole, I am healthy and I am free of cancer', healing chemicals will be released to bring about what you have just said? Yes, it may take a longer time than the short while it took for your facial muscles to be affected by saying 'I am happy', but the principle is the same.

"I hope you have understood the point of affirmations. Say as often as you can the words you choose to say. Write them down and make sure there are no negatives in them at all. If necessary, ask someone to check your affirmation statement for you, or I will be happy to do it for you. And don't forget, you can add something else any time you want to.

"Affirmations can be said wherever you are and whenever you want to say them. While washing up, standing in a queue, falling asleep or if you happen to wake up in the middle of the night, are good times to say them. In fact I find that is a good way of helping me to fall asleep, and I have to concentrate to complete what I want to say. I often fail to complete them, falling asleep in the meantime.

"Being happy is far better for you than being unhappy. Yes, I know it can sometimes be hard to be happy under certain circumstances with cancer, especially if you are in pain. But, if you can somehow manage to change your attitude, you will be surprised how it will help. In fact, laughter is a very good way of relieving pain, and, for the same reason, if you remain miserable and depressed, the 'bad' chemicals that are produced as a result, make it all worse.

"You may think that your problem is worse than that of anyone else. And to you it may well be very serious. But, however serious it is, I can assure you there is someone somewhere who is worse off than you are. Think of all those starving, thirsty people in Africa. Remember the old Chinese saying 'The man who has no shoes should weep for the man who has no feet'. Yes, I know it is hard to think of other people's hardships when you are suffering yourself, but at least you have food, warmth, a roof over your head and people who care for you and will help you.

"So try to minimise your own problems. Try to put them to the back of your mind. Instead of thinking about the bad things in your life, try to concentrate on your good fortune. Be positive rather than negative. Keep your cup half full rather than half empty. Try to smile as much as you can. If necessary, practise smiling in front of a mirror so that you can turn a smile on if you are feeling down. You never know, just doing that may make you smile or even laugh.

"Think about laughter. Who are your favourite comedians? Is there someone on TV at present whose programmes make you laugh? Would you enjoy watching them again, and would you laugh at the same jokes, if you watched them again? If so, record them so that you can watch them whenever you feel a bit low or in pain. Try to obtain recordings of old laughter makers. Who were your favourites from the past? Old recordings are so much easier to obtain nowadays. Have you seen the film 'Patch Adams' starring Robin Williams? He is such a brilliant actor and very funny[♥].

"Ignore all the bad news in the world. Avoid watching the main Evening News on TV. It's nearly all bad news. Just don't turn the TV on at that time. For some unknown reason, the people responsible for what is shown seem to think that bad news is what we are all interested in. Perhaps they are right. Someone tried to produce a 'good news' newspaper some time ago, and it failed to sell. Perhaps we prefer to hear of other people's misfortunes than their good fortune. I suppose people are jealous of lottery winners, rather than pleased for them. If someone has had an accident, perhaps we need to hear about it to feel lucky that it didn't happen to us.

"Whatever the truth is, you can change the effect it has upon you. There isn't anything you can do about it anyway, so why even be aware of it in the first place? When most people go on holiday, the bad news still happens and they don't know it has happened. When they arrive home, the bad news has passed and they don't even know what they missed.

"Are there any beautiful walks or parks near where you live? When did you last visit them? Are there any beautiful buildings anywhere near you? When did you last look at them? Do you live in or near an old city? If you go into the city centre, lift your eyes above the usual shop front at eye level. The buildings above them, usually not seen by most people because they don't look up, are often very beautiful.

[♥] To obtain a copy of the film 'Patch Adams, see Appendix 2 note 15

"When did you last go to the theatre? All of us have a habit of taking for granted all the beautiful things around us. I have a beautiful home at the bottom of a fairly long drive. Every single time I turn into it, I fully appreciate what I have been fortunate to have acquired. It never fails to please me. You may not be as lucky as I am in this respect, but there must be no end to the beauty around you to lift your spirits. You merely have to look for it.

"What I am encouraging you to do is to consider all the ways in which you are lucky. Think positively all the time, if you can. Always think of your cup as being half full rather than half empty. Ignore any unhappiness around you, and, if necessary, give up a relationship with a so-called friend who depresses you at the present time. Smile as much as you can, and laugh every so often. If you are feeling a bit down, make yourself smile. To repeat what I said earlier, if necessary, look in a mirror and practice smiling, like a model who has to turn on a smile as soon as the photographer tells her to do so. You never know. Doing so may make you laugh.

"Well that's enough talking for now. That's a lot for you to take in, but I will give you some sheets with all this fully described. Don't forget, all this is absolutely free. Your attitude doesn't cost you a penny.

"There are many preparations I will want to give you as time goes on, but I want you first to modify your diet and start doing the relaxation, visualisation and affirmation exercises. As a final point of things to talk about today, I would like to give you an intravenous infusion of vitamins and minerals to boost you up and give your immune system a helping hand. After I have checked a particular blood test I will build the dose of vitamin C up to about fifty or seventy-five grammes. Vitamin C is very good at killing cancer cells. Such an infusion will take up to two hours, so it may be better to organise it on another day."

Alison, Dave and her parents sat back exhausted. None of them could speak for a while. There was so much to take in. Dr. James gave them a copy of their discussions, and gently sent them home.

Chapter 43

About a week after Patrick and Lynda had arrived to take care of Maud, she was feeling almost back to her old self.

"I think it's about time you two went home," she said to them. "You have been so kind to me. I have never been ill in my life before, so it was a new experience for me. I suppose it's one of the things you have to put up with when you get old like me. Perhaps some part of me is beginning to wear out. No doubt the whole lot will soon. Anyway, I've had a good innings, so I can't complain. I expect one day you will come to my funeral. I want to be buried in the cemetery of our church. I don't want to be cremated. I know cremation leaves more space, but I think I am entitled to my own little lot. I want to be buried next to my Ted. We booked a space together. I don't know what to expect when I leave here, but I don't want to leave anything to chance. Perhaps Ted and I will be reunited, perhaps not. Who knows?

"Any way, talking of people dying, Dr. James popped in to see me the other day," said Maud. "He said he was just passing by and hoped I was at home as usual. Perhaps he wondered if I was still alive. I suppose I am a bit like the Queen. She must have seen fourteen or fifteen Prime Ministers go by. I have been here through half a dozen doctors. Anyway, it was great to see him again. He must have been retired about six or seven months by then. He said he had moved a few miles away so as not to get in the way of the new doctor. He hadn't wanted to go too far away as he really loved this part of the country.

"We got round to talking about all his former patients, especially the older ones. He wondered how they all were, presumably meaning were they still alive. We talked about Howard Gregson who had had such bad arthritis, but who refused to take anything for it. He reminded me of the day Howard got stuck under his car and they had to lift the car off him to get him out from under it. He was particularly reminded of Howard because he was the only person who had died on Christmas Day. He was also fascinated by

Howard's fatalistic approach to life, although he was prepared to avoid being the fatal result of someone else's doings.

"His visit made me think of people who had survived against all the odds, because they came to see him."

Gerald Walker was in his sixties when he moved into the Stead Norton area with his young wife Cindy. Gerald was Chairman of a large international corporation, whose headquarters had been in London. However the board had decided to move to larger premises in the country and they eventually chose the city about thirty miles from Stead Norton, where the council was offering generous terms to companies to move there. Gerald and Cindy had lived in a large house in Surrey, which had taken him more than an hour to get to work in the City of London and home every day, so to have to drive thirty miles to and from work was a pleasure, especially as much of it was along country roads.

A couple of years before they moved, Gerald had developed a swelling on his left leg, just below the knee, but he ignored it and hoped it would go away. As his wife Cindy was a Nutritional Therapist, she gave him various herbs and supplements to improve his immune system, hoping his body would sort it out. Neither of them knew what it was. About two years later the lump had grown to the size of a small egg, and, as it was producing an annoying bulge in his otherwise smart trousers, he decided to consult his GP at the time, who referred him to a Specialist who recommended that he remove it in a simple operation and have it examined under a microscope to see what it was.

When Gerald saw the Surgeon after the operation, he was duly told that the lump was a sarcoma. He then told him that the only thing to do was to have Gerald back into hospital as soon as possible to amputate his leg above the knee, to prevent the cancer spreading. Gerald was unsure what to do, but his wife Cindy was naturally unhappy at the recommended treatment.

Gerald went back to his GP as a courtesy visit, assuming he would have received a letter from the Surgeon by then. He had, and repeated that the best option was for Gerald to have his leg amputated as soon as possible. The GP became very angry when Gerald said that it was not convenient at the present time as they were moving house very soon.

So it was only a few weeks later when they had moved that Gerald visited Dr. James for the first time. He listened to Gerald's story very carefully. Cindy had had the commonsense to photograph the lump at various stages. They were astonished that Dr. James was really interested in them, especially in the lump as it was before the Surgeon removed it. They were even more amazed when Dr. James asked Cindy what treatment she had given him for the past two years, especially when he told her he was sure her treatment had effectively cured Gerald. He told them of a book he had read entitled 'A Time To Heal' by Beata Bishop♥, in which she wrote about the way her malignant melanoma had developed into a similar egg-like lump after she had spent over two years following the harsh Gerson Regime, having been to Mexico to learn what to do.

"I think you may well have treated your husband so well, Mrs Walker," said Dr. James, "that his body simply put a wall round it and tried to push it out of his body. Unfortunately the pathology report hasn't described the capsule that may have surrounded it, but I wouldn't expect them to think of anything so simple. They wouldn't think the body could do such a thing, but I know it can if it is given the right approach. So I congratulate you. Those photographs tell me all I need to know.

"As for the idea that your leg needs to be amputated, I have a feeling that that is totally unnecessary, but it would be sensible to do some tests first, if you are in agreement, just to make sure?"

"I can't believe what I am hearing," said Gerald. "I assumed you would agree with my former GP and Surgeon and refer me on to a local Surgeon."

"If you stay around here for long, you will find I think differently from most other doctors. I look more carefully at the problem. Yes, I often do exactly the same as all other doctors, but I

♥ To obtain a copy of this book, see Appendix 2 note 16.

prefer to consider whether there might be an alternative. Your photographs convinced me that you had done all that was necessary. What I would like to do is arrange for a detailed scan to be carried out on your leg. I could ask the local Specialist to do it for you, but he is absolutely orthodox and is not likely to see things the way I would like. If you are prepared to pay for it, I would like to send you to a friend, Dr. Thackeray in London, who will look at your scans the way I ask him to."

"That will not be a problem," said Gerald. "I am covered by a company private medical insurance policy. What will you say to your friend?"

"I will tell him the relevant facts of your history, in particular that I think your body has extruded to sarcoma naturally, with your wife's help, of course. The photographs should help, so I would like to send them to him, if I may. They are very clear. I can't understand why your former advisers wouldn't have been impressed by them. They tell a most important story. But there you are. That's life and a closed mind for you.

"I will specifically ask Dr. Thackeray to see if there is any trace of sarcoma left in your leg. I will make sure he rings me with his report before he sends it, so that I can ask him pertinent questions. I will let you know as soon as I hear from him."

A very happy and smiling Gerald and Cindy left Dr. James's surgery. They couldn't believe their luck at finding such an unusual doctor in this tiny country practice. By the time they left, Dr. James had already telephoned Dr. Thackeray's practice and arranged for Gerald to have an appropriate scan within three days. Dr. James wrote his referral letter there and then so that they could take it with them, and the photographs. Two days after their visit to London, Dr. James rang them to say he had the report and there was nothing to worry about, but he would like to see them as soon as convenient. They came the next day.

"I spoke to Dr. Thackeray in the evening of your scan. He was so intrigued by my letter that he said he couldn't wait to look at the pictures, so stayed late to study them. He said he had looked very carefully indeed and could find absolutely no sign of any sarcomatous changes in your leg whatsoever. He assured me he had searched thoroughly.

"He rang me the next day to say he had showed your pictures to two other Specialists, one a Professor of Radiology, asking them to give an opinion. He said a group of his colleagues had a club where every so often they showed each other scan pictures and asked them to comment, without giving them any history at all. That way they were 'blind' so would have to read the pictures very carefully. Only then were they given the history. All anyone could find was the scar from the operation to remove the tumour. They were all absolutely fascinated by it all, and said they would like to write it up for their specialist journal. They may well contact you for the full story."

"How fascinating!" Said Gerald. "So we had the opinion of three Specialists for the price of one. Not bad, eh?"

"Actually I was aware of their academic club and hoped that others would be asked to verify Dr. Thackeray's opinions. I have sent a few patients to this group, and they have always used them for training purposes. When they had had a discussion of the test pictures, and had been told what the problem was, the Professor apparently said to Dr. Thackeray, "I suppose this is one of Dr. James's patients. They are always so unusual."

"That was over twenty years ago," said Maud. "Gerald is now in his eighties, all hail and hearty. Cindy says she can't keep up with him. He happily walks around with two normal legs. 'This is the special one,' he once explained to a group of friends at the local golf club. 'Without my local doctor, some others would have lopped it off a long time ago. Rather difficult to swing a club with only one leg, I should imagine.'

"All of your stories are so fascinating," said Lynda. "They all seem to have a special message. Can you imagine what a difference it would make to so many people if all doctors were like Dr. James?"

"Interesting things didn't only happen to other people," said Maud. "When he visited me recently, he told me of an experience he himself had had with the Grim Reaper not so long ago. He said he had just picked up his lovely old sports car from the garage where it had had its annual service, and he had driven along the motorway towards London. When he got up to a fairly fast speed he felt something was not quite right with the car. There was something unsteady about the vehicle.

"So he slowed down and drove onto the emergency hard shoulder, got out of the car and checked everything he could. He even kicked each tyre and checked the nuts to make sure everything was ok. Satisfied, he got back into the car and drove off back up to his previous fast speed, but this time he was even more sure there was something wrong, so once again he slowed down and stopped on the emergency hard shoulder. He had virtually come to a halt when there was a thump and one of his back wheels fell off completely and the back end of the car landed on the road.

"He rang his wife to tell her what had happened after he had rung the emergency services. Even a police patrol car stopped to try to help and protect him from other passing cars, as it can be very dangerous to stop at the side of a motorway. His car was lifted onto a breakdown truck and taken to the garage that had serviced the car the previous day and any repairs made. He drove his wife's car to the meeting he had originally been planning to attend even though he was a bit late.

"When he arrived home that evening, his wife showed him a cutting from that day's newspaper. It was from the Obituary Pages and described the death of 'Dr. Sir David James', who had died at almost exactly the same time the rear wheel of his car had fallen off the night before. He said the Grim Reaper must have sent out orders for the death of 'David James', but, just at the last minute, realised he had picked the wrong one!"

"The stories of Dr. David James you have told us are absolutely fascinating. I have been trying to find a subject for my next book. If I were to come back next week with a tape-recorder," said Patrick Carlisle, "do you think you could repeat them all?"

Appendix 1

Results of an Open Study of the use of Juice Plus capsules in pregnancy, as mentioned on pages 84 and 285, which has led to the Mississippi Medical Centre's gold standard study currently under way.

	Group 1 N=178 Control	**Group 1 N=179 Juice plus**
Caesarean delivery	**66%**	**47%**
Preterm delivery	**4%**	**0%**
Pre-eclampsia	**21%**	**0%**
Birth weight < 2500 gm	**12%**	**1%**
Admission to Neonatal ICU	**10%**	**0%**
Respiratory distress syndrome	**8%**	**0%**

Appendix 2

Footnote References

1. Mentioned on page 15. To obtain a copy of the book 'Not All In The Mind' by Dr. Richard Mackarness, go to www.abacopublishing.com. Note, this book may be hard to obtain as it is out of print.
2. Mentioned on pages 84, 232, 285 and 307. See Appendix 1 for details of the study mentioned on pages 84 and 285. For more information about the capsules and how to obtain them, look up www.juiceplus.co.uk/+pk025727.
3. Mentioned on page 88 and 288. For more detailed information about preparing for pregnancy and what to consider if you have already had a miscarriage or an unfortunate pregnancy experience, read the book 'Beautiful Babies Fabulous Families Wonderful World' by Belinda Barnes. To obtain a copy go to www.abacopublishing.com.
4. Mentioned on page 108. To obtain a copy of the book 'The Journey' by Brandon Bays go to www.abacopublishing.com.
5. Mentioned on page 131. To obtain a copy of the book 'Eat Fat And Grow Slim' by Dr. Richard Mackarness, go to www.abacopublishing.com. Note that this is an old book so may not be readily available.
6. Mentioned on page 133. Described fully in the book 'Conquering Cystitis' by Dr. Patrick Kingsley. To obtain a copy go to www.abacopublishing.com.
7. Mentioned on page 197. To obtain a copy of the book 'Living Proof. A medical mutiny' by Michael Gearin-Tosh, go to www.abacopublishing.com.
8. Mentioned on page 211. To obtain a supply of transdermal magnesium, contact wellbeing.research@virgin.net mentioning code PC100 for a 10% discount off the retail price.

9. Mentioned on page 248. For information about this test contact www.alcat.com, quoting ref CC200 to obtain a 5% discount on the cost of the test when ordering it in Canada, North America and the Caribbean or phone 001-954-426-2304. For Europe, the Middle East and South Africa phone 0049–33022–023800 quoting reference AK200 for a 5% discount off the retail price.
10. Mentioned on page 256. 'Natural Progesterone; The multiple roles of a Remarkable Hormone' by Dr. John Lee can be obtained from www.abacopublishing.com.
11. Mentioned on page 269. For more information on this piece of equipment, contact www.get-fitt.com, quoting reference FITT13 for a 5% discount off the retail price.
12. Mentioned on page 284. To obtain a copy of the book 'Hypothyroidism: The Unsuspected Illness', by Broda O. Barnes, MD, go to www.abacopublishing.com.
13. Mentioned on page 303. 'Your Life In Your Hands' by Professor Jane Plant. ISBN 9-781852-278090. To obtain a copy go to www.abacopublishing.com.
14. Mentioned on page 305. This has recently been expanded in his book 'Cancer is a Fungus' by Dr. Tulio Simoncini. To obtain a copy go to www.abacopublishing.com.
15. Mentioned on page 312. To obtain a copy of the film 'Patch Adams', starring Robin Williams, go to www.abacopublishing.com.
16. Mentioned on page 316. To obtain a copy of the book 'A Time To Heal' by Beata Bishop, go to www.abacopublishing.com.